TREE GROWTH

Edited by

THEODORE T. KOZLOWSKI

UNIVERSITY OF WISCONSIN

THE RONALD PRESS COMPANY · NEW YORK

Library of Congress Catalog Card Number: 62–9752

PRINTED IN THE UNITED STATES OF AMERICA

To

A. E. DOUGLASS

Preface

This book provides a broad coverage of various aspects of tree growth including tree physiology, genetics, dendrochronology, mensuration, and effects of soil and climate on growth. Not only the physiological and biochemical aspects of tree growth are presented but also growth correlations, historical events, silvicultural implications, tree improvement, and measurement of growth of individual trees and stands. There are critical evaluations and strong overtones throughout of the role of the principal climatic and edaphic factors which influence growth through the intermediation of internal physicochemical processes and conditions. Hence, this one volume summarizes the early developments and, with considerably greater emphasis, the current state of knowledge of main aspects of the nature, control, and measurement of the growth of trees. For these reasons the book will be especially useful as a text or reference for a wide variety of scientists including foresters, physiologists, ecologists, geneticists, soil scientists, horticulturists, and archeologists, among others.

The eminent roster of contributors to this book presented their papers at the International Conference on Forest Tree Growth held during April 1–10, 1960, at the University of Arizona in Tucson. Our sincere thanks are due to each of these authors for their scholarly presentations, patience, and cooperation in reviewing their papers. T. L. Smiley, who worked indefatigably as general chairman of the Organizational Committee, probably contributed more than any one individual to the success of the conference. Special thanks must also be given to A. L. McComb, C. O. Minor, and F. W. Went, who provided stimulating leadership throughout as members of the Organizational Committee. The editor and his co-moderators, R. Zahner, A. L. McComb, H. A. Fowells, G. S. Allen, and G. M. Furnival, arranged the programs in the various subject-matter sections. The work of the co-moderators in selection of topics and their skill in guiding the subject-matter presentations and intellectually exciting discussions, resulted in an unusually high level of excellence.

Organizations sponsoring the conference included the Tree-Ring Society, founded in 1934 at Flagstaff, Arizona, to encourage scien-

v

tific work in dendrochronology; the Laboratory of Tree-Ring Research at the University of Arizona, the site since 1906 of research on tree-ring chronologies, climate, tree-growth relationships, and dating of prehistoric specimens; the Department of Watershed Management at the University of Arizona; and the Division of Forestry at Arizona State College in Flagstaff. Financial support was provided by Resources for the Future, Inc., Washington, D. C., and by private sources, to whom all those concerned wish to express their appreciation.

THEODORE T. KOZLOWSKI

Madison, Wisconsin
   January, 1962

Contents

vii

TREE
GROWTH

1

The Vascular Cambium
and Tree-Ring Development

M. W. BANNAN

The major part of this paper will be devoted to a consideration of the development of the growth ring from the vascular cambium. Certain features of the cambium will be dealt with such as its cellular organization, the site and extent of periclinal divisions, seasonal changes, the march of growth, and the time factor in xylem and phloem production. Factors influencing latewood development and the problem of variation in different parts of the tree will also be discussed. The descriptions will relate to the conifers because these have been more intensively studied than the broad-leaved trees.

Structure of the Cambium

In 1853 Hartig suggested that the cambium was a biseriate layer of cells, each radial file across the cambium consisting of two mother cells which stood back to back and produced wood and bast cells in opposite directions. Twenty years later Sanio (1873) presented another concept. He proposed that the source was a single layer of cells. Each division of the initial produced two daughter cells one of which continued as an initial while the other became a xylem or phloem mother cell. The latter cell sometimes divided once or twice before maturation into vascular elements. Support for Sanio's theory was given by Mischke (1890), Schoute (1902) and Beijer (1927), although these workers claimed that the tissue mother cells had greater capacity for redivision than noted by Sanio. Raatz (1892) and Kleinmann (1923), on the other hand, argued that all cells in the multiseriate zone of division existent in periods of active growth were similar and equivalent. They rejected the hypothesis of a specific layer of initials.

The concept of the cambium as proposed by Sanio, namely a uniseriate initiating row of cells producing tissue mother cells on either side which divide again, is supported by the following evidence:

1. The radial continuity of cells across the cambium, and the generally simultaneous origin of new radial files and cessation of old ones in both xylem and phloem demonstrate derivation of both tissue systems from a common source, a tier of initials.

2. Although the multiplication of radial files of xylem and phloem elements, achieved by pseudotransverse division of the initiating cambial cells (Bailey, 1923; Klinken, 1914), usually takes place toward the end of the growing season when the zone of division is narrow, careful study has shown that it may occur at any time during the growing season. This demonstrates the existence, at least through the major part of the growing season, of a specific tier of cells which is functioning as an initiating layer.

3. Temporary changes in basic cell pattern are of relatively rare occurrence. Such alterations usually involve a short-lived doubling of a radial file of xylem elements without a similar change in the phloem. Here there has evidently been a pseudotransverse division in a xylem mother cell rather than in the functioning initial. However, study of many thousands of pseudotransverse divisions has shown that the proportion of these taking place outside the initiating layer is very low (Bannan, 1957b). The most frequent occurrence was found in a tree of *Cedrus deodara* with growth rings up to 1 cm. wide, but even here the proportion of extrainitial divisions was only one-fifth of the total. This low incidence of extrainitial divisions under conditions of rapid growth is particularly significant. Even when several cells in each radial file are undergoing periclinal division, sensitivity to the stimuli associated with anticlinal division is restricted to a very narrow part of the broad zone of growth.

4. The cells of the constituent layers in the meristem can be distinguished in radial sections by their tips. The initial and phloem mother cells are slightly shorter than the xylem mother cells.

The initiating layer is functionally uniseriate, but the width of the phloem and xylem mother cell layers varies with the time of year, vigour of growth, and cycle of periclinal division (Bannan, 1955). In white-cedar the phloem mother cell layer is uniseriate or absent according to the local stage of development. The layer of xylem mother cells ranges from one to many rows of cells. Minimum extent is found in the dormant cambium, and the maximum during active growth when the layer of dividing cells is 10–15 or

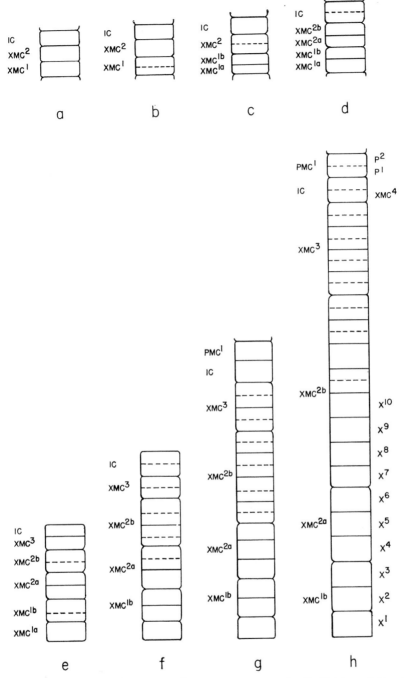

FIG. 1–1. Series of diagrams showing sequence of cell divisions following reactivation of the cambium in the spring. Divisions are shown as beginning in xylem mother cells, extensive redivision of which results in rapid production of xylem-destined cells. Less frequent divisions in the tier of initial cells yield new xylem mother cells on the inside and phloem mother cells toward the outside. Symbol IC denotes initial cell; XMC, xylem mother cell; PMC, phloem mother cell; X, differentiating xylem element; and P, phloem element.

5

occasionally more cells wide. In this connection it might be pointed out that some botanists prefer applying the term cambium only to the layer of initials, while others, including the author, use it in the broader sense to denote the entire zone of cell division.

Vernal Cambial Activity

In the dormant condition the width of the cambium in conifers ranges from one to four or five cells but is usually two or three cells wide (Fig. 1–2). In the general two- to three-tiered condition the outermost row, lying next to the more or less immature phloem, is recognizable as the layer of initials. The one or two rows of slightly longer xylemward cells are the xylem mother cells. All cells have restricted radial dimensions, the mean diameter generally being 5–6 microns. The radial walls are relatively thick and the protoplasts dense.

When frost leaves the ground and water becomes available, cambial reactivation takes place. As noted by several authors (De Bary, 1884; Kruger, 1892; Knudson, 1913; Brown, 1915; Bailey, 1930; Cockerham, 1930; Priestley, 1930; Priestley et al., 1933; Wight, 1933; Fraser, 1952; Ladefoged, 1952) the first observable change is swelling of the cells and thinning of the radial walls (Fig. 1–3). With increasing vacuolation the radial diameter increases to 10 microns or more.

Periclinal cell divisions follow soon after vacuolation. Sometimes these begin in the Great Lakes area as early as mid-April. The first divisions occur in any of the two or three rows of cells that generally comprise the generative zone at this time of year, but it is noteworthy that the usual site of the first division is not the initiating layer, as might be supposed, but rather the tangential tier of xylem mother cells contiguous to the wood (see also Grillos and Smith, 1959). This tier is designated as XMC[1] in Figs. 1–1a and 1–1b. The radial longitudinal aspect of the cambium at this stage is shown in Fig. 1–4 for a two-tiered zone. The xylem mother cell adjoining the latewood of the previous year has divided, the two daughter nuclei appearing to the right of center in the photograph, while the enlarged nucleus of the initial cell, on the left-hand side, is still in a predivision state. Figure 1–5 shows a slightly later stage in a three-tiered zone. The two xylem mother cells toward the right have already divided to make four cells whereas the initial cell, on the left-hand side, is still in an early phase of division, the incipient cell wall extending only a short distance to the migrating phragmoplasts recognizable above and below the two new-formed daughter

FIGS. 1–2—1–6. Cambium in eastern white-cedar (*Thuja occidentalis*).

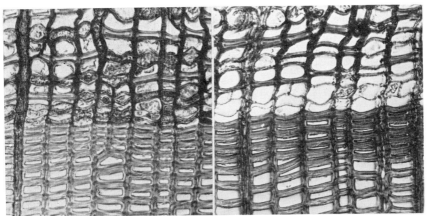

FIG. 1–2.   FIG. 1–3.

FIG. 1–4.   FIG. 1–5.   FIG. 1–6.

FIG. 1–2. Transverse section showing dormant cambium in February.

FIG. 1–3. Swelling of cambial cells on reactivation in mid-April.

FIG. 1–4. Radial longitudinal section showing first division in late April. The xylem mother cell toward the right has divided, the initial cell on the left is undivided.

FIG. 1–5. Radial section of cambium in early May, showing two divided xylem mother cells on the right and the dividing initial on the left.

FIG. 1–6. Radial section of the cambium during the vernal surge of activity in late May, showing nuclei of dividing xylem mother cells. The great width of the zone of division is demonstrated by the fact that the center of the photographed area is 80 microns inward from the initial cell.

nuclei. The stage of development is similar to that diagramed in
Fig. 1–1d. The general inception of division in the cells nearest the
mature xylem is of interest. It would seem to indicate the importance of water, as well as growth hormones, in the resumption of cell
multiplication.

By the end of April or early in May in the Toronto area the
second in the cycle of divisions is generally under way, divisions
taking place for the most part in the central part of the expanding
cambium, now four or five cells wide (Fig. 1–1e). Activity is usually noticeable first in the derivatives of the second xylem mother
cell (cells 2a and 2b, Fig. 1–1e) and in the outermost derivative of
the first xylem mother cell (cell 1b). The interval between the first
and second divisions in the generative cycle of the xylem mother
cells is sometimes as much as two weeks. Divisions usually become
general in the initiating layer slightly before or simultaneously with
the second division of the xylem mother cells.

With continued cell division the cambium rapidly widens out
due largely to redivision of the xylem mother cells (Fig. 1–1, f–h).
Sometimes a considerable portion of the earlywood is formed by
redivision of xylem mother cells which were in existence at the
time of cambial reactivation, as shown in the schematic presentation in Fig. 1–1. At other times, especially when the cambium is
only two-tiered at the beginning, almost all the earlywood is derived
from xylem mother cells newly arisen from the initiating tier during
the current year. It should be emphasized that much variation
exists in the width of the cambium and in the pattern of periclinal
division during the early growth stages.

During the month of May the successive periclinal divisions tend
to follow one another at shorter intervals. An approximate time
table can be constructed by utilizing data on the number of cells
produced, the width of the zone of division, and the relative rates
of division across that zone. In the stem bases of vigorous open-
grown white-cedar trees in the Toronto area the first division occurred about April 15–20 in the year of study (Bannan, 1955), the
second on or about May 1, the third on approximately May 10, and
the fourth somewhat less than a week later. By the end of May
the cambium in some trees was in the sixth or seventh successive
division. The rate is thus similar to that discovered in pine by
Raatz (1892), where six cambial divisions were observed in 42 days.
As already noted, the intervals between the successive divisions are
not uniform but decrease from approximately two weeks between
the first and second to probably as little as 4–6 days between the
later divisions. This interval is considerably longer than in apical

meristems where the lapse is 8–18 hours (Baldovinos, 1953). No doubt a factor in the relatively slow division of cambial cells is the time required for the phragmoplasts to reach the tips of the cells which are a few millimeters long. Synthesis over the enormous area of the cambium also doubtless poses a problem.

Through the successive periclinal divisions the cambium in vigorous open-grown trees expands to a width of 100–150 microns (Fig. 1–6) or occasionally to 300 microns. Counts of the mitoses in radial sections show that the frequency of division is greatest in the central part of the zone of division, comprising the dividing and redividing xylem mother, cells (Fig. 1–7). The frequency of division in the phloemward part, which includes the phloem mother cell, when present, and the layer of initials, is approximately one-half that in the central area. In the peripheral zone toward the xylem the frequency falls off in straggling divisions, and the cells enlarge and maturate to tracheids (Fig. 1–1, g and h). In the trees of slower growth, with annual increments of 0.5–1.0 mm., the zone of redivision amongst the xylem mother cells is much narrower and the total width of the cambium is usually only 50–60 microns.

By the end of May the aggregate of xylemward production in the Toronto area, including the dividing, enlarging, and maturing elements, ranges up to 60 cells in vigorous trees. This amounts to 35–40 per cent of the growth for the year in terms of linear distance, or nearly 50 per cent if rated in cells.

Aestival Growth

In southern Ontario narrowing of the zone of periclinal division becomes evident early in June, and by the end of the month the cambium is reduced to a width of 50–60 microns in most trees of average or better growth. Constriction continues through July, sometimes down to a width of a 30–35 microns, or three to four rows of cells. The zone of division now comprises the row of phloem mother cells, the single tier of initials, and one or two rows of xylem mother cells. The diminution in width is thus due to reduction in extent of redivision among the xylem mother cells. These cells, which divided to the second, third, or fourth order during the surge of vernal growth, now apparently divide only once or rarely twice before maturing into xylem elements. The presence of numerous mitotic figures in radial sections attests to active division in the layer of initials and the immediate derivatives on either side, but the zone of redivision on the xylem side, and hence the production of xylem, is now drastically reduced.

Some authors (Mischke, 1890; Jost, 1892; Friedrich, 1897; Brown, 1915; Kienholz, 1934; Kaufman, 1945) reported an early summer reduction in activity, the growth cycle being characterized by spring and summer maxima with a lull between. Brown (1915) suggested that the early summer slackening was related to food supply,

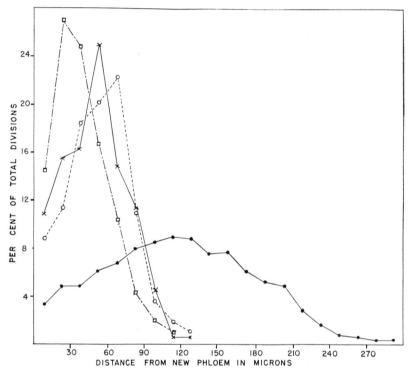

Fig. 1–7. Graph showing relative frequency of periclinal divisions across the cambia of four fast-growing white-cedar trees sampled on May 24 or May 30. The site of the initial cell is to the extreme left, within the first 20 microns. Most active division is in the approximate center of the generative zone, among the dividing and redividing xylem mother cells. The data are based on 1,200 division figures observed in radial longitudinal sections.

but others (Mischke, 1890; Daubenmire and Deters, 1947; Byram and Doolittle, 1950) who noted temporary halts in growth believed that climatic influences, such as drought or a drop in temperature, were responsible. The majority of the studies (Buckhout, 1907; Korstian, 1921, Gäumann, 1928; Fowells, 1941; Daubenmire, 1945; Daubenmire and Deters, 1947; Byram and Doolittle, 1950; Warrack and Joergensen, 1950; Belyea et al., 1951; Fraser, 1952; Jackson, 1952; Schneider, 1952; Eggler, 1955; Fritts, 1958; Grillos and Smith, 1959) have been in general agreement in revealing a vernal surge of activity, the grand period of growth, followed by a marked slowing down which began as early as June or as late as August or early September. Gäumann (1928) stated that 95 per cent of the ring was laid down by mid-July in *Picea* and 86 per cent in *Abies*. The author (Bannan, 1955) estimated that in *Thuja occidentalis* 70–80 per cent of the ring was in existence by the end of June and 90 per cent or more by the end of July.

The transition from early- to latewood is extremely varied both in the anatomical manifestation and in the precise period of the growing season when it is effected. Bailey and Faull (1934) have illustrated the great variation in proportion of latewood and in cellular aspect which may be found in a single species. As to the time at which latewood formation begins, it is interesting to note that Eggler (1955) reported radial growth as having ceased as early as June 1 in *Taxodium* growing in Louisiana. For *Picea* in northern temperate latitudes, the time of latewood inception has been given as mid-June (Gäumann, 1928), the beginning of July (Ladefoged, 1952), mid-July (Rees, 1929), the end of July (Wieler, 1898), and mid-August (Mer, 1892).

The extent of development of latewood is influenced by both inherent and environmental factors. Age of the tree seems to have a bearing on latewood production. Several studies (Turnbull, 1937; Paul, 1950, 1957; Chalk, 1953; Larson, 1957; Rendle and Phillips, 1958) have shown that the wood laid down in the middle life of the tree is denser, with a higher proportion of latewood, than wood produced early in life. In the last-formed wood of very old trees various conditions obtain. For instance, in the peripheral growth of large sequoias latewood makes up a large part of the ring in some stems and a very small proportion in others. Rate of growth is another important factor in that young fast-growing trees tend to have a lower proportion of latewood than slow-growing trees of the same age (Paul, 1930; Luxford and Markwardt, 1932; Rendle and Phillips, 1958). The significant role of nutritional factors has been demonstrated by the circumstance that one of the first effects of defoliation is a marked reduction in latewood (Church, 1949; Harper, 1913). Conversely Marts (1950) noted more latewood in open-grown trees.

The relation between water supply and latewood development has been considered by several investigators (Schwarz, 1899; Paul and Marts, 1931; Paul and Smith, 1950; Priestley and Scott, 1936; Schulman, 1942; Chalk, 1951, 1953). It has been shown that irrigation increases the amount of latewood whereas summer drought reduces it. Dobbs (1953) noted that the formation of bands of thick-walled cells ("lines") was associated with rainfall after a dry period. While the development of latewood usually takes place when available soil moisture is at a low level, it is significant that an increase in water supply at this time of year is reflected in expanded latewood formation. The deduction thus follows that latewood formation is not caused simply by low water supply. The effect of growth hormones on the development of early- and latewood has been touched upon by Fraser (1952). Wareing (1954) and Wareing and Roberts (1956) have dealt with the problem of photoperiod in relation to auxin concentration and tree growth. Larson also discusses auxin and latewood formation in another paper of this volume. For reviews on the earlier literature on the causes of latewood formation reference may be made to Büsgen and Münch (1929), Ladefoged (1952), and Studhalter (1955).

The time of cessation of cell division varies widely with altitude, latitude, climate, and site. As a rule growth ceases earlier at the higher altitudes (Daubenmire, 1945). In warm countries growth may continue through the greater part of the year (Fahn, 1958; Studhalter, 1955) whereas in North Temperate Zones radial accretion usually terminates in the period from the end of August to the end of September. Local circumstances, such as high or low temperatures, drought, and the density of stand also have a profound influence. In warm climates with a prolonged summer dry spell two periods of growth may occur, resulting in double rings (MacDougal, 1938). Under special circumstances multiple rings sometimes develop (Glock, 1955; Studhalter, 1955).

Growth of the Phloem

It has been demonstrated for certain conifers and broad-leaved trees that the last-formed phloem elements of the annual production do not complete maturation until the following year (Strasburger, 1891; Elliott, 1935; Abbe and Crafts, 1939; Artschwager, 1945; Ladefoged, 1952; Grillos and Smith, 1959). It has also been stated that a portion of the phloem of the previous year functions through the early part of the growing season (Raatz, 1892; Gill, 1932; Huber, 1939; Esau, 1948). Observations on the inception of new phloem, particularly in respect to its synchronization with xylem development, are at variance. Knudson (1913) believed that phloem production preceded that of xylem. Lodewick (1928) reported a simultaneous beginning. Others (Strasburger, 1891; Rees, 1929; Elliott, 1935; Artschwager, 1945) decided that phloem development began after that of xylem.

In white-cedar the initiating layer in the cambium adjoins the phloem (Bannan, 1955). Phloem mother cells are cut off periodically from this layer, each mother cell usually dividing to produce two cells, the outer of which generally differentiates into a sieve element and the inner into a parenchyma cell or fiber according to the standard pattern of cell sequence. Intermittently with the production of phloem mother cells the initials give rise to xylem mother cells, but during the vernal surge of growth production of the latter exceeds that of the former. In most vigorous trees the first phloem mother cell of the new year does not divide until the middle or latter part of May. The amount of new phloem at the end of May thus ranges from 0 to 4 cells, with 2 as the usual number. The sparse production of 0 to 4 phloem cells by the end of May contrasts with as many as 30 to 60 dividing, differentiating, and mature cells on the xylem side of the initiating row. The preponderance of vernal xylem production has also been noted in other species (Raatz, 1892; Brown, 1915; Gill, 1932; Artschwager, 1945, 1950; Esau, 1948; Fraser, 1952; Grillos and Smith, 1959).

In actively growing white-cedar trees the timetable of phloem development in the lower part of the stem was found to be as follows: 4 new cells by late May or early June, 6 cells at the end of June, 8 cells in mid-July, 10 cells at the end of July, 12–16 cells in mid-August, and by the end of August production was about to cease if it had not already done so. The growth curves of phloem and xylem are thus quite different (Fig. 1–8). Xylem development is characterized by a grand period of growth in May, tapering off through June, July, and August, whereas the production of new phloem begins later and continues at a more or less uniform pace through the remainder of the growing season.

Another noteworthy feature of phloem development, pointed out by Holdheide and Huber (1952) and Artschwager (1945), is that the annual increments vary less than those of the xylem. In white-cedar it was found that on the average a quadrupling in width of the xylem rings from 0.5 to 2.0 mm. was accompanied by only a twofold expansion in phloem accretion.

Root Growth

In conifers the form of the root system varies with the species and habitat. For instance, jack pine trees growing on deep, well-drained soils usually have a prominent tap root, widely spreading laterals, and sinkers descending from the laterals (Pulling, 1918; Cheyney, 1932; Hansen, 1937; Bannan, 1940). On certain sites, however, the tap root is lacking (Adams, 1928). In black spruce, by way of contrast, the tap root and sinkers are absent or feebly developed even in deep sand (Bannan, 1940). In all species the lateral roots are extensive and constitute the major part of the root system. Kalela (1950) estimated that 85 per cent of pine roots and

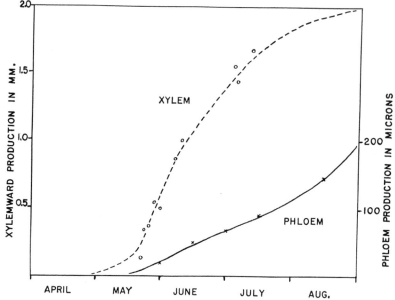

Fig. 1–8. Graph showing the march of xylem and phloem production during the growing season for a hypothetical white-cedar tree having an annual xylem increment of 2 mm.

90 per cent of spruce roots were in the top 20 cm. of soil. The spread of the laterals is often very great, some having been traced for 20 m. or more from the trunk (Heyward, 1933; Bannan, 1940).

Studies of root growth have been concerned mostly with longitudinal growth of the laterals. In northern latitudes growth in length begins shortly after the removal of frost and ceases when the ground becomes too cold (McDougall, 1916; Preston, 1942). Certain workers concluded that longitudinal growth was rhythmic, taking place mainly in the spring and again in the autumn with a slackening or cessation in July and August (Resa, 1877; Peterson, 1898; Büsgen and Münch, 1929; Stevens, 1931). Others believed that a summer rest period occurred only when climatic conditions, such as lack of rainfall, interfered with growth (Wieler, 1894; McDougall, 1916; Turner, 1936; Pessin, 1939; Preston, 1942; Kaufman, 1945; Morrow, 1950).

Diameter growth of roots has received scant attention. According to the literature (see review by Ladefoged) there is much variation in the time of inception of radial growth. Cambial activity apparently begins first in exposed roots or surface roots near the stem and extends to the deeper layers. Radial accretion in the latter often does not begin until several weeks after bud break. Thereafter wood formation evidently proceeds irregularly and may continue later than in the stem (Hartig, 1863; Gulbe, 1889; Lodewick, 1928; Rees, 1929). Brown (1915) has commented on the fact that the rings are sometimes very narrow at one point and wide at another. Some rings are incomplete, and others appear to be multiple.

A notable feature of roots is the wide range in wood structure in different parts of the root system (Bannan, 1941). In the early growth of lateral roots the tracheids are usually large, the walls are thin, and latewood is often restricted to one or two rows of cells (Fig. 1–9). By way of contrast, in the peripheral growth of the larger laterals, in the tap root, and in the sinkers dropping down from the laterals the tracheids are smaller, the walls are thicker, and latewood constitutes a larger proportion of the growth rings (Fig. 1–10). The wood is essentially stemlike. Sensitivity to environmental conditions is shown in the development of a stemlike wood in lateral roots exposed by soil erosion (Kny, 1908; Bannan, 1941). Conversely Wieler (see Büsgen and Münch, 1929, p. 295) produced an open-textured wood like that in lateral roots by placing a stem under water. The author, however, was not able to find such a dramatic alteration in wood texture in the proximal, rooted portions of layered branches of *Abies* and *Picea*. Although some of these branches had been rooted for several years and were well covered with litter, there was in most cases little or no change in wood texture.

The existence of such variability in the wood structure of roots underlies the difficulty of finding the identity of the factor or complex of factors involved in determining wood texture and, more especially, the formation of latewood. The very low proportion of latewood in the inner growth rings of lateral roots is obviously not attributable simply to the fact that the roots are covered by soil. If this were the case the tap and sinker roots should have a similar kind of wood, but they do not. While it might be suggested that the deeper roots are subjected to greater pressure than the laterals, there has been no convincing demonstration that increased pressure favors the development of latewood. In his experiments designed to refute the theory of bark pressure, Krabbe (1884) noted a diminution in ring width and reduction in proportion of latewood after the application of pressure. In areas of compression in stems of *Thuja occidentalis* the author (Bannan, 1957a) found that the

FIGS. 1–9 and 1–10. Wood structure in spruce roots.

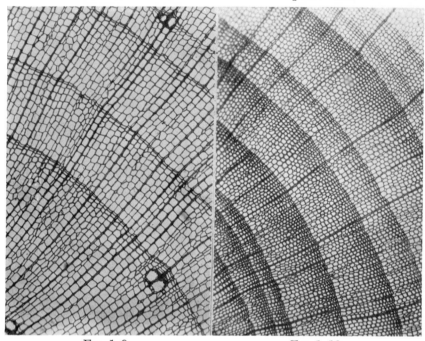

FIG. 1–9.   FIG. 1–10.

FIG. 1–9. *Picea mariana,* open type of wood in lateral root 24 ft. from stem and 2 in. deep in soil. ×40.

FIG. 1–10. *Picea glauca,* stemlike wood in sinker root 3 ft. deep in sand. ×40.

tracheid walls were no thicker, and in the latewood were possibly thinner, than in ordinary wood, and latewood did not exceed the usual proportion. The problem with respect to latewood formation is to find a causal mechanism which is clearly operative under all the varied conditions in different parts of the tree.

Discussion

WALDO S. GLOCK

The initiation of cambial activity, the sequence of events involving cambial initials and xylem and phloem mother cells, the variable rate of cell division, and growth slow-down and cessation—all these and the factors which control them should be of vital interest to everyone seeking to understand tree growth. In other words, *how* a tree grows transcends in importance, perhaps, all other facets of the problem of tree growth. *When* growth occurs, *where* on the plant body it occurs, *how often* it occurs, and *what* factors promote or inhibit growth can be investigated fruitfully only through the understanding of the processes of growth.

Dr. Bannan has given us a picture of tree growth which is lucid and vivid. Painstaking, arduous labor on his part in tracing growth from its inception to its conclusion, through its rate rhythms and physiological rhythms, seems to be establishing the principles upon which later work may be based. Such detailed studies carried on meticulously over protracted periods could well be spread into tree growth under various climatic regimes, various lengths of growing season, and contrasting topographic and edaphic conditions.

Other examples of Dr. Bannan's own detailed work for his region can be found listed under "Literature Cited" at the end of this paper.

Several more specific points should, perhaps, be mentioned. The sequence of cell divisions among cambial initials and mother cells is especially noteworthy. In the matter of growth slow-down, the author keeps in mind the impact of environmental factors. This appears to be proper.

The amount of xylem formed by the end of May in the Toronto area may be a surprise to some workers. On the High Plains of West Texas, the writer has found growth layers with both light and densewood complete by the first of May, and the cambium again actively engaged in setting off xylem cells before the end of the month. All this suggests that the careful work of Dr. Bannan could well be expanded to many other regions.

Dr. Bannan calls attention to the fact that the last-formed phloem elements of the annual increment in certain trees may not complete maturation until the following year. We have found the same thing to be true of the last-formed xylem cells in trees growing on the High Plains of Texas.

Emphasis is placed by Dr. Bannan on the spread and arrangement of the members of a root system. This it seems is justifiable emphasis. If a root system possesses extensive lateral development with many rootlets just below the surface, the tree can make use of many more of the small rains than it could were the roots at some distance below the surface. Measurements of soil moisture during the past 4 years indicate rapid decline of available soil moisture after a rain during the active growing season.

The sequence of events traced by Dr. Bannan for cambial activity throws welcome light on growth processes. We hope that work of this type will be carried on even more vigorously and will bo initiated in many diverse environments.

LITERATURE CITED

ABBE, L. B., and A. S. CRAFTS. 1939. Phloem of white pine and other coniferous species. Bot. Gaz. 100: 695–722.

ADAMS, W. R., JR. 1928. Studies in tolerance of New England forest trees. VIII. Effect of spacing in a jack pine plantation. Vt. Agr. Expt. Sta. Bull. 282: 1–51.

ARTSCHWAGER, E. 1945. Growth studies on guayule (*Parthenium argentatum*). U.S. Dept. Agr. Tech. Bull. 885: 1–19.

———. 1950. The time factor in differentiation of secondary xylem and phloem in pecan. Amer. Jour. Bot. 37: 15–24.

BAILEY, I. W. 1923. The cambium and its derivative tissues. IV. The increase in girth of the cambium. Amer. Jour. Bot. 10: 499–509.

———. 1930. The cambium and its derivative tissues. V. A reconnaissance of the vacuome in living cells. Z. Zellforsch. U. Mikroskop. Anat. 10: 651–682.

BAILEY, I. W., and A. F. FAULL. 1934. The cambium and its derivative tissues. IX. Structural variability in the redwood, *Sequoia sempervirens*, and its significance in the identification of fossil woods. Jour. Arnold Arboretum 15: 233–254.

BALDOVINOS, G. 1953. Growth of the root tip. In: Growth and Differentiation in Plants. W. E. LOOMIS (ed.) Iowa State College Press, Ames, Iowa.

BANNAN, M. W. 1940. The root systems of northern Ontario species growing in sand. Amer. Jour. Bot. 27: 108–114.

———. 1941. Variability in wood structure in roots of native Ontario conifers. Bull. Torrey Bot. Club 68: 173–194.

———. 1953. Further observations on the reduction of fusiform cambial cells in *Thuja occidentalis*. Can. Jour. Bot. 31: 63–74.

———. 1954. Ring widths, tracheid size and ray volume in stem wood of *Thuja occidentalis*. Can. Jour. Bot. 32: 466–479.

———. 1955. The vascular cambium and radial growth in *Thuja occidentalis* L. Can. Jour. Bot. 33: 113–138.

———. 1956. Some aspects of the elongation of fusiform cambial cells in *Thuja occidentalis*. Can. Jour. Bot. 34: 175–196.

———. 1957a. Girth increase in white cedar stems of irregular form. Can. Jour. Bot. 35: 425–434.

———. 1957b. The relative frequency of the different types of anticlinal divisions in conifer cambium. Can. Jour. Bot. 35: 875–884.

———. 1957c. The structure and growth of the cambium. Tappi 40(4): 220–225.

BANNAN, M. W., and I. L. BAYLY. 1956. Cell size and survival in conifer cambium. Can. Jour. Bot. 34: 769–776.

BEIJER, J. J. 1927. Die Vermehrung der radialen Reihen im Cambium. Rec. tray. botan. Néerl. 24: 631–786.

BELYEA, R. M., D. A. FRASER, and A. H. ROSE. 1951. Seasonal growth of some trees in Ontario. Forestry Chron. 27: 300–305.

BROWN, H. P. 1915. Growth studies in forest trees. II. *Pinus strobus* L. Bot. Gaz. 59: 197–241.

BUCKHOUT, W. A. 1907. The formation of the annual ring of wood in the European larch and the white pine. Forestry Quart. 5: 259–267.

BÜSGEN, M., and E. MÜNCH. 1929. Structure and life of forest trees. English translation. John Wiley & Sons, Inc., New York.

BYRAM, G. B., and W. T. DOOLITTLE. 1950. A year of growth for a shortleaf pine. Ecol. 31: 27–35.

CHALK, L. 1951. Water and the growth of wood of Douglas-fir. Quart. Jour. Forestry. 45: 237–242.

———. 1953. Variation of density in stems of Douglas fir. Forestry 26: 33–36.

CHEYNEY, E. G. 1932. The roots of a jack pine tree. Jour. Forestry 30: 928–932.

CHURCH, T. W., JR. 1949. Effects of defoliation on growth of certain conifers. Northeast Forest Expt. Sta. Paper 22: 1–12.

COCKERHAM, G. 1930. Some observations on cambial activity and seasonal starch content in sycamore (*Acer pseudoplatanus*). Proc. Leeds Phil. and Lit. Soc., Sci. Sect. 2: 64–80.

DAUBENMIRE, R. F. 1945. Radial growth of trees at different altitudes. Bot. Gaz. 107: 463–467.

DAUBENMIRE, R. F., and M. E. DETERS. 1947. Comparative studies of growth in deciduous and evergreen trees. Bot. Gaz. 109: 1–12.

DE BARY, A. 1884. Comparative Anatomy of the Vegetative Organs of the Phanerogams and Ferns. English Translation. The Clarendon Press. Oxford.

DOBBS, C. G. 1953. A study of growth rings in trees III. Forestry 26: 97–110.

EGGLER, W. A. 1955. Radial growth in nine species of trees in southern Louisiana. Ecol. 36: 130–136.

ELLIOTT, J. H. 1935. Seasonal changes in the development of the phloem of the sycamore, *Acer Pseudo Platanus* L. Proc. Leeds Phil. and Lit. Soc., Sci. Sect. 3: 5–67.

ESAU, K. 1948. Phloem structure in the grapevine, and its seasonal changes. Hilgardia 18: 217–296.

FAHN, A. 1958. Xylem structure and annual rhythm of development in trees and shrubs of the desert. I. *Tamarix aphylla, T. Jordanis* var. *negevensis, T. gallica* var. *Maris mortui*. Trop. Woods 109: 81–94.

FOWELLS, H. A. 1941. The period of seasonal growth of ponderosa pine and associated species. Jour. Forestry 39: 601–608.

FRASER, D. A. 1952. Initiation of cambial activity in some forest trees in Ontario. Ecol. 33: 259–273.

FRIEDRICH, J. 1897. Über den Einfluss der Witterung auf den Baumzwachs. Mitt. Forstl. Versuch. Osterreichs 22:1–160.

FRITTS, H. C. 1958. An analysis of radial growth of beech in a central Ohio forest during 1954–1955. Ecol. 39: 705–720.

GÄUMANN, E. 1928. Die chemische Zusammensetzung des Fichten-und Tannenholzes in den verschiedenen Jahreszeiten. Flora 123: 344–385.

GILL, N. 1932. The phloem of ash (*Fraxinus excelsior* Linn.): Its differentiation and seasonal variation. Proc. Leeds Phil. and Lit. Soc., Sci. Sect. 2: 347–355.

GLOCK, W. S. 1955. Tree growth. II. Growth rings and climate. Bot. Rev. 21: 73–188.

GRILLOS, S. J., and F. H. SMITH. 1959. The secondary phloem of Douglas-fir. Forest Sci. 5: 377–388.

GULBE, L. A. 1889. Über die periodische Thätigkeit des Cambiums in den Wurzeln unserer Bäume. Jahrb. St. Petersburger Forstinst. 3: 1–47. 1888. Review in Bot. Centbl. 40: 43–44.

HANSEN, T. S. 1937. Ecological changes due to thinning jack pine. Minn. Agr. Expt. Sta. Tech. Bull. 124: 1–77.

HARPER, A. G. 1913. Defoliation: Its effects upon the growth and structure of the wood of *Larix*. Ann. Bot. 27: 621–642.

HARTIG, T. 1853. Über die Entwickelung des Jahresringes der Holzpflanzen. Bot. Zeitung 11: 553–556, 569–579.

———. 1863. Über die Zeit des Zuwachses der Baumwurzeln. Bot. Ztg. 21: 288–289.

HEYWARD, F. 1933. The root system of longleaf pine on the deep sands of western Florida. Ecol. 14: 136–148.

HOLDHEIDE, W., and B. HUBER. 1952. Ähnlichkeiten und Unterschiede im Feinbau von Holze und Rinde. Holz. Roh-u. Werkstoff 10: 263–268.

HUBER, B. 1939. Das Siebröhensystem unserer Bäume und seine jahreszeitlichen Veränderungen. Jahrb. f. Wiss. Bot. 88: 176–242.

JACKSON, L. W. R. 1952. Radial growth of forest trees in the Georgia Piedmont. ECOL. 33: 336–341.

JOST, L. 1892. Beobachtungen über den zeitlichen Verlauf des secundären Dickenwachsthums der Bäume. Ber. Deut. Bot. Ges. 10: 587–605.

KALELA, E. K. 1950. On the horizontal roots in pine and spruce stands. 1. Acta Forest. Fenn. 57: 1–79.

KAUFMAN, C. M. 1945. Root growth of jack pine on several sites in the Cloquet Forest, Minnesota. Ecol. 26: 10–23.

KIENHOLZ, R. 1934. Leader, needle, cambial, and root growth of certain conifers and their interrelations. Bot. Gaz. 96: 73–92.

KLEINMANN, A. 1923. Über Kern-und Zellteilungen im Cambium. Bot. Arch. 4: 113–147.

KLINKEN, J. 1914. Über das gleitende Wachstum der Initialen im Kambium der Koniferen und den Markstrahlverlauf in ihrer sekundären Rinde. Biblioth. Bot. 19: 1–37.

KNUDSON, L. 1913. Observations on the inception, season, and duration of cambium development in the American larch (*Larix laricina* [Du Roi] Koch). Bull. Torrey Bot. Club 40: 271–293.

KNY, L. 1908. Über das Dickenwachstum des Holzkörpers der Wurzeln in seiner Beziehung zur Lotlinie. Ber. Deut. Bot. Ges. 26: 19–50.

KORSTIAN, C. F. 1921. Diameter growth in box elder and blue spruce. Bot. Gaz. 71: 451–461.

KRABBE, G. 1884. Über das Wachsthum des Verdickungsringes und der jungen Holzzellen in seiner Abhängigkeit von Druckwirkungen. Abhandl. Köningl. Akad. der Wiss. Berlin.

KRUGER, F. 1892. Über die Wandverdickungen der Cambiumzellen Bot. Ztg. 50: 633–640, 649–657, 665–670, 681–688, 702–708.

LADEFOGED, K. 1952. The periodicity of wood formation. Kgl. Danske Videnskab Selskab. Biol. Skrifter 7: 1–98.

LARSON, P. R. 1957. Effect of environment on the percentage of summerwood and specific gravity of slash pine. Yale Univ., School Forestry Bull. 63.

LODEWICK, J. R. 1928. Seasonal activity of the cambium in some northeastern trees. Bull. N. Y. State Col. Forestry, Syracuse Univ. Tech. Publ. 23: 1–87.

LUXFORD, R. F., and L. J. MARKWARDT. 1932. The strength and related properties of redwood. U.S. Dept. Agr. Tech. Bull. 305: 1–48.

MACDOUGAL, D. T. 1938. Tree growth. Chronica Botanica Co., Leiden.

McDOUGALL, W. B. 1916. The growth of forest tree roots. Amer. Jour. Bot. 3: 384–392.

MARTS, R. O. 1950. Wood quality of bud-pruned longleaf pine. South. Lumberman issue of Dec. 15, 1950: 1–3.

MER, E. 1892. Réveil et extinction de l'activité cambiale dans les arbres. Compt. Rend. Acad. Sci. 114: 242–245.

MISCHKE, K. 1890. Beobachtungen über das Dickenwachstum der Coniferen. Bot. Cent. 44: 39–43, 65–71, 97–102, 137–142, 169–175.

MORROW, R. R. 1950. Periodicity in growth of sugar maple surface layer roots. Jour. Forestry 48: 875–881.

PAUL, B. H. 1930. The application of silviculture in controlling the specific gravity of wood. U.S. Dept. Agr. Tech. Bull. 168: 1–19.

———. 1950. Wood quality in relation to site quality of second-growth Douglas-fir. Jour. Forestry 48: 175–179.

———. 1957. Growth and specific gravity responses in a thinned red pine plantation. Jour. Forestry 55: 510–512.

PAUL, B. H., and R. O. MARTS. 1931. Controlling the proportion of summerwood in long-leaf pine. Jour. Forestry 29: 784–796.

PAUL, B. H., and D. M. SMITH. 1950. Summary on growth in relation to quality of southern yellow pine. U.S. Dept. Agr. Forest. Ser., Forest Prod. Lab. D1751: 1–19.

PESSIN, L. J. 1939. Root habits of longleaf pine and associated species. Ecol. 20: 47–57.

PETERSON, O. G. 1898. Études sur les Phénomènes vitaux des racines des arbres (Französisches resumé). Bot. Cent. 75: 272–274.

PRESTON, R. J., JR. 1942. The growth and development of the root systems of juvenile lodgepole pines. Ecol. Monog. 12: 449–468.

PRIESTLEY, J. H. 1930. Studies in the physiology of cambial activity III. The seasonal activity of the cambium. New Phytol. 29: 316–354.

PRIESTLEY, J. H., and L. I. SCOTT. 1936. A note upon summer wood production in the tree. Proc. Leeds Phil. and Lit. Soc., Sci. Sect. 3: 235–245.

PRIESTLEY, J. H., and L. I. SCOTT, and M. E. MALINS. 1933. A new method of studying cambial activity. Proc. Leeds Phil. and Lit. Soc., Sci. Sect. 2: 365–374.

PULLING, H. E. 1918. Root habit and plant distribution in the far north. Plant World, 21: 223–233.

RAATZ, W. 1892. Die Stabbildungen im secundären Holzkörper der Bäume und die Initialentheorie. Jahrb. f. Wiss. Bot. 23: 567–636.

REES, L. W. 1929. Growth studies in forest trees Picea rubra Link. Jour. Forestry 27: 384–403.

RENDLE, B. J., and E. W. J. PHILLIPS. 1958. The effect of rate of growth (ring width) on the density of soft woods. Forestry 31: 113–120. 1958.

RESA, F. 1877. Über die Periode der Wurzelbildung. Inaug. Diss. Bonn (cited by Brown, 1915).

SANIO, K. 1873. Anatomie der gemeinen Kiefer (Pinus silvestris L.) Jahrb. f. Wiss. Bot. 9: 50–126.

SCHNEIDER, H. 1952. The phloem of the sweet orange tree trunk and the seasonal production of xylem and phloem. Hilgardia 21: 331–366.

SCHOUTE, J. C. 1902. Über Zellteilungsvorgänge im Cambium. Koninkl. Akad. Wetenschap. Sect. II, 9: 3–59.

SCHULMAN, E. 1942. Dendrochronology in pines of Arkansas. Ecol. 23: 309–318.

SCHWARZ, F. 1899. Physiologische Untersuchungen über Dickenwachstum und Holzqualität von Pinus sylvestris. Parey. Berlin. 372 pp.

STEVENS, C. L. 1931. Root growth of white pine. Yale Univ., School Forestry Bull. 32: 1–62.

STRASBURGER, E. 1891. Über den Bau und die Verrichtungen der Leitungsbahnen in den Pflanzen Hist. Beiträge Bd. 3. Gustav Fischer. Jena.

STUDHALTER, R. A. 1955. Tree growth. I. Some historical chapters. Bot. Rev. 21: 1–72.

TURNBULL, J. M. 1937. Variations in strength of pine timbers. So. African Jour. Sci. 33: 654–682.

TURNER, L. M. 1936. Root growth of seedlings of Pinus echinata and Pinus taeda. Jour. Agr. Res. 53: 145–149.

WAREING, P. F. 1954. Growth studies in woody species. VI. The locus of photoperiodic perception in relation to dormancy. Physiol. Plant. 7: 261–277.

WAREING, P. F., and D. L. ROBERTS. 1956. Photoperiodic control of cambial activity in Robinia pseudacacia L. New Phytol. 55: 356–366.

WARRACK, G., and C. JOERGENSEN. 1950. Precision measurement of radial growth and daily radial fluctuations in Douglas fir. Forestry Chron. 26: 52–66.

WIELER, A. 1894. Über die Periodicität in der Wurzelbildung der Pflanzen. Forstwiss. Centbl. 16: 333–349.

———. 1898. Über die jährliche Periodicität im Dickenwachsthum des Holzkörpers der Bäume. Tharandter Forstl. Jahrb. 48: 39–139.

WIGHT, W. 1933. Radial growth of the xylem and the starch reserves of Pinus sylvestris: A preliminary survey. New Phytol. 32: 77–96.

2

Rainfall and Tree Growth

WALDO S. GLOCK AND SHARLENE R. AGERTER *

Introduction

The relation of rainfall to tree growth impinges so constantly on the processes of, and results achieved by, cambial activity and cambial rhythms that investigators are tempted to devote themselves exclusively to the physiology and anatomy of growth. Cambial division, differentiation, maturation, and growth in all aspects hold the key to an understanding of what it is we wish to investigate in the relationship of rainfall to tree growth.

The literature on the relationship between tree growth and climate has been reviewed by Studhalter (1955) and by Glock (1941, 1955).

In this paper attention will be directed toward an analysis of tree-growth—rainfall (or soil moisture) relations, first, by means of a new method recently discovered and called the "incidence of reversals," second, by means of what may be called "pattern analysis," and, third, by means of a few detailed comparisons of a specific pattern type. All this has to do more with cambial activity, perhaps, than with simple comparisons between growth layers and spot rainfall. However, certain complicating aspects bear directly upon the linear relationship between growth-layer thicknesses and spot rainfall; these complicating items are optimum and limiting factors,

* The studies of which the present material is in the nature of a progress report have been supported generously during the past years by the Smithsonian Institution, the American Philosophical Society, the National Science Foundation, Texas Technological College, and Macalester College. To these organizations the authors owe deep gratitude. They are also indebted to the personnel of the U.S. Forest Service, the Rocky Mountain Forest and Range Experiment Station, the Texas Agricultural Experiment Station, and the Walnut Canyon National Monument, for long-continued and generous cooperation.

23

multiplicity of growth factors, and uniformity within the trunk of a tree.

Correlations of spot or multispot rainfall with growth-layer thicknesses have yielded coefficients of approximately 0.4 to 0.8, hovering around 0.55 to 0.60. In a comparison which gave a coefficient of 0.50, trend showed 32 cases parallel and 12 opposite. The introduction of a lag effect gave a coefficient of 0.82, whereas trend showed 22 cases parallel and 21 opposite.

In reference to the use of the Pearsonian correlation coefficient, J. Bartels of Germany told the writers its use is legitimate for data gained by random sampling but ill-advised for data of a continuous time series. However that may be, the trend coefficient (Glock, 1942) gives results little better than the correlation coefficient. A collection of increment cores from near the forest interior at about 9,000 feet in north-central New Mexico (Glock, 1950) gave a trend coefficient of 0.965 with 12 per cent opposite trends between tree growth and rainfall of March–July, 5 miles distant over a span of 33 years.

With January–August rainfall the coefficient was 0.95 with 19 per cent opposite trend, and with March–June rainfall 0.89 with 16 per cent opposite trend. Other month intervals and other rainfall stations gave decreasing correspondence. Figure 2–1A shows the poor quality of cross-dating near the forest interior where trend cofficient is high. This should be compared with Fig. 2–1B which shows high-quality cross-dating near the lower forest border in northern Arizona. The graphs of Fig. 2–1C show the close trend relationship between growth-layer thicknesses and March–July rainfall 5 miles distant.

Both types of correlation are beset by problems inherent in the use of rainfall records. These problems include variations in rainfall from spot to spot; inconsistent rainfall amounts in sequence (Henry, 1931), for instance a month above average may be followed by one far below, or vice versa; the particular month interval of rainfall which controls the amount of soil moisture present when actual growth requires it; the percentage of any given precipitation becoming available soil moisture; and the time relationships between precipitation and physiological requirements—the speed and course of the journey from rainfall to the hydrostatic system of the plant.

Limiting factors constitute the first complicating aspect of study. Growth depends upon a complex of factors and the proper balance among them. If one factor is too scarce or too plentiful in relation to others, it becomes limiting. The very nature of growth, complex as is the process, makes it nearly if not quite impossible to separate

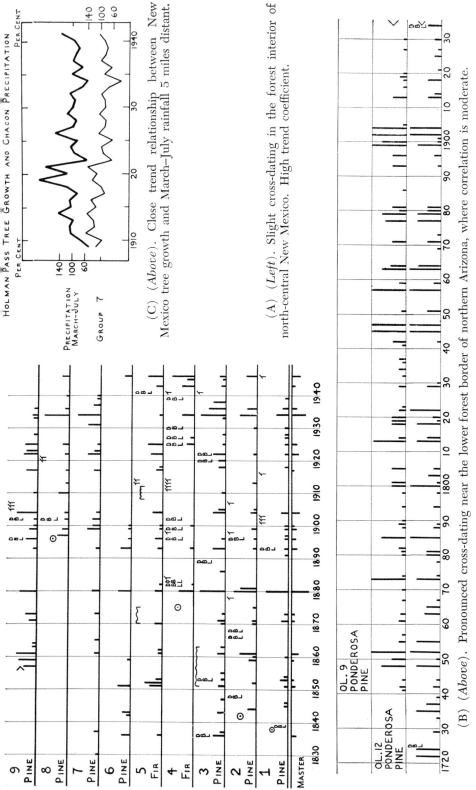

HOLMAN PASS TREE GROWTH AND CHACON PRECIPITATION

(C) (*Above*). Close trend relationship between New Mexico tree growth and March–July rainfall 5 miles distant.

(A) (*Left*). Slight cross-dating in the forest interior of north-central New Mexico. High trend coefficient.

(B) (*Above*). Pronounced cross-dating near the lower forest border of northern Arizona, where correlation is moderate.

FIG. 2–1. Cross-dating.

25

completely the effects of water supply from those of all other factors. This goes so far as to suggest that a truly 100 per cent correlation of rainfall and tree growth would be highly suspect.

If rainfall maintains soil moisture at the optimum amount in relation to other factors which themselves are in proper balance, growth may attain its maximum as expressed in growth-layer thicknesses. Sequences are highly uniform; in fact, factors in proper balance and in uniform amounts from season to season give growth layers with little visual differences in thickness. Away from such an idealized optimum in water supply, variations in growth-layer thicknesses, although slight, do appear and in one case at least show high correlation with rainfall. Figure 2–2A shows fluctuating soil moisture (or rainfall) which yields minimum variation in growth-layer thicknesses depending upon the position of the mean line within the optimal zone. Such conditions will result in no violent decrease in thickness from one growth layer to another.

If average rainfall lies close to the lower (Fig. 2–2B) limit or to the upper (Fig. 2–2C) limit of the optimal zone, certain fluctuations will penetrate downward into the minimal zone and others upward into the maximal, both being recorded decidedly in resultant growth.

It seems clear that the interplay of many factors, even though an attempt is made to simplify the picture by a threefold division into optimum, minimum, and maximum, presents manifold complexities when considering the vivid contrasts in habitat conditions from the desert at the extreme lower forest border with its scant and uncertain water supply to the forest interior and beyond with its abundant water supply.

The multiplicity of growth factors, the second of the complicating aspects, may be classified briefly as internal: genetic, physiologic, reproductive, growth substances, pathologic, electrical potential, and polarity; as external: rainfall and temperature (popular), wind and storms, evaporation and humidity, soil and rock, sunlight and radiation, competition, fire, and topography and exposure. Known to be multiple in number as well as multiple in action, these factors either promote or inhibit tree growth.

Genetic factors may cause differences in sensitivity, whereas ecologic factors may cause differences in variability of growth-layer sequences. Physiologic factors include, for instance, cambial activity, maturation, and so-called invisible growth layers. Coming periodically as they do, heavy seed years are included under reproductive factors which influence growth. Pathologic factors include periodic pest attacks. Hormones, either promoting or inhibiting growth, assume great importance with respect to the factors which control hormone formation and dissipation. Among the ecologic factors, rainfall (or soil moisture) and temperature have popular

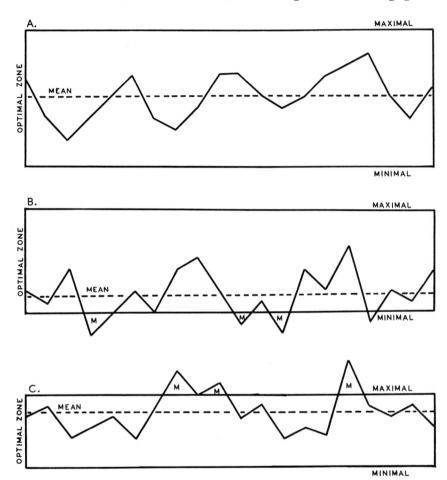

FIG. 2–2. Optimum and limiting factors, diagrammatically expressed. (A) Fluctuations within the optimal zone, yielding uniform sequences. (B) Average rainfall sufficiently low so that at points "M" rainfall becomes limiting and there is a direct response in tree growth. (C) Average rainfall sufficiently high so that at points "M" rainfall becomes limiting and there is an inverse response in tree growth.

appeal and undoubtedly stand high in importance in many habitat situations. It is known that they fluctuate in degree and in time. Their fluctuations cover less than a year, approximately a year, and more than a year. If growth is indeed strongly affected by rainfall and temperature it seems clear that one should remain alert to anatomical evidence for such fluctuations and cycles.

Figure 2–3 illustrates annual and less-than-annual fluctuations diagrammatically; in the first instance the fluctuations yield thick and thin annual growth layers, in the second they yield multiple growth layers within the annual increment. If this is essentially true, the identification of the annual growth layer depends upon

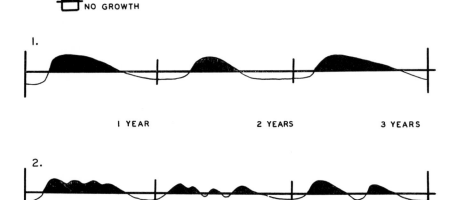

■ GROWTH
□ NO GROWTH

1.

I YEAR   2 YEARS   3 YEARS

2.

FIG. 2–3. Diagrammatic representation of (1) thick and thin growth layers, and (2) multiple growth layers.

the lack of decisiveness with which growth factors terminate and re-initiate growth among the other growth layers within the annual increment.

The third complication is composed of the many problems of uniformity which beset the growth layers themselves. If volume represents the true measure of growth in a tree the following questions may be asked:

To what extent does one radius represent a section or a whole tree?
To what extent does one section represent a tree?
To what extent does one tree represent a group?

A partial answer to these questions is being sought at the present time by the analysis of three sectioned ponderosa pine trees which grew within 2.5 miles of each other north of Flagstaff, Arizona, near the lower limit of the ponderosa pine zone. Perhaps the lack of uniformity of absolute and relative thicknesses of growth layers within the stem of a tree explains partly or completely the rather poor correspondence between amount of rainfall and thicknesses of growth layers.

Sections were taken at an average distance of 4 feet apart in each of the three trees and either three or five radii were measured on each section. The following tabulation summarizes pertinent results to date:

Absolute thickness: unless thickness is zero, no growth layer on any section has the same thickness on three radii.

Site of thickest portion of growth layers: chiefly on north radius, but by no means universal (Fig. 2-4).

Relative thicknesses; uniformity of trend: decrease of uniformity with additional radii, 146 years.

	1st tree	2nd tree
3 radii	77 per cent	73 per cent
5 radii	70 per cent	65 per cent

Circuit uniformity; sectional averages, three trees:

71 per cent to 84 per cent (circuit uniformity for individual sections falls within this range).

Minimum, 1800–1899: 42 per cent.

Total circuit uniformity; comparison of the individual section averages for the entire trunk:

Tree 1—80 per cent.
Tree 2—79 per cent.
Tree 3—78 per cent.

Total circuit uniformity; comparison of tree averages:

Tree average, three trees—66 per cent.
Second section above ground—62 per cent.
Sixth section above ground—62 per cent.
Ninth section above ground—54 per cent.
1700–1941—No reversals anywhere in the three trees—18 per cent.

Longitudinal uniformity; section averages:

	Tree No. 1	Tree No. 2	Tree No. 3
2 sections	94 per cent	94 per cent	94 per cent
11 or 12 sections	63 per cent	55 per cent	62 per cent

Longitudinal uniformity, three separate radii, three trees:

	Tree No. 1	Tree No. 2	Tree No. 3
N radius	57 per cent	68 per cent	59 per cent
SE radius	60 per cent	66 per cent	57 per cent
SW radius....................	63 per cent	62 per cent	59 per cent

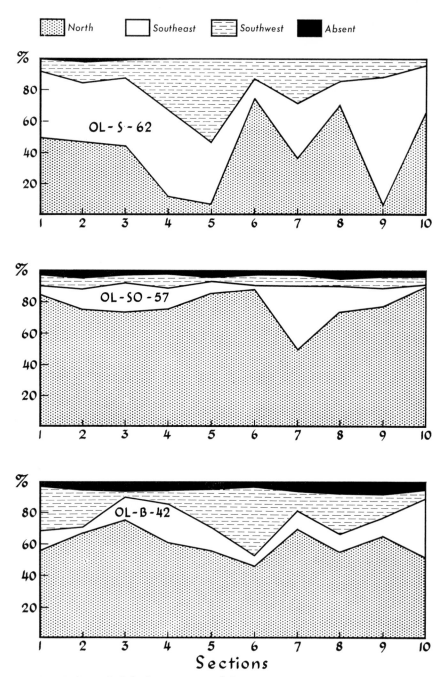

Fig. 2–4. Radial thicknesses around the circuit in per cent.

Trend agreement in trunk as a whole; all radii, all sections:

Tree 1—47.6 per cent (10 sections, 3 radii, 7,260 total).
Tree 2—51.6 per cent (10 sections, 3 radii, 7,260 total).
Tree 3—46.4 per cent (12 sections, 3 radii, 8,712 total).

Figure 2–5 gives the reversals of trend, their numbers and their distribution on three radii vertically along the trunk for some 40 feet, 1800–1899. In the first 8 sections, 54 per cent of the growth layers do not have reversals on any radius; in the first 9 sections 50 per cent do not have reversals; and in the 10 sections 41 per cent do not have reversals.

It seems quite clear that variations and reversals in thickness relations among growth layers throughout a tree are amply sufficient to explain the lack of high correlation between growth-layer thicknesses and precipitation records. A single radius, or an entire section, agrees with the entire trunk (as represented by 10 to 14 sections of three to five radii each) from 40 to 80 per cent as brought out in the critical analysis of three trees from near the lower part of the ponderosa pine zone. How can one determine whether a given radius or section represents the total response of a tree poorly, fairly, excellently, or perfectly? If to this lack of uniformity there are added the problems inherent in the multiplicity of growth factors, spot rainfall, and available soil moisture when and where the trees need it, the quality of linear relationships between growth-layer thicknesses and spot rainfall appears to be surprisingly high. Because of the high quality of the comparisons more should not be read into the results than is justified.

Tree-Growth–Rainfall Relations

INCIDENCE OF REVERSALS. The unsatisfactory and sometimes frustrating nature of growth-rainfall correlations served as a sharp motivation to determine other methods of gaining climatic, specifically rainfall, information from growth layers. Uniformity by means of reversal incidence and pattern analysis suggests, in the first case, a means of detecting change in rainfall distribution or amount and, in the second, of deriving the rainfall regime.

Incidence of reversals—New Mexico: During work at Holman Pass in north-central New Mexico (Glock, 1950), a puzzling abundance of reversals in trend appeared in the interval 1850–1897 as contrasted with the interval 1898–1941. An immediate search was made for other contrasts between the two intervals. A resumé of

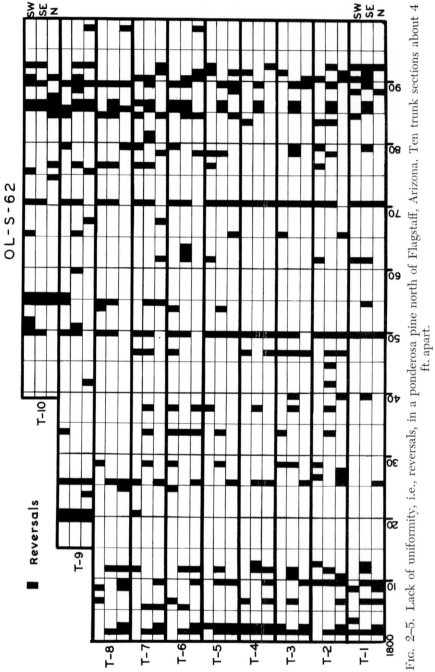

Fig. 2–5. Lack of uniformity, i.e., reversals, in a ponderosa pine north of Flagstaff, Arizona. Ten trunk sections about 4 ft. apart.

results is given here in order that they may be compared with those detailed later:

Tree Averages	1850–1897	1898–1941
Parallel trends (9 trees)	9	15
Average thickness, millimeters	1.99	1.83
Average departure, per cent	35	31
Average variation, per cent	33	32
Average departure from mean variation, per cent	13	10.5

Santa Fe Rainfall		
March–July, inches	6.34	6.74
Average departure, per cent	33	22
Average variation, per cent	42	33
Average departure from mean variation, per cent	25	22

The data given are by no means the complete picture but do represent seven out of nine trees. If the other two trees are included the contrasts are not so sharply drawn except for average departure from mean variation. If the parameters of four of the trees which grew on the sites judged to be somewhat drier than those of the other five are isolated, they yield mixed data. Average variation for these "dry site" trees actually increased during the later interval in comparison with the earlier one. In similar fashion, calculation showed that average variation for April–May rainfall likewise increased, thus contrasting with that for March–July rainfall. Average rainfall of March–June began to increase sometime near 1898 whereas that of July–August decreased. If the physiology of growth is to be understood it is necessary to recognize and study the complexities involved in even one growth-influencing factor such as indicated above for rainfall.

Leopold (1951) published an excellent analysis of Santa Fe rainfall. In this analysis he discovered a marked difference in the number of small rains between the two periods 1849–1895 and 1896–1939. These dates, surprisingly enough, coincide almost exactly with those found in Holman Pass tree growth. Leopold grouped daily rains into three categories:

Small rains	0.01–0.49 inch
Intermediate rains	0.50–0.99 inch
Large rains	1.00 inch or more

	1849–1895	1896–1939
Number of small rains per year	66	81
Number of rains over 1.00 inch, average per year	1.7	1.1

Apparently, small rains at close intervals have more uniform influence on growth than do heavy, widely spaced rains. This is strikingly true, we believe, for trees with shallow root systems.

Figure 2–6 shows one example among hundreds which have been observed over the years in New Mexico, Arizona, California, Texas, and many other states.

Growth at Holman Pass showed poorer correlation with rainfall during the earlier period than it did during the later. Thus, cor-

Fig. 2–6. "Pancake" root system which lay just below the surface, where small rains can be effective.

relations were higher when frequency of small rains was greater and when variations of rainfall were less.

Incidence of reversals—Arizona: After the three dissected ponderosa pines from north of Flagstaff, Arizona, had been analyzed for general uniformity, a restudy of the data revealed that a marked change in trend uniformity, or incidence of reversals, had occurred within the decade 1895–1904. A summary of initial results follows:

	1850–1897	1900–1947
Reversals (tree averages), per cent	36	46
Reversals (section 2), per cent	36	44
Mean sensitivity	0.57	0.43
Average growth-layer thickness, millimeters	0.91	1.30
Average departure, per cent	45	49
Average variation, per cent	33	42
Average departure from mean variation, per cent	23	25

A greater number of reversals for 1900–1947 was accompanied by thicker growth layers, increase in values of parameters, and a decrease in mean sensitivity (Douglass, 1928). This contrasts vividly with the results in New Mexico where the greater number of reversals occurred during the interval 1850–1897. However, the limits of the intervals are significantly the same.

It seems clear that trees record changes in both amount and distribution in the rainfall regime. Perhaps the indications here revealed in trees from New Mexico and Arizona offer a highly profitable field of investigation for information on the nature, distribution, and amount of rainfall. Root systems, soil moisture, and perhaps above all the physiology of growth itself must be studied. A study such as that carried on by Leopold accomplishes more in emphasizing the complexities of a single growth factor and reveals more basic information on tree growth than does ever so much work on correlation and trend coefficients. As a next direct step using the "incidence of reversals," it is necessary to define, clarify, and evaluate all parameters or indexes known at present or yet to be discovered. In this manner it may be possible to point the way for future physiological and anatomical studies into the fundamentals of tree growth.

GROWTH PATTERNS AND THE RAINFALL REGIME. Before much field work had been done and before much thought had been given to complexity of growth patterns, growth layers were rather simply classified, from highly variable to extremely uniform types. Studies of cross-sections of trees from the desert and near desert, from the forest interior, and from high altitudes in northern Arizona confused rather than clarified growth characteristics, continuity, and relationships.

An extension of field work into California, New Mexico, and over a greater area of northern Arizona further complicated the picture of growth sequences and growth patterns. Growth patterns are complex, not simple. It was not until after 10 years of intensive work in West Texas and continued studies in northern Arizona and the central Sierra Nevada of California that a tentative classification of growth layers began to emerge with any degree of clarity.

Initially, three pattern types, which were named the California, the West Texas, and the Northern Arizona, were recognized. These types corresponded roughly to three rainfall regimes: winter rainfall, summer rainfall, and a combination of the two. Figure 2–7 shows the maximum, average, and minimum monthly rainfall of Lubbock, Texas, on the east and San Francisco on the west, with the intermediate stations at Winslow, Flagstaff, and Kingman, Arizona. Lubbock experiences dominantly summer rainfall, San Francisco winter rainfall, and Flagstaff both summer and winter rainfall. To a certain extent, the Winslow rainfall regime is intermediate between that of Lubbock and Flagstaff; the Kingman regime is somewhat intermediate between Flagstaff and San Francisco. Juiz de Fora, Brazil, and Darwin, Australia, have summer rainfall whereas Auckland, New Zealand, has accent on winter rainfall.

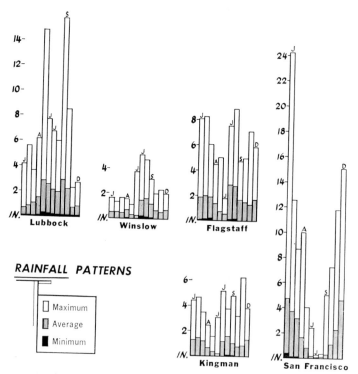

RAINFALL PATTERNS

☐ Maximum
▦ Average
■ Minimum

FIG. 2–7. Maximum, average, and minimum monthly rainfall of Lubbock, Texas; Winslow, Flagstaff, and Kingman, Arizona; and San Francisco, California. Three stations from the Southern Hemisphere are given for comparison:

Under the California regime a rainy season occurs in the winter and a dry season in the summer. Growth begins at the start of the growing season when all or nearly all the soil moisture, which the trees will find available until the next winter, is present in the soil. Soil moisture, commonly at an initial maximum, diminishes steadily to such an extent at some places and at some times as to halt growth. Marked differences in elevation, proximity to the coast, and latitude may intensify or modify the type.

In the California pattern of tree growth, growth layers are seldom partial; they possess low variability, probable unity of growth layers in the annual increment, a lack of diffusely margined growth layers, and rather high uniformity of absolute and relative thicknesses. Cross-dating exists but is typically abortive and localized. Figure 2–3A from the forest interior of New Mexico, illustrates the quality of cross-dating in the California pattern. Although annual increments probably possess unity of growth layers, the matter awaits careful study, especially in light of the fact that a second tip flush

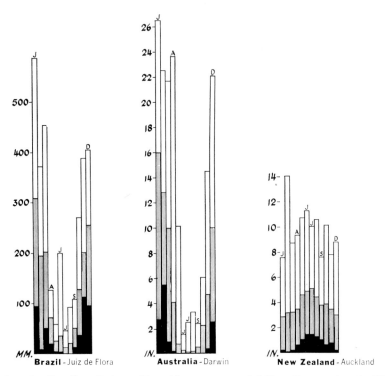

Brazil - Juiz de Flora   Australia - Darwin   New Zealand - Auckland

stations in Brazil and Australia with summer rainfall and a station in New Zealand with winter rainfall.

was observed to occur on conifers in August in the central Sierra Nevada at an elevation of 9,000 feet.

Illustrations of the California pattern of regularity are so common in lumber from California, the Northwest, and the northern states that photographs are perhaps unnecessary. However, two are pertinent here. Figure 2–8 gives a sequence of growth layers in *Agathis* from New Zealand and illustrates the California pattern grown in a regime of winter rainfall. In contrast, a section of Western Juniper (*Juniperus occidentalis*) from above 8,400 feet elevation in the central Sierra Nevada (Fig. 2–9) probably shows the effects of a water supply above the optimum. Pattern characteristics diverge from the ideal California in the matter of fluctuations of absolute and relative thicknesses around the circuit and thus, but no further, resemble patterns in trees grown under a water supply considerably below the optimum. In fact, the 19-foot juniper from which the section of Fig. 2–9 was taken grew near and within the head of a broad shallow upland valley (Glock, 1937). Snow was off the ground less than 2 weeks when the tree was felled on July 5. The current growth layer was one-third to one-half the thickness of the previous growth layer and about equal in thickness to the average growth layer of the section. Tip growth exceeded 3 inches. There can be little doubt that growth commonly begins among the high-altitude junipers before the snow cover disappears and that in some cases more than half the seasonal growth is completed within 2 weeks after the disappearance of the snow cover. Because such high percentage of growth occurs before seasonal temperature has reached a maximum it would appear that the length of the growing season, as represented by the interval during which temperature is favorable for growth, has little effect on the thickness of annual increments unless there is a second flush of growth in the season.

Under the West Texas regime, summer rainfall dominates the annual picture (Fig. 2–7). The total supply of the season's soil moisture seldom if ever is present when growth begins in the spring; the bulk of the rainfall comes after the first burst of growth. During the summer rainy season brief wet spells are separated by dry spells which are sometimes of short duration and at other times prolonged and intense. Here, latitude, altitude, and continentality may be vital factors.

Partial growth layers are a common feature of the West Texas pattern of tree growth. The pattern is also characterized by high variability, multiplicity of growth layers within the annual increments, many diffusely-margined growth layers, and uniformity of relative and absolute thicknesses which varies from low to high

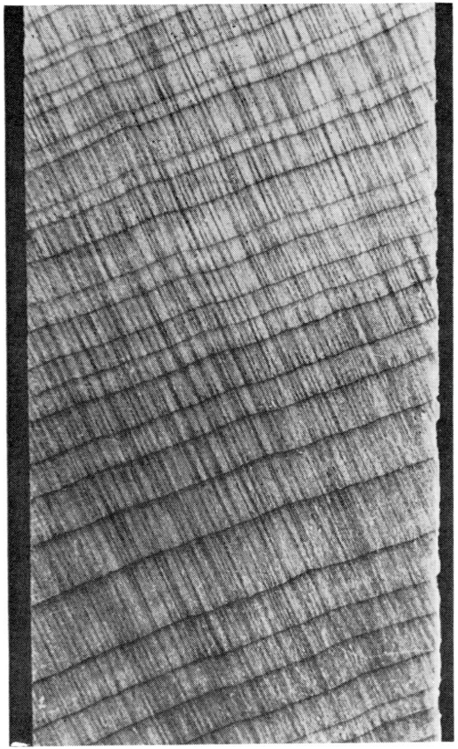

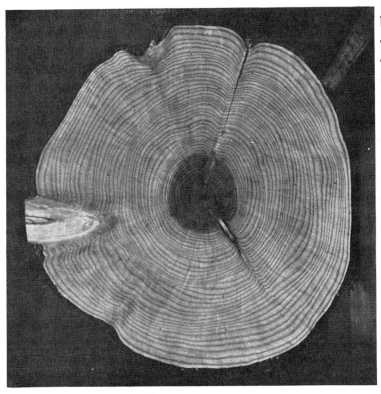

FIG. 2–8 (left). An example of the California type of growth pattern in *Agathis* (the Kauri) from New Zealand. The rainfall regime is shown on Fig. 2–7.

FIG. 2–9 (right). Section of *Juniperus occidentalis* from an elevation of over 8,400 ft. in the central Sierra Nevada of California.

degree. Quality of cross-dating is weak and, because of multiplicity and partial growth layers, cross-dating commonly is futile.

The great number of partial growth layers (lenses) and the high degree of radial variability in thickness constitute the two most readily visible diagnostic features of the West Texas pattern of tree growth. A two-dimensional view of growth layers reveals little

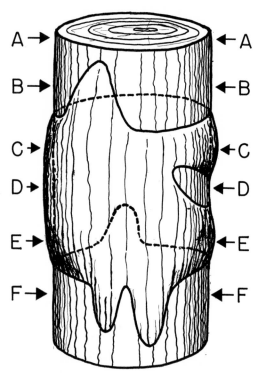

FIG. 2–10. A partial growth layer, diagrammatically expressed, to show the different positions on the trunks where transverse sections could be taken. See Fig. 2–11 (from Smithsonian Institution).

about the actual areal distribution of the sheath of xylem on the trunk, the nature of the sheath if the "ring" is partial, or whether the ring is truly entire. This problem of areal distribution in three dimensions is illustrated in Figs. 2–10 and 2–11. The cross-sections of Fig. 2–11 were taken at the designated places on Fig. 2–10 and clearly illustrate how the same partial growth layer can appear in a variety of different forms when viewed in two dimensions only. If one were to make inferences based on any single cross-section of Fig. 2–11, grave errors might result. The same sheath of xylem appears as: an absent growth layer, a short lens, an entire growth layer, a long lens, a "different" long lens, and two short concurrent lenses. It is obvious that a three-dimensional viewpoint is of critical importance.

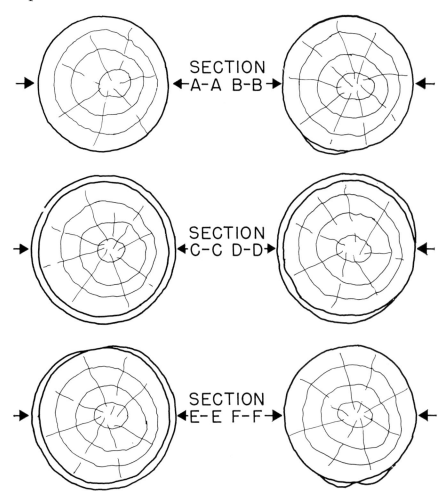

FIG. 2–11. Transverse sections taken at the positions designated in Fig. 2–10. The following classes of growth layers all refer to the same sheath: "absent" growth layer, short lens, entire growth layer, long lens, long lens (different from former one), and two concurrent lenses (from Smithsonian Institution).

Figure 2–12 shows the type specimen of the West Texas pattern. It came from a native juniper (*Juniperus* sp.) which grew in the Break of the Plains near Post, Texas, some 40 miles southeast of Lubbock. Figure 2–13 gives a clearer idea of the West Texas pat-

Fig. 2–12 (left). Transverse section of the type specimen of the West Texas pattern of tree growth. *Juniperus* sp. from near Post, Texas, 41 miles southeast of Lubbock.

Fig. 2–13 (right). Secondary type specimen of the West Texas pattern. *Juniperus* sp. from near Post, Texas, in the Break of the Plains, 41 miles southeast of Lubbock. Part of the same stand with the tree of Fig. 2–12.

tern by a somewhat exaggerated display of pattern characteristics. Both trees represented by the two figures were of the same species and part of the same stand. In eastern Australia, with summer rainfall, the West Texas pattern of tree growth exists in *Araucaria* * (Fig. 2–14) in a form as vivid and typical as in West Texas itself.

Under the Northern Arizona regime, two rainy seasons occur, one in summer and the other in winter (Fig. 2–7). Growth commonly begins, and the initial period of rapid growth is made, on the basis of soil moisture supplied by winter rains. Subsequent growth, if any, may or may not respond to summer rains. Here, latitude, longitude, altitude, and exposure are important factors. In a measure, the rainfall east of Flagstaff, at Winslow, Arizona, is intermediate between that of Lubbock and that of Flagstaff; the winter rainfall at Winslow appears to be greater in relation to summer rainfall than at Lubbock. Also, the spring–early-summer decrease in rainfall (May–June) becomes evident at Winslow. Winter rainfall has increased further at Flagstaff, and the late spring dry interval is more pronounced than at Winslow. Rainfall at Kingman, Arizona, west of Flagstaff, is intermediate between those of Flagstaff and San Francisco; the rainfall of winter has again increased relative to summer rainfall and appears to dominate the annual picture.

In the Northern Arizona pattern, lenticular or partial growth layers may be present locally in time. Variability ranges widely, low for a series of growth layers, then high for a succeeding series. Diffuse-margined growth layers may or may not be common. Uniformity also ranges widely from high uniformity among growth layers of a highly variable series to low uniformity among those of a slightly variable series. Cross-dating may or may not be of high quality depending upon the degree of variability.

The typical Northern Arizona pattern is composed of alternating groups of growth layers, certain of the groups possessing California characteristics whereas alternate groups possess West Texas characters. At times the groups contain many growth layers, at other times very few. Figure 2–15 shows rather rapid alternation of groups in a Northern Arizona pattern on a cross-section of Douglas-fir. In Fig. 2–16, showing a typical Northern Arizona pattern in piñon, the groups of uniform growth layers reach over longer intervals than do those of variable growth layers.

* Wood of *Agathis* and *Araucaria* were kindly supplied by the Chicago Museum of Natural History in connection with a study for the Carnegie Institution of Washington.

Fig. 2–14 (left). Typical West Texas pattern in *Araucaria* from Australia.
Fig. 2–15 (right). Northern Arizona growth pattern on a cross-section of Douglas-fir. Rather rapid alternation of groups of uniform and variable growth layers.

The phenological history of individual ponderosa pine in northern Arizona stands out as a critical problem in relation to tree growth in all its phases. For instance, second tip flushes were observed to begin in mid-August at 7,400 feet near Flagstaff. It is a problem which needs close attention over a number of years.

The many modifications inherent in what is recognized as the typical Northern Arizona pattern present fascinating problems. With increasing elevation, the Arizona growth pattern resembles more and more the California pattern; with decreasing elevation more and more the West Texas pattern. It seems clear that the

Fig. 2–16. Typical Northern Arizona growth pattern on a cross-section of pinyon pine. Long intervals of uniform growth layers alternate with short intervals of variable growth layers (from A. E. Douglass).

West Texas pattern extends westward at low elevations and the California pattern eastward at high elevations. A contact between the two appears to exist on the Coconino Plateau and in the San Francisco Peaks area of northern Arizona.

Thus, the Arizona pattern consists of a combination of the other two patterns, the California portions of a growth-layer sequence representing an intrusion downward (eastward?) and the West Texas portions representing an intrusion upward (westward?). It is thought that the area of contact between the two patterns creates a tension zone with vertical (and horizontal?) mobility which migrates downward during periods of high rainfall and upward during periods of low rainfall. Cross-dating is at its best in the tension zone where there exists a rhythmic and sufficiently rapid alternation of California and West Texas patterns to provide acceptable cross-identification among trees. Any decided departure from the tension zone toward the West Texas region makes attempts at cross-dating futile; any decided departure toward the California regime makes cross-dating weak and uncertain.

In summary, it seems clear that certain complicating factors militate against a high correspondence between spot rainfall and the linear thicknesses of growth layers. An effort has been made to devise other methods of obtaining climatic, or rainfall, information from tree growth. At present two methods are being developed: the incidence of reversals in relative thickness between successive growth layers and the analysis of growth patterns in the wood of trees. Both methods merit intense and prolonged investigation.

DETAILS OF THE WEST TEXAS PATTERN. The characteristic growth pattern of the West Texas rainfall regime was studied intensively for 11 years by observation, measurement, and experimentation. Some trees were observed daily, others weekly, monthly, or annually. Four methods of dating growth layers were devised and employed: the use of natural frost effects, the use of artificial frost effects, measured tip growth, and ratio of diameter flushes to tip flushes. The application of these methods permitted the exact positioning of growth layers with respect to their annual increments. Because a detailed analysis of West Texas tree growth is being published, or will have been when the present report appears, only a few highlights of the study of West Texas tree growth are given here (Glock *et al.*, 1960).

Figure 2–17 shows an enlarged portion of a transverse section of an Arizona cypress (*Cupressus arizonica*) branch which was under observation for 3 years. The section includes the following:

1937: Outer part of increment
1938: Natural frost injury and recovery of April 7–9
      1 thick growth layer
      1 thin growth layer
1939: 1 thick growth layer
      1 thin growth layer
1940: Artificial frost injury and recovery of April 8
      Incomplete growth layer
      Branch cut off May 10

Of special interest here in connection with the West Texas pattern, the section illustrates high radial variability and multiplicity; of secondary interest, perhaps, the section shows frost effects, both natural and artificial, which serve as dating enclosures.

Figure 2–18 includes nearly an entire transverse section from the branch of an Arizona cypress which grew approximately 100

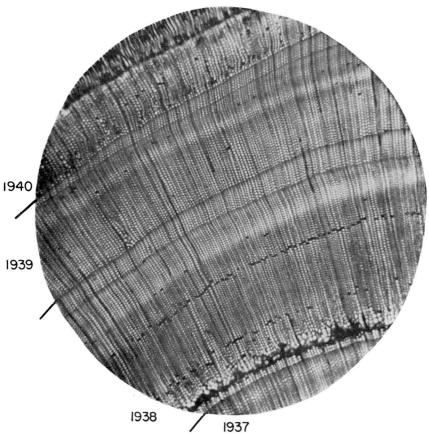

1940

1939

1938   1937

Fig. 2–17. Enlarged transverse section of Arizona cypress (*Cupressus arizonica*) branch from a tree at the Texas Agricultural Experiment Station, near Lubbock. Includes complete increments for 1938 and 1939, and outer part of 1937 and inner part of 1940. Increment for 1938 contains effects of natural frost of April 7–9, increment of 1940 contains effects of artificial frost of April 8. Branch cut off May 10, 1940.

feet from the tree whose section is shown in Fig. 2–17. The section of Fig. 2–18 includes from center to bark:

1937:   Central growth layer
1938:   Natural frost effects of April 7–9
        1 thick growth layer
        2 thin growth layers
        1 long lens
1939:   Spots of frost effects
        1 thick growth layer

Fig. 2–18. Enlarged transverse section of Arizona cypress (*Cupressus arizonica*) branch from a tree at the Texas Agricultural Experiment Station, near Lubbock. Time range is from 1937 to 1941. Includes complete increments for 1938–41. Frost effects in 1938, 1939, and 1940.

<pre>
        1 lens-like growth layer
        1 thin growth layer
1940:   Frost effects
        1 thick growth layer
        2 thin growth layers
        Lensing
1941:   A complete growth layer
        Cut from tree Oct. 11
</pre>

This figure gives an excellent example of the West Texas pattern of tree growth.

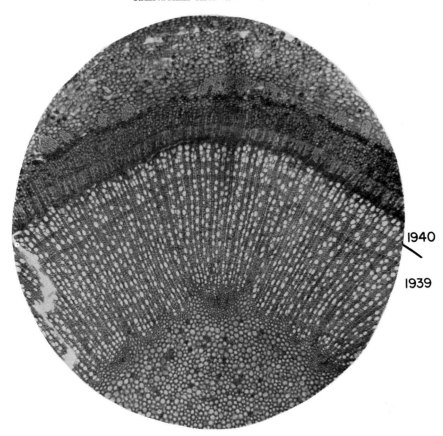

1940

1939

FIG. 2–19. Enlarged transverse section of a branch of the apple, *Malus sylvestris*, on the campus of Texas Technological College. The two completed growth layers were formed in 1939, and the outer, incomplete one formed up to the cutting date of April 21. The thin outer growth layer of 1939 in this experimental tree was grown after a 4-in. irrigation on July 25; control trees grew no second growth layer in 1939.

In Fig. 2–19, the transverse section of a branch of apple, *Malus sylvestris*, contains xylem of 1939 and 1940. The section includes:

1939:   1 thick growth layer outside of pith
        1 thin growth layer
1940:   1 incomplete growth layer
        Cut from tree April 21

The thin growth layer terminating the 1939 increment was caused by a 4-inch irrigation on July 25. Obviously growth had ceased prior to the application of water, only to resume afterward.

Fɪɢ. 2–20. Enlarged transverse section of a branch of *Citrus maxima* from the University of Arizona Experimental Farm at Yuma. The section shows two years of growth, 1939–40, under irrigation. Cut from tree November 26, 1940.

Control trees, with no irrigation, did not add a second growth layer in 1939.

Figure 2–20 gives an enlarged section of a portion of a branch of *Citrus maxima*, cut from the tree on November 26, 1940, and containing the growth of 1939–40. The tree grew under irrigation at the University of Arizona Experimental Farm at Yuma. Undoubtedly the 12 or so growth layers represent major irrigations. Cambial divisions and the other growth processes began and ended several times during the 2-year period of 1939–40. It is clear that the pattern of growth in the citrus branch and the intermittent cambial activity exhibit similarities to the West Texas pattern and in part support that pattern analysis even without the study of soil moisture in the Texas area which was carried on for 3½ years.

The matter of cambial activity suggested by the analysis of the materials in Figs. 2–17 to 2–20 recalls attention to the first paragraphs of the Introduction where the importance of cambial activity was stressed. Figures 2–21A and 2–21B were constructed to illustrate the problems connected with cambial activity and to suggest a partial solution. Figure 2–21A is a diagrammatic simplification of an enlarged transverse section from a branch of an Arizona cypress.

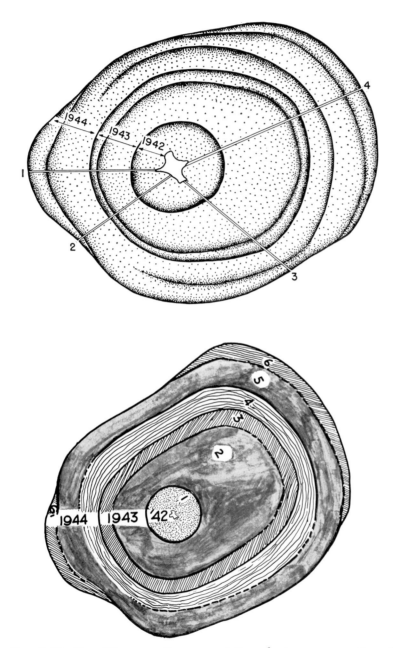

Fig. 2–21. *Top,* Diagrammatic representation of a transverse section of an Arizona cypress branch from the campus of Texas Technological College. Variable cambial and growth history along different radii. *Bottom,* Diagrammatic interpretation of Fig. 2–21. Recognition of an invisible growth layer caused by lack of local densewood formation between growth layers 4 and 5 partially simplifies the sequence of growth events.

51

In following along the four designated radii, or several others equally pertinent, it will be recognized that cambial activity and growth have had a different history along each radius and that the activity is difficult to trace and to correlate around the circuit where such activity changed. To assist in the clarification of cambial activity and to define more clearly the problems involved, Fig. 2–21B has been constructed. There are six growth layers whose borders vary from sharp (solid lines), to diffuse (dashed lines), to absent (white space). Not all of the cambium is active at the same time, and in that part which is active there is a difference in the activity, in the differentiation, and in the maturation processes. Between growth layer 4 and growth layer 5 at the bottom of the figure, densewood * failed to develop in growth layer 4. This failure produces what is called an "invisible growth layer." It may well be asked: Why did densewood fail to develop? In any event, the recognition of an invisible growth layer no doubt permits a clearer and more detailed picture of growth activities than had been known heretofore, although it is not yet known why growth processes form densewood on one radius while not forming it on another.

In summary, the purposes of this paper have been first to mention certain complicating factors in the use of linear relationships between radial thicknesses of growth layers and spot rainfall, and second to describe other methods whereby information may be obtained on the nature of the rainfall regime and changes in that regime, from the incidence of reversals in relative thicknesses and growth-pattern analyses. The relationship between rainfall and tree growth, it is thought, will ultimately be clarified and evaluated through a knowledge of the physiology of cambial activity, cell differentiation, and maturation.

LITERATURE CITED

DOUGLASS, A. E. 1928. Climatic cycles and tree growth. Carnegie Inst. Wash., Pub. No. 289, Vol. II: 1–166. Ref. p. 29.

GLOCK, W. S. 1937. Observations on the western juniper. Madroño IV: 21–28.

———. 1941. Growth rings and climate. Bot. Rev. 7(12): 649–713.

———. 1942. A rapid method of correlation for continuous time series. Amer. Jour. Sci. 240: 437–442.

———. 1950. Tree growth and rainfall: A study of correlation and methods. Smithsn. Misc. Collect. 111(18): 1–47.

———. 1955. Tree growth. II. Growth rings and climate. Bot. Rev. 21(1–3): 73–188.

* The terms *densewood* and *lightwood* are synonomous with the older terms *latewood* and *earlywood* and are here used in conformity with useage in the publication by Glock *et al.* (1960).

GLOCK, W. S., R. A. STUDHALTER, and SHARLENE AGERTER. 1960. Classification and multiplicity of growth layers in branches of trees from the lower forest border. Smithsn. Misc. Collect. Vol. 140(1): 1–294.

HENRY, A. J. 1931. The calendar year as a time unit in drought statistics. Monthly Weather Rev. 59: 150–154.

LEOPOLD, LUNA B. 1951. Rainfall frequency: An aspect of climatic variation. Trans. Amer. Geophys. Union 32: 347–357.

STUDHALTER, R. A. 1955. Tree Growth. I. Some historical chapters. Bot. Rev. 21(1–3): 1–72.

Discussion

M. B. APPLEQUIST

Some 450 years ago Leonardo da Vinci (Stallings, 1937) suggested the existence of a relationship between rainfall and diameter growth. Ever since that time, scientists have been intrigued with the problem of pinpointing just how these two variables are related. The papers of this volume indicate our present state of knowledge, and, more important, how much we still have to learn about this aspect of growth.

Depending on the objective of the worker, this problem has been approached from several angles. The archeologist is intent on dating prehistoric ruins; the astronomer looks for clues to the existence of sunspot cycles; the climatologist seeks evidence of climatic cycles and rainfall regimes; the physiologist is interested in the basic processes within the tree which influence growth; and, finally, the forester is interested in diameter growth for the sake of the wood produced. The comments that follow will be slanted mostly toward the latter viewpoint.

Glock's paper has focused attention on the "pattern analysis" approach to the study of these rainfall-growth relations. His objective has been to pick average trees in a forest stand that would reflect in their growth rings the climatic regime of a given area. He has listed in some detail the many problems inherent in all studies of this type. His recognition of the California, West Texas, and Arizona growth patterns and the relationship each bears to the regional rainfall type should provide a good basis for work in other places. While no two areas will be the same, the occurrence and relative amounts of "complacent" uniform rings, "sensitive" variable rings, false rings, and other distinguishing ring characteristics can be anticipated on the basis of known rainfall records.

Dr. Glock's studies of trees in the Santa Fe and Flagstaff areas emphasized the importance of having detailed precipitation records available for comparisons against growth. Thus he was able to show that lesser rains coming at closer intervals had a greater effect on growth than heavier but less frequent rains. Why the Flagstaff trees reacted the opposite of those in New Mexico for the same general period was not discussed. A comparison of rainfall amounts and timing between the two areas might provide some explanation. He suggested that further study of certain tree-ring parameters as determined from the relative thicknesses of growth layers might yield information on the distribution and type of rainfall.

PROBLEMS IN SHOWING RELATIONSHIPS. The problems involved in demonstrating real rainfall-growth relationships are many. Briefly stated they include:

1. Multiplicity of growth factors. No less than 15 were cited in Glock's paper.

2. Rainfall. Variations in place, time, and availability to the tree affect diameter growth.

3. The growth layer. How many radii should be measured per section? How many cross-sections are needed for each tree? How many trees constitute an adequate sample for a site? The considerable variation in ring width encountered radially and longitudinally in the same tree, plus similar changes between different trees and sites, has been pointed out.

4. Terminology. Tree-ring specialists have developed a set of terms known best within their group. Where there exists any possibility of misunderstanding or lack of understanding, terms should be clearly defined.

5. Reconstruction or prediction. How far back into the past can we logically expect to reconstruct rainfall records based on ring-width measurements of a cross-section? Or can more intensive study of the current rainfall-growth relations better help us to predict future trends?

SUGGESTED APPROACHES. The following suggestions, based partially on equipment, methods, and ideas that have received increased attention in recent years, are offered for consideration in future work of this type:

1. More emphasis on the basic physiology of growth. In his opening paragraph, Dr. Glock emphasized the importance of cambial division, differentiation, and rhythms. An understanding of these fundamental processes will provide many of the real answers we seek. Kramer and Kozlowski's recent text (1960) provides a good summary of present knowledge on this phase of tree physiology.

We still know surprisingly little about the phenology of many trees. So far as is known, only one study (Pearson, 1924) has investigated the beginning and ending of cambial growth in ponderosa pine in the Southwest. This study included only two trees during one season.

2. Use of qualitative characters in tree-ring work. Dobbs (1951) in England, along with other European workers, has criticized the almost exclusive attention given ring width, a quantitative character. He stated that relative size, color, wall thickness, and the distribution of different elements within the ring were useful in dating as well as in the study of general growth relations.

3. Careful selection of study trees. Variation due to numerous external factors already cited should be minimized so as to bring out the effect of the single variable under study. Usually this variable will be rainfall but other possibilities occur. The writer (Applequist, 1959), in a study

of growth in swamp species, found a complete lack of tree-ring work. It is suggested that permanently flooded swamp trees offer a unique opportunity to study the relationship between growth and other external factors with the all-important soil-moisture factor held constant.

4. More detailed rainfall records. Dr. Glock's report has pointed up this need. Such records should be more specific both as to time and place. Continuous or daily records would be ideal; weekly data would be more valuable than monthly records. Rain gauges should be situated on the same site as study trees or in close proximity. The irregular distribution of summer shower rainfall is well known. It seems quite likely that some of the poor correlations obtained in studies of this type were due to the necessity of using rainfall records for a station some miles distant.

5. Use of soil-moisture data. The need for more information about soil moisture and root systems has already been mentioned. A continuous record of soil-moisture fluctuations would more clearly reveal the single most important factor affecting diameter growth. This type of soil-moisture budget has been used by Zahner (1955) to relate soil moisture to growth in southern pine stands.

One aspect of rainfall-growth relations that has been largely overlooked in the past is the effect that *excess* moisture has on diameter growth. How do different species respond when soil moisture is above field capacity? Good rainfall and soil-moisture records will help answer this question.

6. Metal band dendrometers. The problem of radial variation can be largely overcome by encircling bands of this type described by Liming (1957). Such bands are inexpensive and simply constructed, yet sensitive enough to yield valuable information.

7. Statistical procedures. Schumacher and Meyer (1937) have suggested the use of analysis of variance methods in separating ring-width variation into its component parts. In addition to that portion due to the climatic factor, the variations attributable to age and to competition can be isolated and measured. Further, if adequate rainfall data are at hand, the precipitation of different time intervals can be tested to find which is best related to diameter growth.

It appears, then, that present-day instrumentation should make it possible to examine these rainfall–diameter-growth relations more fully than before. An ideal setup might include precipitation records, soil-moisture data, and dendrometers on sample trees. By measuring all three of these basic variables on one site, the pattern of diameter growth should be more complete and meaningful.

LITERATURE CITED IN DISCUSSION

Applequist, M. B. 1959. A study of soil and site factors affecting the growth and development of swamp blackgum and tupelogum stands in southeastern Georgia. D.F. thesis, School of Forestry, Duke University, Durham, N. C.

Dobbs, C. G. 1951. A study of growth rings in trees. I. Review and discussion of recent work. Forestry 24(1): 22–35.

Kramer, P. J., and T. T. Kozlowski. 1960. Physiology of Trees. McGraw-Hill Book Co., Inc., New York.

Liming, F. G. 1957. Homemade dendrometers. Jour. Forestry 55: 575–577.

Pearson, G. A. 1924. The growing season of western yellow pine. Jour. Agr. Res. 29: 203–204.

Schumacher, F. X., and H. A. Meyer. 1937. Effect of climate on timber-growth fluctuations. Jour. Agr. Res. 54(2): 79–107.

Stallings, W. S. 1937. Some early papers on tree-rings. Tree-Ring Bull., 3: 27–28.

Zahner, R. 1955. Soil water depletion by pine and hardwood stands during a dry season. Forest Sci. 1: 258–264.

3

Cambial Growth Characteristics

HUGH WILCOX

Introduction

Cyclic growth is a phenomenon common to trees of the North Temperate Zone. The growth of shoots, roots, and cambium occurs in recurrent cycles, alternating with periods of dormancy or relative inactivity. This periodicity is generally annual, but intraseasonal cycles are also common (Reed, 1928). These cycles are related to physiological conditions, presumably controlled by genetic systems within the plant. The extent to which these oscillations are accentuated or damped depends not only upon factors of the environment but also upon racial or ecotypic variation (Clausen, 1951). The complexity of these interactions has made the interpretation of field studies of growth behavior in woody species very difficult. In general, growth responses have been evaluated in relation to environmental factors, internal physiological factors, or ecotypic variation without acknowledgment that such analyses constitute only part of a whole.

Studies of tree growth under controlled conditions with genetically known stocks have contributed to our knowledge of growth and growth correlations. However, it is impractical to devise growth chambers for the young, thrifty-mature trees which are of interest to foresters. This limitation applies particularly to physiological studies of cambial activity, which is the topic of this paper. Nevertheless, some of the studies of seedlings grown under controlled conditions have contributed toward understanding of the growth of woody plants and have provided new insights to aid in the interpretation and planning of field studies. It is the present purpose to examine the state of knowledge of cambial growth—the occurrence of rhythms of vegetative growth and their relation to cambial activity, the extent and nature of correlations between the various meristematic regions, cambial activity in relation to hormonal factors, and the relation of cambial activity to other physiological processes.

Growth Periodicity

It is, by now, a well recognized fact that a species which grows over a wide range of latitudes generally consists of a number of races or ecotypes (Clausen, 1951; Pauley and Perry, 1954; Clausen *et al.*, 1940, 1945, 1948; Vaartaja, 1954). When individuals of the various climatic races of a species are planted together in a location near the center of the range, obvious differences will be seen in their periods of growth and dormancy. Corresponding differences occur in the beginning and cessation of cambial activity. It is possible to distinguish races on the basis of their response to photoperiod, to day-night temperature differences during the growing season, to edaphic factors, and possibly to other environmental factors. The responses to these differences are primarily physiological and are not generally manifested by discernible differences in morphological characteristics.

It is not easy to obtain information on the range of environmental response that is inherent in a species. Transplant experiments (Turesson, 1922; Clausen *et al.*, 1940, 1945, 1948; Pauley and Perry, 1954) or growth chambers can be used to study seedlings and small woody plants. However, it should be realized that growth characteristics of seedlings may differ considerably from those of the adult tree.

A question sometimes asked of plant physiologists is whether there are any species or ecotypes within our common forest species which might grow continuously under appropriate environmental conditions. An unequivocal answer cannot be given. Downs and Borthwick (1956) found that catalpa, elm, birch, red maple, and dogwood apparently could be kept growing continuously by using daylengths of 16 hours. Other species grew intermittently on long photoperiods or became dormant.

These results partially substantiate the thesis of the German plant physiologist Klebs (1914) who maintained, on the basis of experiments with beech, that growth could be made continuous by providing optimum environmental conditions. MacDougal (1930) also developed a hypothesis that seasonal growth activity was determined by the intensity of environmental factors or by the deterioration of leaves. He claimed that if water supply was adequate and temperature suitable, continuous growth could be attained in those plants whose morphogenic development provides them continually with leaves.

According to Koriba (1958), growth conditions are ideal and nearly uniform in the vicinity of Singapore; but, even there, growth is usually not continuous. He reports that among all tree species of Malaya the evergrowing trees, even with the addition of Palmaceae, Coniferae, and the tree ferns, amount to less than 20 per cent, probably 15 per cent. The deciduous trees total about 5 per cent and the evergreen trees with intermittent growth 75 per cent.

A word of caution should be introduced at this point. Natural periodicity may be subject to the influence of age as well as environment. The studies of Downs and Borthwick and of Klebs mentioned above were made on seedlings of woody plants. It is well known that youthful vigor is reflected in longer growing seasons as compared with mature individuals. Coster (1927, 1928) found in Java that typically deciduous species retained their foliage throughout the year while they were saplings, but with the approach of maturity the annual resting period manifested itself and gradually became longer each year until it reached its normal duration. Similar observations have been made by Koriba (1958) and Richards (1942).

One other interesting characteristic of periodic growth behavior deserves consideration. It is commonly assumed that the period of dormancy in the aerial portions of woody plants is largely systemic. However, reference to Coster's work in Java indicates that this is not always so. In the uniform climate of Buitenzorg, Coster found that leaf fall, dormancy, and leaf-renewal processes showed a variable pattern. The majority of trees passed through an annual resting period. Some species shed all their leaves and stood bare for a considerable period of time, but there were other species which displayed an annual periodicity in their separate branches, each of which became independent of the tree as a whole. The important point is that individual meristems are capable of regulating their own growth behavior to an extent which is not generally appreciated because it seldom occurs. The limits of seasonal activity are generally determined by those factors of the external or internal environment which depart from the optimum. If the external environment is uniform and optimum, the individualized growth behavior which is frequently characteristic for individual roots in the more uniform soil environment may be achieved. Under these circumstances the internal environment becomes predominant in determining growth behavior.

Coster showed that in all cases there was a correlation between vegetative and cambial activity, and variations in vegetative growth were correlated with formation of corresponding growth zones in the trunk. The renewal of leaves on a deciduous tree was accompanied by a burst of cambial activity.

The foregoing considerations have been presented to illustrate the universality and inherent nature of growth periodicity. These considerations may be summarized as follows:

1. Growth periodicity is an inherent feature of most woody plants.

2. The cyclic growth behavior is determined by the coordinated interplay of environmental factors and the internal physiological processes of the plant.

3. Although usually masked, individual meristems are to a degree self-determining. Their mutual relationships are maintained by internal correlating mechanisms.

4. The cyclic growth behavior of the cambium, in particular, is strongly correlated with leaf-renewal processes in the tree.

Growth Correlations

Many nineteenth century botanists were aware that there was a close correlation between the initiation of cambial activity and expansion of buds in the spring. The history of their investigations was reviewed by Priestley (1930) and, more recently, by Wareing (1951) and Fraser (1958). A number of important aspects of this relationship will be discussed later. However, at this point it would be well to inquire whether there have been any attempts to obtain an even broader picture of growth correlations in woody plants. A complete study of growth correlations would include periodic and coincident observations on the growth of primary vascular tissues and of the vascular cambium, in both shoot and root systems of individual plants.

Very few such inclusive studies seem to have been made. One such investigation was that of Kienholz (1934) who studied leader growth, needle growth, and cambial activity in certain conifers near Keene, New Hampshire. In addition, he supplemented his data from the work of Stevens on root elongation of white pine, in order to obtain a composite picture of growth interrelationships. His results suggest that there is an internal balance among the times of maximum development of needles, cambium, and roots which is determined by internal competition for foods, water, and possibly mineral nutrients. The data on cambial activity were obtained by means of dendrographs attached to two red pine trees at about 1 foot above the ground. Although the interrelationships are suggestive, the applicability is limited because of the small number of samples and the uncertainties introduced by using the dendrometer method unsupported by anatomical samples (Fraser, 1956). Also, data on cambial activity at various other positions would have made the correlations more meaningful.

Reed and MacDougal (1937) attempted a similar multiple correlation between periodicity in elongation of shoots and roots and cyclic growth of the vascular cambium in the trunk of orange trees. They concluded that the tendency of the various cycles to alternate with one another was evidence of growth correlations between these meristems. Like Kienholz, they examined the activity of the cambium at only one position on the tree trunk.

Although these broad studies have established the pervasiveness of growth correlations among the meristems within a plant, they have done little to enhance understanding of the internal mechanisms involved. To comprehend the physiological features of the correlating mechanisms, it will be necessary to restrict our attention to the better-detailed studies which have been made of the somewhat more limited relationship between the cambial activity and growth of the shoot.

Bark-peeling Studies

The activity of the cambium first came to the attention of early botanists and foresters through the recognition of the so-called sap-peeling season, a period during which the bark can be easily removed from the tree. Forestry practice soon led to the development of rules of thumb for determining the best time to remove bark on the basis of phenological observations of foliar development. Thus was crudely developed the first formulation of a growth correlation between primary and secondary growth activities.

Early disputes arose as to whether the relationship between bark peeling and leafing-out was actually in the nature of a correlation or whether both phenomena depended on common factors. The better modern understanding regarding the transformation of cambial cells and the seasonal ontogeny of cambial derivatives (Bailey, 1954; Bannan, 1955), together with methods for evaluating bark-peeling resistances (Huber, 1948; Wilcox et al., 1956), have afforded means for the more rapid investigation of correlations between cambial activity and bud expansion (Fig. 3–1). These investigations, in turn, have furnished a broad picture which can be used as a basis for the visualization of problems requiring more exact anatomical or physiological methods for their solution. Before turning to the more refined studies of growth correlations, some of the results obtained from bark-peeling studies will be examined.

FIG. 3–1. Use of the bark-testing tool for measurement of bark-peeling resistances. (A) Cutting bark disc with hole saw mounted on borer shaft. (B) Peeling head in position for making the test. (C) Measurement of torque required to twist bark disc loose from the wood. (D) Test completed; bark disc separated from wood. From Wilcox *et al.* (1956).

EARLY SAP-PEELING STAGE. A number of alterations occur in the cambium prior to the resumption of cell division in the spring: the cells expand radially; the radial walls become thinner; and the cytoplasm takes up a parietal position about a large central vacuole (Bannan, 1955). It is at this time that the bark first starts to peel. It was found by Wilcox *et al.* (1956) that peeling first started in eight species in the Adirondack region of New York State during a single 1-week period in which the mean weekly temperature had passed 40° F. This onset of peeling preceded leafing-out by about 3 weeks and preceded cambial divisions by approximately a month.

This same delay between the alterations in the cambium and the time of first divisions was also noted for the coniferous and hardwood species investigated in Denmark by Ladefoged (1952).

An important feature of this early awakening of the cambium and the consequent advent of bark slippage is that these changes first occur below the buds and move basipetally down the branches and stem. Huber (1948) found that in spruce the peelability moved downward at the rate of 1 m. per day in favorable weather. He found that in oak peelability moved down the stem too rapidly to detect a difference between the crown and the base of the trunk. This early start of peeling, which occurs considerably ahead of cambial divisions, has been discussed in detail by Huber (1948).

INITIATION OF CAMBIAL ACTIVITY. Measurements of bark-peeling resistances show a progressive decrease during the interval between awakening of the cambium and cambial divisions. Once cambial activity is initiated, it aids further in promoting the peelability. Anatomical samples show that the first cambial divisions follow the same sequence as the earlier changes in bark stripability. Divisions start first beneath the buds and progress basipetally down the tree. Rate studies of the different tree species could not be determined with the bark-peelability tool, but results from anatomical studies have shown a similar pattern of movement to that of the initial cambial changes. In general, rates of basipetal movement of cambial divisions are fastest in ring-porous trees, in most cases being too rapid to detect a time lapse. In large diffuse-porous trees, time intervals of from 3 weeks to a month have been reported (Lodewick, 1928; Priestley et al., 1933; Ladefoged, 1952). Cambial divisions in coniferous species move at an intermediate rate, generally requiring about a week in larger trees.

Conflicting results have been reported on the time of inception of cell division in relation to bud break. Part of this confusion may have arisen from the failure to recognize the time lapse between the early changes in the cambium and the beginning of divisions. This, in turn, may have contributed to the controversy on the correlation between primary and secondary growth mentioned earlier.

Ladefoged's (1952) careful study of the interval between bud break and cell division at the base of the bud shows results which are representative of the general differences in species behavior. In diffuse-porous hardwoods the interval depends on how much the buds extend before bursting. Where the extension is slight, cambial divisions start simultaneously with, or at the most 2 days before, bursting. Where the shoot extension is relatively great, cell division occurs up to a week before bud break. In ring-porous hardwoods divisions begin 1 to 9 days before bud break, regardless of bud extension. In conifers, cell division begins 9 to 12 days before bud break. Certainly, these time intervals are short enough for it to seem reasonable to assume that the primary growth occurring within the bud before bud break could provide a stimulus for secondary growth activity at the base of the bud. Evidence will be presented later to show that this is so.

CESSATION OF CAMBIAL ACTIVITY. Although measurements of bark-peeling resistance do not distinguish between different stages of cambial development during the period of active cambial divisions, the peelability tool is of value for the determination of the approach of dormancy in different species and for the investigation of conditions associated with cessation of cambial activity (Fig. 3–2). The investigations of Adirondack species mentioned earlier showed that the peeling season is generally longer for conifers than for hardwoods. Anatomical studies confirmed that this was due to cambial divisions extending over a longer period of time. For any particular tree, the cessation of cambial divisions and the increase in peeling resistance did not appear to be related to prevailing weather conditions. On the other hand, tree vigor appeared to influence the peeling season significantly, with vigorous trees peeling the longest. Huber (1948) showed that in a comparison by crown classes, dominant trees peeled longer than intermediate or suppressed trees. Trees on south-facing slopes peeled longer than those on north-facing slopes, and trees on moist, well-drained sites peeled longer than those on dry and swampy sites.

Huber also found that changes in bark-peeling resistances following various experimental treatments were in harmony with earlier anatomical studies and tended to support a hormonal theory of cambial regulation. These results will be discussed later in conjunction with the physiological studies of other investigators.

Normal Cambial Activity in Relation to Growth Hormones

HORMONE THEORY OF CAMBIAL INITIATION. The fact that cambial activity starts in the twigs below the swelling buds was first interpreted as due to a more favorable distribution of food materials, mineral nutrients, and water supply. The developing leaves were assumed to mobilize these materials and to bring greater supplies to the twigs.

The German botanist Ludwig Jost (1891, 1893) interpreted this relationship differently. In a series of careful experiments with both coniferous and dicotyledenous species, he observed the relationship between the awakening of the cambium and the development of buds and leaves. In a moment of prescience, he tentatively postulated a theory of correlation dependent upon the movement of some substance or stimulus. Later he abandoned his theory of correlation and stated that both the formation of leaves and the formation of earlywood were dependent upon common factors and that the relationship was not in the nature of a correlation (Jost, 1907). Had he displayed greater conviction, the discovery of hormones might have been made earlier.

Gradually, however, Jost's original idea of a cambial stimulus was adopted by other investigators, and a hormone theory was proposed by Kastens (1924) and by Coster (1927, 1928). The experimental verification of a hormone stimulus was made by Snow (1933), who clearly demonstrated that leaves promote the growth of the cambium beneath them, that this stimulus travels in a morphologically downward direction, and that it can cross a protoplasmic discontinuity from one species of plant to another. Later Snow (1935) activated cambial growth by pure indoleacetic acid and concluded that normal cambial growth is activated by the same hormone which, formed by the young leaves, promotes extension of cells in stems.

Other investigators have contributed to this evidence by demonstrating physiological concentrations of hormone in swelling buds and developing leaves (Zimmerman, 1936; Avery et al., 1937; Söding, 1937) or in the growing cambium (Söding, 1937, 1940). Other evidence of divers and sundry types has been contributed by various investigators. No effort will be made to recapitulate all the findings here. It will suffice to indicate that the belief that a hormone is involved in the awakening of the cambium is based on what might be considered circumstantial evidence. Physiologists are inclined to accept this evidence, although they understand neither the role of a hormone in stimulating cambial divisions nor the nature of the part it may play in promoting the differentiation of the various products of cambial division.

NATURE OF THE GROWTH HORMONE. Before more detailed consideration of growth hormones in relation to cambial activity, sites of production, and paths of movement, it is advisable to clarify the use of terms. The phenomenon of correlation, in common with most biological phenomena, has proved to be more complicated than it first seemed. The term *hormone* was applied to plant substances that serve as correlating agents by moving from one location to another, being produced in the first location and controlling

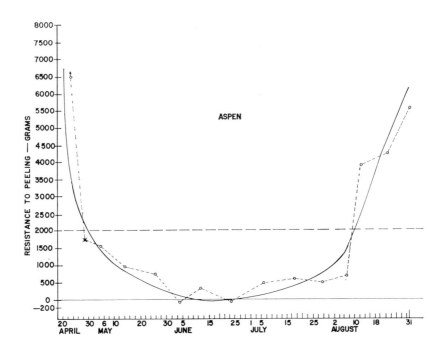

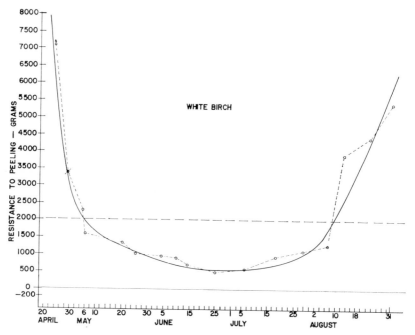

FIG. 3–2. Curves of bark-peeling resistance for aspen, ash, white birch, and red maple. Resistances below 4,000 grams indicate a sap-peeling condition. Best sap peeling corresponds to a measurement of 2,000 grams or less as indi-

66

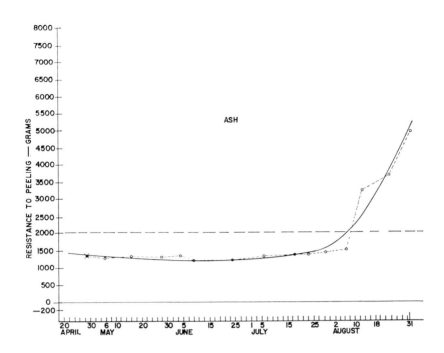

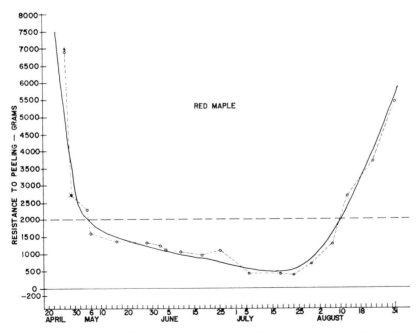

cated by the portions of the curves below the horizontal broken line. From Wilcox *et al.* (1956).

growth in the second. The term is used in this paper in its original sense as a morphological agent. It is acknowledged that there are numerous growth-regulatory or morphogenetic stimuli, as clearly pointed out in a recent review on the chemical regulation of growth (Steward and Shantz, 1959).

The perfection of the Went techniques for collection and assay of hormone by diffusion from plant tissue and measurement by *Avena* curvatures has focused attention on those hormones which stimulate cell enlargement in shoots. The generic term *auxin* has been applied to substances eliciting this response, the term being applied to both natural and synthetic substances. A considerable amount of evidence indicates that the naturally occurring auxin is the chemical indoleacetic acid, although this is by no means proven. However, auxin will be used here in its generic sense. Any pure chemical substance such as indoleacetic acid will be referred to by specific designation.

The hormonal effects on cambial division mentioned in the last section are influenced by those hormones which are measured in the *Avena* curvature test, i.e., by auxin. Therefore, physiologists have become accustomed to thinking of auxin as synonymous with the cambial stimulus. However, it should be pointed out that there are other diffusates which influence the *Avena* test. Also, as pointed out in various reviews, the auxin economy in plants is complicated by the uncertain identity of such substances as bound auxin, auxin precursors, stored auxin, diffusible auxin, extractable auxin, etc. (Gordon, 1953). One can only echo the sentiment of Steward and Shantz (1959) that the time has come for isolation and chemical identification of substances causing specific growth effects. Since knowledge is at present so primitive, investigators will be forced to examine the physiology of cambial activity in the light of what is known about auxin. At present, the writer is inclined to accept the evidence that the readily diffusible auxin or free auxin is a priori the most important form of auxin for the immediate physiological needs of the plant.

DISTRIBUTION OF AUXIN. Soon after development of the Went (1928) technique for the collection and assay of auxin, many attempts were made to collect hormone from expanding buds and growing vegetative organs (Zimmermann, 1936; Avery *et al.*, 1937; Söding, 1937, 1940; Mirov, 1941). Zimmermann's (1936) studies are of particular interest to tree physiologists. He investigated the auxin content of dormant buds of 11 different species of hardwoods and conifers and failed to obtain diffusible hormone from any of these. However, he found that as soon as the buds began to swell he was able to collect diffusible auxin. The amount of auxin increased very rapidly and reached a peak value during the elongation of the new shoot and had already started to decrease slowly by the time elongation was completed. A much lower hormone content was found in the newly developed terminal buds at the ends of the current annual shoot, and this amount diminished progressively to the low values of the dormant winter bud. Zimmermann further investigated the distribution of hormone in current shoots during their development and in the successively older annual shoots through the previous three or four increments of shoot length (Fig. 3–3). He found a relatively high auxin content

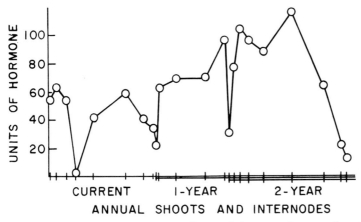

FIG. 3–3. Growth hormone content of annual shoots and internodes of *Acer pseudoplatanus*. Vertical markings along the abscissa show the internode lengths for the last three successive annual shoots. Redrawn from W. A. Zimmermann (1936).

in all portions of the current shoot up to the time of its completed development. By the end of May or June, no more hormone was found in the outgrown shoot. During the development period the distribution was erratic but there was a comparatively high maximum in the center portion of the shoot. A similar distribution has since been found by Hatcher (1959) in shoots of apple and plum rootstock varieties. In pine, the peak concentration has been found near the base of the annual shoot (Mirov, 1941; Brown and Wetmore, 1959) and in ginkgo a few internodes above the base (Gunckel and Thimann, 1949). An approximate but imperfect correlation was found by Zimmerman between auxin content and internode length in the current shoot (Fig. 3–3). Appreciable auxin was also demonstrated in the 1-year (previous annual shoot) and the 2-year-old shoot, with peak concentrations in the central portion of these shoots as well. He did not study the hormone distribution in larger branches and in the trunk, and subsequent efforts by other investigators to demonstrate auxin in these large parts of a tree have been largely unsuccessful.

MOVEMENT OF AUXIN. The ease with which these various hormone concentrations diffuse basipetally through the tissue into agar receiver blocks indicates that the hormone distribution pattern represents a dynamic rather than a static situation. The distribution in the current shoot is further complicated by the uncertain identification of centers of production and consumption and the quantitative relationships associated therewith. Nevertheless, it seems reasonable to assume that excess auxin from the current shoot flows into the shoot of the previous year and for indefinite distances downward.

Gregory and Hancock (1955) found that endogenous auxin moves through the woody stem tissue of apple at a rate of 7 mm./hr. at 20° C., and at half this rate at 10° C. They found an optimum rate of transport between 27° C. and 32° C. Brown and Wetmore (1959) studied transport of both endogenous and exogenous auxin in the long shoots of pine and found the former relatively independent of oxygen tension in comparison to the latter. They voiced a word of caution on studies with exogenous auxin because the problem of initial uptake may mask the phase of basipetal transport. They also pointed out the weakness in determining rates of transport of endogenous auxin from the evacuation rate of a limited supply contained in a stem segment. Such measurements might be affected by differences in transport capacity (as separate from rate) or by the constantly changing auxin gradient. One feature which Brown and Wetmore point to with surety is the strict retention of polarity in the stem segments of the pine that they investigated. However, the work of Jacobs (1954) and Jacobs and Morrow (1957) indicates that polarity of transport may be overstressed because acropetal movements of endogenous auxin do occur in some tissues. This work demonstrated such movement in the regeneration of vascular strands of *Coleus* and also in certain phases of normal xylem differentiation in the shoot apex. Obviously, further studies are necessary to elucidate the rate and direction of auxin movement during various phases of shoot ontogeny. Another problem which does not seem to be completely solved is the path of movement of auxin in the stem. Söding (1937, 1940) tested auxin distribution in the immediate derivatives on both sides of the cambium and in the xylem and phloem (Fig. 3–4). He found a consistently higher amount in the cambium and concluded that auxin moves in the cambium itself. Bannan (1955) supports this theory from observations on cambial behavior in *Thuja occidentalis.* During the spring surge of growth the greatest mitotic activity occurs in the median position in a broad zone of periclinal divisions. He interprets this to mean that the stimulants to division are produced or activated in this central region which is relatively far removed from the mature xylem and phloem.

These views of Söding and Bannan are entirely consistent with the claim of Jacobs and Morrow (1957) that procambium is probably the preferred pathway for auxin transport in the shoot apex.

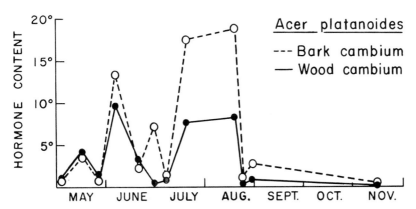

FIG. 3–4. Seasonal content of auxin in the "bark cambium" and "wood cambium" of *Acer platanoides.* Sampling was performed by slipping the bark and removing strips of new tissue (recent cambial derivatives) from the outer face of the wood or from the inner face of the bark. From Söding (1940).

Anatomists look upon the procambium and the cambium as two developmental stages of the same meristem (Esau, 1953).

In contrast to Söding's results, Huber *et al.,* (1937) found auxin in sieve-tube sap and assumed movement in the phloem. Söding tends to discount movement in the phloem because he feels that there would be no functioning phloem at the time that the cambial stimulus is first propagated. Such a belief is supported by the many studies of seasonal ontogeny of phloem which report that secondary sieve tubes commonly become functionless during the season when they are initiated in the cambium (Esau, 1950). However, it has been reported for both dicotyledonous and gymnospermous tree species that certain of the phloem elements formed toward the end of the growing season complete their maturation during the following spring (Esau, 1950; Bannan, 1955). It is also possible for a few of the last-formed sieve tubes to remain open over winter. Gill (1932) has reported such instances for *Fraxinus excelsior* and *Quercus robur*, Elliott (1935) for *Acer pseudoplatanus*, and Huber (1939) for various Abietineae. Thus, it can be seen that phloem cannot be ruled out for all species as a channel for hormone movement. It is noteworthy that two of the species just mentioned with surviving functional phloem are ring-porous hardwoods in which the cambial stimulus moves downward with great rapidity.

EFFECTS OF AUXIN ON CAMBIAL ACTIVITY. Soon after auxin was recognized as responsible for the initiation of cell divisions in the cambium, various investigators began to report effects on the differentiation of cambial derivatives. The first investigators came to associate a high auxin content with development of large-diameter earlywood vessels or tracheids. Later, with the administration of pure indoleacetic acid, it was found that supraoptimal concentrations resulted in the formation of heavily lignified cells, which, in conifers, had the appearance of compression wood (Fraser, 1949). Thus, physiologists interested in the effects of auxin on cambial activity have been confronted with two interrelated problems, that of cambial activation and that of differentiation of cambial derivatives. Numerous other physiological and biochemical responses to auxin and other growth hormones are doubtless involved.

Investigations of cell division in the cambium have been essentially descriptive, but they have provided more adequate knowledge of the locations of the first cambial divisions, the direction and rate of movement of the first surge of cambial activity, the intensity of cambial divisions at various positions and times, and the time and manner of decline and cessation of cambial activity (Bannan, 1955). Answers to the manner in which auxin influences these processes await the elucidation of the biochemical mechanism of auxin action.

Both descriptive and experimental evidence indicate that auxin has an active and perhaps a specific role in controlling the differentiation of cambial derivatives. The evidence seems conclusive for its participation in xylem differentiation. This is indicated by its role in xylem differentiation in wound healing and in root-culture work (Torrey, 1953). Its role in the differentiation of phloem is uncertain, and there is reason to believe that a number of growth substances may be involved for various phases of cambial activity. For example, Söding (1936), Gouwentak (1936, 1941), Brown and Cormack (1937), and Gouwentak and Maas (1940) have reported that auxin combines with wound hormone to produce cambial activity for only a short distance below the wound in a dormant shoot. The stimulus extends further in non-dormant shoots, thus indicating participation of another factor. Gibberellin-like factors may influence the nature of cambial activity. Wareing (1958) was able to produce an annual ring without differentiation of vessels in disbudded ash shoots treated with gibberellin. Bradley and Crane (1957) obtained a similar type of annual ring in the spur shoots of apricot after treatment with gibberellin. Various other substances have been reported to influence differentiation of cambial tissues.

Quantitative relationships have recently been established by Jacobs and Morrow (1957) between leaf length, auxin content, and primary xylem differentiation in growing shoots. They were working with a herbaceous plant and did not extend their investigations to a consideration of secondary xylem. However, according to the generally accepted view of plant anatomists (Esau, 1953), the later stages of primary vascular differentiation and the early stages of secondary growth may overlap in the same portion of a stem. This may occur while the internodes are still undergoing some elongation. Thus it is likely that primary xylem differentiation and secondary xylem differentiation have many features in common, including a similar response to auxin. Certainly the acropetal movement of secondary xylem differentiation in the current shoot and the basipetal differentiation in the 1-year-old shoot have parallels in the simultaneous acropetal and basipetal developments which are frequently reported in primary xylem differentiation.

If secondary xylem differentiation obeys the same rules as primary xylem differentiation, it might also be possible to establish quantitative relationships between auxin concentration and differentiation of the first annual ring of combined primary and secondary xylem in the current annual shoot or between auxin concentration and the width of the current annual ring in 1-year, 2-year, 3-year, or older shoots. An examination of the current annual shoot at various times during its elongation does not necessarily show a wider ring of xylem in the portions of the shoot where the peak hormone contents are highest, the center of the shoot for some species (Zimmerman, 1936; Hatcher, 1959) and the base for others (Gunckel & Thimann, 1949). Observations of ring width of the current annual shoot suggest that the relationship is not uniform. Hämmerle (1900) found a continuous and uniform decrease in ring width in the current shoot of *Acer pseudoplatanus*. Huber (1928) reported that in *Abies concolor* and *Picea excelsa* the width of xylem at the base of the new shoot was always greater than at its apex and was even greater than the combined width of the two annual rings of the preceding annual shoot measured at a position below the first branch (at the distal end of the 1-year shoot). When Huber compared the conducting area of the xylem at any level with the fresh weight of needles being supplied by these conducting elements, he found a progressive increase in relative conducting area toward the apex of the main shoot (leader) in both fir and spruce (Fig. 3–5).

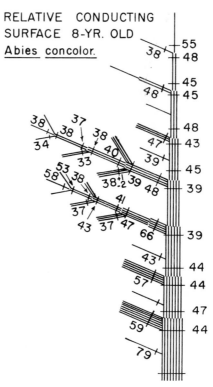

FIG. 3–5. Value of relative conducting surface at various positions in the crown of an 8-year-old white fir (*Abies concolor*). The relative conducting surface at any level is determined from the ratio between the cross-sectional area of the xylem and the fresh weight of needles being supplied by these conducting elements. The age of each shoot is represented schematically by the number of parallel lines, except that the weak epicormic branches are represented by single lines. The positions of the measurements are indicated by the short orthogonal lines. Redrawn from Huber (1928).

The lack of agreement between ring width in the current annual shoot and auxin distribution has several possible explanations. One possibility is that the relationship would tend to be obscured by the different relative ages of the two ends of the shoot and the acropetal differentiation of the secondary xylem. Another is that other substances which act synergistically with auxin may be limiting factors. The correct explanation awaits clarification of the role of auxin in controlling xylem differentiation.

The fact that the current annual ring in the 1-year shoot possesses essentially the same age throughout the length of the shoot might make it easier to establish a relationship between the width of this ring and the hormonal distribution pattern. Huber reported the consistent increase in relative conducting surface from base to apex in each of the last five or six annual shoots, with the differences becoming progressively less in the older shoots (Fig. 3–5). His computations for relative conducting surfaces showed a diminution with the various orders of shoot branching, and in beech he also found consistent differences for branches bearing sun and shade leaves. All of these relationships seem to vary in a manner analogous to the hormone concentration distributions reported by Zimmerman. Zimmerman (1936) found that buds in the upper part of the tree crown had less hormone than buds situated lower. He also found differences between main and side buds related to the branching order.

SITE OF AUXIN PRODUCTION. The distribution patterns just discussed indicate that diffusible auxin is found in most growing tissues—elongating stems, growing leaves, dividing cambium, developing flowers and fruits, etc. The formation of active free auxin is usually associated with embryonic or meristematic cells, but this may not always be the case, as there is some evidence of auxin production in mature leaves (Münch, 1938). Apparently there are differences in production of hormone by leaves depending on species, ontogenetic development, position in the crown, etc. There also appear to be differences in the site of auxin production within the growing regions of stems. Gunkel and Thimann (1949) found that in the long shoots of ginkgo auxin was not produced by the leaves or the apical meristem but by the elongating stem itself, possibly from a precursor supplied by the leaves. They found a peak yield of auxin in the lower, rapidly extending internodes at a position about two nodes above the base. Titman and Wetmore (1955) found in the long shoots of *Cercidiphyllum* that the major auxin production center was in the rib meristem of the apical meristem and in the elongating stem rather than in the leaves or shoot initials themselves.

Some of the difficulties in determining site of auxin production are illustrated by Hatcher (1959). He found that the peak of accumulated auxin occurred several internodes below the stem apex, as previously mentioned. He assumed that this auxin originated in the stem apex and young developing leaves. The declining auxin concentrations in the lower stem were difficult to explain, and it was not clear whether the hormone was consumed in cambial activity, inactivated by auxin oxidase, converted to a bound condition, or unable to move through older internodes. The fact that auxin production was found to occur in the lower portion of the stem after a temporary arrest of growth due to drought made Hatcher favor the possibility that auxin can readily be converted to a bound form which can again be set free.

The fact that auxin concentrations decrease in a basipetal direction and may become undetectable in the larger branches or trunk has raised the question of whether the sites of auxin production in the growing shoots are adequate for cambial activity in the lower portions of the tree. Söding (1940) presented evidence to show that the amount of auxin required to initiate cambial activity is extremely small, less than the amount contained in a single coleoptile tip. He believes that this amount of auxin is received from above and is consumed in initiating growth. Once active, the cambium produces its own auxin by a process of autocatalysis, and the excess moves basipetally to the cambium below to repeat the process. The amount of auxin present in the cambium at any one time might be below the limits detectable by the *Avena* test. Hatcher (1959) discounts this theory on the basis of his own results and tends to favor some kind of auxin release as a more probable explanation for low auxin contents in the lower cambium. Wareing (1951) also postulates the presence of bound auxin or auxin precursor in the cambium of ring-porous hardwoods to account for the extremely rapid basipetal movement of the cambial stimulus in the spring. It is evident that there is need for work on auxin biogenesis in woody plants.

Abnormal Cambial Activity in Relation to Experimental Treatments

Important information on the physiology of cambial activity has accrued from various experimental techniques such as decapitation of seedlings, disbudding and defoliation, felling of trees for peeling studies, ringing, treatment with exogenous auxin supplies, and culture of cambial tissues. Some of the results of these treatments will be considered briefly in light of the information that has just been presented on auxin relationships in woody plants.

The experiments of Snow in which seedlings were decapitated and then provided with auxin as a means of verifying the hormonal nature of the cambial stimulus were cited earlier. Similar experiments were repeated by Jost and Reiss (1936) and by Snow (1935). Aside from demonstrating the stimulation of cambial divisions, these experiments also demonstrated that auxin can serve as a general cell-division factor and stimulate divisions in the cells of the primary tissues. Söding (1940) used the decapitated stem of *Helianthus* as a test object for determining the amounts of indoleacetic acid necessary to produce cambial activity and to determine the comparative effectiveness of various hormonal diffusates from plants. He found that auxin collected from the active cambium of *Acer circinatum* was able to stimulate more cambial activity in *Helianthus* than a comparable amount of indoleacetic acid (*Avena* curvatures were used to determine comparable amounts). He thus postulated the presence of other hormones or cofactors effective in cambial stimulation but not in cell elongation.

Disbudding and ringing experiments have also indicated hormonal control of cambial divisions. If shoots of diffuse-porous hardwoods are disbudded before the start of cambial activity, it will generally be found that no cambial activity will occur. Similarly, if a ring of bark is removed from the shoot there will be no cambial activity below the ring. Both results are generally accepted as supporting the conclusion that cambial activity after a period of dormancy is dependent upon a stimulus from the developing buds. If indoleacetic acid is added to the scars left by the disbudding or to the ring, cambial activity will be stimulated. These experiments have been repeated by many investigators and are interpreted as demonstrating the hormonal nature of the cambial stimulus.

Disbudding and ringing experiments with ring-porous hardwoods and with coniferous species have not always prevented cambial activity. However, recent experiments by Wareing (1951) on ring-porous hardwoods have demonstrated that the cambial stimulus is still dependent upon bud growth but that the stimulus is provided by adventitious buds and that vessels are developed at a very early stage of these buds. Wareing was further able to show that the stimulus developed earlier and was effective over a considerably greater distance than were any stimuli which might develop from adventitious buds in diffuse-porous hardwoods. He thus postulated the presence of a hormone precursor in ring-porous species.

Ringing experiments on evergreen conifers have given a somewhat different result. Both Münch (1938) and Huber (1948) noted that ringing of conifers results in a cessation of cambial activity immediately below the ring but that cambial activity appears gradually with distance below the ring until nearly a normal ring width is obtained. Münch (1938) performed his experiments at various positions on 1-, 2-, and 3-year-old branches of *Pinus* and came to the conclusion that hormones effective in cambial division are provided primarily by the young developing needles but that small quantities can be supplied by older needles. However, this hormone supply will move only downward and any twig that is defoliated or shaded and topped will die.

Huber's (1948) experiments were performed on the trunks of trees at considerable distances from the crown. He found that, if a trunk was peelable at the time of ringing, it became non-peelable about 14 days later. It is not known whether cambial divisions ceased immediately; presumably this interval could correspond to the time for the xylem mother cells to mature to the cambium. However, a few weeks later he observed weak cambial activity and an increase in peelability, due to an autonomous production of hormone. He observed that the autonomous production of growth hormone below a ring was greatest during the best sap-peeling time in the second half of June. The peelability began later and ended earlier than in the non-ringed stem. Furthermore, cambial activity did not become as vigorous, as shown by the higher peeling resistances. A similar production of autonomous hormone seemed to occur in trees which had been felled and topped in the late winter and allowed to remain on the ground. However, these felled trees did not peel in the upper part of the bole but only in the center portion, indicating a basipetal movement and gradual augmentation of the autonomous hormone stream. The peelability of felled trees also began later and ended earlier than that of standing trees, the hormone regeneration being thus comparable to the situation occurring below a ring.

Further evidence of the production of hormone in older needles and possibly for its autonomous production in the cambium of evergreen conifers is shown by the disbudding experiments of Münch (1938) (Figs. 3–6 and 3–7). Münch explained the added diameter growth at the base of disbudded trees as due to utilization of the food material which normally would have been used for shoot elongation. This utilization for diameter growth was made possible by the downward movement and accumulation of sufficient hormone.

The experimental treatments with indoleacetic acid mentioned earlier have also yielded important results on the physiology of cambial activity. Especially interesting are those treatments in which hormone has been used to determine whether cambial be-

havior below a ring was due to starvation or to hormone depriva-
tion. Repeated observations have confirmed that the extent of
cambial activity resulting from auxin doses administered below a
ring is dependent upon the responsiveness of the cambium. Treatments made during the early spring or sap-peeling time are effec-

DIAMETER GROWTH - 10 YR. OLD
Pinus strobus

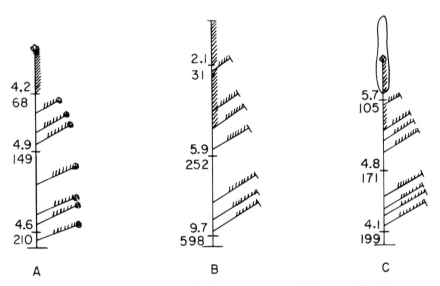

FIG. 3–6. Diameter growth of the main stem of 10-year-old white pine
(*Pinus strobus*) trees: (A) untreated; (B) completely disbudded but with
needles retained; (C) terminal bud covered and all other buds removed. In
the pairs of numbers to the left of the stems, the upper number corresponds to
the increase of diameter in millimeters and the lower to the total increase in
conducting surface in square millimeters. Measurements were made at three
locations in each stem: a few centimeters below the base of the leader, in the
center of the stem, and a little above the ground line. Redrawn from Münch
(1938).

tive in stimulating cambial activity for a considerable distance
below the point of application. Treatments made in the autumn are
ineffective, indicating that factors other than hormones are required
for normal cambial activity.

These various experimental procedures involve wounding, which
also has an effect on cambial activity. Brown and Cormack (1937)
tested the response of the vascular cambium to wounding both in

the winter months and during the growing season. In the latter treatments, they found that the wound cambium was promoted by the development of buds and leaves distal to a wound, and that the effect was noticeable before the basipetal gradient of normal cambial activity from the developing extension growth had reached the

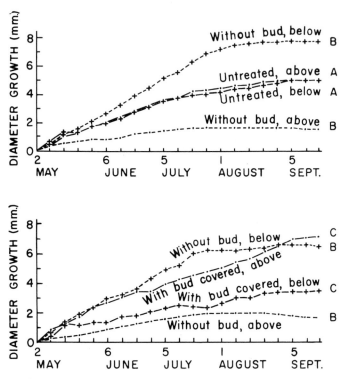

Fig. 3–7. Growth curves of the 10-year-old white pine (*Pinus strobus*) trees shown in Fig. 3–6. "Above" refers to the uppermost measurement and "below" to the basal measurement. From Münch (1938).

cambium. The wound stimulus itself is apparently capable of producing cell division only, because there is a slight basipetal gradient below a girdle in which differentiation does not occur, and a normal differentiation above the girdle where there could be a reaction between the wound substance and the cambial hormone.

The methods of tissue culture have been applied to the cambium in an effort to determine its nutritional requirements. Jacquiot (1950) made cambial cultures throughout the winter of various native trees growing near Fontainebleau, France, and reported that there were sufficient growth substances for a normal 6- to 8-week development of cambium at all times during the dormant season. He concluded that cambial activity was limited in nature only by low ambient temperatures. Sussex and Clutter (1959) studied seasonal growth periodicity of tissue explants of secondary phloem from woody perennial plants, grown in sterile culture with carbohydrates, vitamins, and growth substances. They found that maximum growth was obtained from explants removed from the donor plant near the time of bud break in the spring. Tissues removed progressively later in the summer proliferated less. The decreasing growth trend was reversed several months before bud break so that there was a gradual increase toward the spring peak. These results indicate a periodicity in growth potential, probably due to some unrecognized growth substance. It is not known whether the differences observed by Jacquiot and by Sussex and Clutter represent a difference between the requirements of xylem and phloem derivatives for growth factors.

Cambial Activity in Relation to Water Contents

The hypothesis of the hormonal control of seasonal periodicity has challenged the older view that the water contents of the soil and of the tree itself are the most important factors causing a cyclic behavior of the cambium. Detailed studies of seasonal water contents in the various species of trees showed a spring maximum coinciding with the swelling and bursting of buds (Gibbs, 1957; Craib, 1918, 1920, 1923). This relationship led some investigators to the conclusion that water replenishment initiated terminal growth which, in turn, by basipetal influence initiated radial growth (Priestley and Scott, 1936). Production of false rings in connection with lammas shoots during wet summers after an early dry spell also contributed to this conclusion.

An even more prevalent belief has been that the cessation of cambial activity is due to decreased water contents. Priestley (1930) advanced an elaborate hypothesis to explain the mechanism whereby decreasing water contents could bring about the cessation of cambial activity in dicotyledonous species.

One of the most thorough efforts to relate cambial activity to water contents was made by Huber (1948). He sampled small blocks 2 cm. square, consisting of cambium with 1 mm. of bark and 1 mm. of wood on opposite sides, and found a very low correlation between water content and peelability. A further argument noted by Huber against a relationship of cambial activity to water saturation was the fact that trees felled in winter exhibited cambial activity at the customary time without external water supply.

It should be emphasized that the above remarks apply to the influence of internal water contents on the cyclic behavior of trees and are not meant to imply that water is unimportant for cambial activity. The width of the annual ring does reflect environmental conditions, and there are many circumstances under which there is a strong positive correlation between growth-layer widths and internal and external water supplies.

Cambial Activity in Relation to Food Reserves

Studies of the food reserves of trees in relation to cyclic growth behavior have had a parallel history to those of water contents and distributions. However, the number of studies on food reserves far exceeds the number on seasonal water contents.

The relationships between cyclic growth behavior in the cambium and cyclic fluctuations in food reserves are further complicated by seasonal changes of food reserves in relation to frost hardiness. It seems rather unlikely that a causal relationship exists between carbohydrate reserves and the initiation and cessation of cambial activity. Ringing studies have shown that food reserves generally are adequate in any portion of the stem to support cambial activity in that location once the cambium has been stimulated by the developing vegetative organs. The fluctuations in nature and amount of carbohydrate reserve probably are associated with growth phenomena and are not causal in nature.

There appears to be a relationship, in some cases, between phloem reactivation or early phloem differentiation, the spring flush of growth, and the seasonal fluctuations in starch reserves. In many trees there is a bimodal seasonal fluctuation in starch reserves with one maximum in late summer and early fall and the other maximum in late winter and early spring just prior to shoot growth (Preston and Phillips, 1911; Cockerham, 1930; Swarbrick, 1927; Wight, 1933). The two periods of phloem activity which have been noted by some investigators (Elliott, 1935; Ladefoged, 1952) closely follow the two maxima of starch content. Perhaps, in these cases, phloem differentiation provides channels for food transport for subsequent height growth and for xylem differentiation. Enough starch is present to provide for both phloem differentiation and the surge of height growth. Once the channels of food movement are provided the phloem may cease its activity and lose the balance of its food to the differentiating xylem. Xylem formation is triggered by auxins from the elongating shoot. Further food supplies for xylem differentiation are provided from the newly expanded leaves of the current shoot. The starch content gradually rises through the growing season, and the late-season differentiation of wood probably is associated with ample carbohydrate supplies. The maintenance of cambial activity may depend upon the continued production of auxin in mature leaves under suitably long photoperiods (Wareing and Roberts, 1956).

Distribution of the Annual Ring

It is evident that our knowledge is still too meager to allow formulation of a physiological explanation of the form of tree trunks and the radial distribution of growth. The early literature contains numerous accounts of empirical investigations of annual ring width and stem form together with various hypotheses of causal factors. Most investigators have sought an explanation of growth inequalities on the basis of differences in nutrition or in force stimuli affecting the cambium. These early theories, which have been summarized by Büsgen and Münch (1931), have been largely superseded by recognition of the importance of hormones in the regulation of growth. However, the *modus operandi* of these substances is still obscure.

A multiplicity of causes may be responsible for eccentricities in ring configuration at various levels in the stem. Foresters and wood technologists are well acquainted with conditions leading to elliptical growth rings and production of compression or tension wood. In addition to the more obvious and predictable eccentricities, there are others which are of random nature.

Young, thrifty forest trees with uniform crowns and slender cylindrical boles display uniform and predictable variations in growth increments. A measurement of ring widths along a radius at any vertical position shows a gradual increase in widths in the first few rings from the center, followed by a slow diminution toward the outside. If the annual increments are followed vertically, it will be seen that the annual rings are widest near the base of the crown. These variations in ring width originate from operation of the internal correlating mechanisms within the tree.

Duff and Nolan (1953, 1957, 1958) have investigated the patterns of ring development in *Pinus resinosa* and have called attention to the importance of studying ring sequences obtained by measuring ring widths from internode * to internode at a uniform ring number from the pith. For example, such a sequence might consist of all the rings laid down during the sixth year from the origin of the internode. They claim that such a sequence exhibits a configuration that varies with site and stand conditions, and also exhibits random yearly fluctuations. The effect of internal variation would be uniform throughout a series because the rings would have been laid down in their respective internodes when these internodes and cambia were at a uniform age. It would thus appear that means are at hand to more clearly delimit the spheres of internal physiology from those arising from quality of the locality.

Summary and Conclusions

Growth of the vascular cambium in woody plants is probably never continuous, even in the so-called ever growing species of the tropical rain forest. Rather, cambial activity is cyclic, with periods of activity alternating with periods of rest or relative inactivity. This growth periodicity is heritable and is controlled by internal correlating mechanisms which are probably hormonal in nature. The intensity and period of the rhythms are usually determined by fluctuations of environmental conditions. Each new surge of cambial activity is initiated by a period of new vegetative development. Plant hormones produced in the growing primary body move morphologically downward into the vascular cambium and thence down the tree. There is a lapse of time after the hormones reach the cambium before divisions commence. During this time lag, the bark becomes easily peelable from the surface of the wood and a number of distinctive changes occur in the cambium. These changes in the cambium move with great rapidity down the stem to the base of the trunk of ring-porous trees, but may take several weeks in large diffuse-porous trees. Once cambial divisions commence, they, too, progress down the tree at rates comparable to those of the initial changes.

The belief that a hormone is involved in the awakening of the cambium is based on circumstantial evidence of divers and sundry types. Elongating shoots and developing leaves have been found to produce high concentrations of diffusible auxin and at the same time have been shown to promote the growth of the cambium beneath them. The resulting cambial activity can be interrupted by

---

* "Internode" is here used in the sense employed by foresters to refer to the interval between branch whorls along the main stem.

such experimental treatments as decapitation, ringing, or disbudding. Restoration of cambial activity can be attained by treatment of the stump, girdle, or bud scar with exogenous auxin. The responsiveness of the cambium to treatment with exogenous supplies of auxin varies with season. Indications are that other hormonal factors are involved besides auxin.

Efforts have been made to study, in woody shoots, the centers of hormone production, the rates and directions of movement, and the role of auxin in the processes of division and differentiation in the cambium. None of these problems is satisfactorily solved and there is obviously need for further studies. These should be made during various phases of shoot and cambial ontogeny.

Knowledge of the *modus operandi* of hormones in the regulation of cambial growth will enable foresters to successfully formulate explanations of the form of tree trunks and the radial distribution of growth. Some progress has been made in distinguishing variations in ring width which originate from the operation of the internal correlating mechanisms within the tree from those due to the operation of external factors. Tree physiologists are steadily enlarging the circle of knowledge regarding tree growth.

LITERATURE CITED

AVERY, G. S. JR., P. R. BURKHOLDER, and H. B. CREIGHTON. 1937. Production and distribution of growth hormone in shoots of *Aesculus* and *Malus*, and its probable role in stimulating cambial activity. Amer. Jour. Bot. 24: 51–58.

BAILEY, I. W. 1954. Contributions to Plant Anatomy. Chronica Botanica Co., Waltham, Mass.

BANNAN, M. W. 1955. The vascular cambium and radial growth in *Thuja occidentalis* L. Can. Jour. Bot. 33: 113–138.

BRADLEY, M. V., and J. C. CRANE. 1957. Gibberellin-stimulated cambial activity in stems of apricot spur shoots. Sci. 126: 972–973.

BROWN, A. B., and R. G. H. CORMACK. 1937. Stimulation of cambial activity, locally in the region of application and at a distance in relation to a wound, by means of heteroauxin. Can. Jour. Res. Sect. C., Bot. Sci. 15: 433–441.

BROWN, C. L., and R. H. WETMORE. 1959. Auxin transport in the long shoots of pine. Amer. Jour. Bot. 46: 586–590.

BÜSGEN, M., and E. MÜNCH. 1931. The structure and life of forest trees. 3rd ed. Translated by T. THOMPSON. John Wiley & Sons, Inc., New York.

CLAUSEN, J. 1951. Stages in the Evolution of Plant Species. Cornell University Press, Ithaca, N. Y.

CLAUSEN, J., D. D. KECK, and W. M. HIESEY. 1940, 1945, 1948. Experimental studies on the nature of species. I, II, III. Carnegie Inst. Wash. Pubs. 520, 564, 581.

COCKERHAM, G. 1930. Some observations on cambial activity and seasonal starch content in sycamore (*Acer pseudoplatanus*). Proc. Leeds Phil. and Lit. Soc. Sci. Sect. 2: 64–80.

COSTER, C. 1927, 1928. Zur Anatomie und Physiologie der Zuwachszonen und Jahresringbildung in den Tropen. Ann. Jard. Bot. Buitenzorg. 37: 49–160; 38: 1–114. Reviewed by B. J. RENDLE in Forestry Quart. 2: 127–130. 1928,

CRAIB, W. G. 1918, 1920, 1923. Regional spread of moisture in wood of trees. Roy. Bot. Gard. Edinb. Notes 11: 1–18; 12: 187–190; 14: 1–8.

DOWNS, R. J., and H. A. BORTHWICK. 1956. Effects of photoperiod on growth of trees. Bot. Gaz. 117: 310–326.

DUFF, G. H., and N. J. NOLAN. 1953. Growth and morphogenesis in the Canadian forest species. I. The controls of cambial and apical activity in Pinus resinosa Ait. Can. Jour. Bot. 31: 471–513.

——— and ———. 1957. Growth and morphogenesis in the Canadian forest species. II. Specific increments and their relation to the quantity and activity of growth in Pinus resionsa Ait. Can. Jour. Bot. 35: 527–572.

——— and ———. 1958. Growth and morphogenesis in the Canadian forest species. III. The time scale of morphogenesis at the stem apex of Pinus resinosa Ait., Can. Jour. Bot. 36: 687–706.

ELLIOTT, J. H. 1935. Seasonal changes in the development of the phloem of the sycamore, Acer Pseudo Platanus L. Proc. Leeds Phil. and Lit. Soc. Sci. Sect. 3: 55–67.

ESAU, K. 1950. Development and structure of phloem tissue. II. Bot. Rev. 16: 67–114.

———. 1953. Plant Anatomy. John Wiley & Sons, Inc., New York.

FRASER, D. A. 1949. Production of spring wood with B-indole acetic acid (heteroauxin). Nature (London) 164: 542–543.

———. 1956. Ecological studies of forest trees at Chalk River, Ontario, Canada. II. Ecological conditions and radial increment. Ecol. 37: 777–789.

———. 1958. Growth mechanisms in hardwoods. Pulp and Paper Mag. Canada. 59: 202–209.

GIBBS, R. D. 1957. Patterns in the seasonal water content of trees. In: The Physiology of Forest Trees. K. V. THIMANN (ed.). The Ronald Press Co., New York. Pp. 43–69.

GILL, N. 1932. The phloem of ash (Fraxinus excelsior Linn.): Its differentiation and seasonal variation. Proc. Leeds Phil. and Lit. Soc. Sci. Sect. 2: 347–355.

GORDON, S. A. 1953. Physiology of hormone action. In: Growth and Differentiation in Plants. W. E. LOOMIS (ed.). Iowa State College Press, Ames, Iowa.

GOUWENTAK, C. A. 1936. Kambiumtätigkeit und Wuchsstoff. I. Meded. Landbouwhoogesch. (Wageningen) 39: 3–23.

———. 1941. Cambial activity as dependent on the presence of growth hormone and the non-resting condition of stems. Proc. Acad. Sci. Amsterdam 44: 654–663.

GOUWENTAK, C. A., and A. L. MAAS. 1940. Kambiumtätigkeit und Wuchsstoff. II. Meded. Landbouwhoogesch. (Wageningen) 44: 3–16.

GREGORY, F. G., and C. R. HANCOCK. 1955. The rate of transport of natural auxin in woody shoots. Ann. Bot., n.s. 19: 451–465.

GUNCKEL, J. E., and K. V. THIMANN. 1949. Studies of development in long shoots and short shoots of Ginkgo biloba L. III. Auxin production in shoot growth. Amer. Jour. Bot. 36: 145–151.

HÄMMERLE, J. 1900. Zur Organisation von Acer pseudoplatanus. Biblioth. Bot. 50: 100–101.

HATCHER, E. S. J. 1959. Auxin relations of the woody shoot. The distribution of diffusible auxin in shoots of apple and plum rootstock varieties. Ann. Bot., n.s. 23:409–423.

HUBER, B. 1928. Weitere quantitative Untersuchungen über das Wasserleitungssystem der Pflanzen. Jahrb. f. Wiss. Bot. 67: 877–959.

———. 1939. Das Siebröhresystem unserer Bäume und seine jahreszeitlichen Veränderungen. Jahrb. f. Wiss. Bot. 88: 176–242.

———. 1948. Physiologie der Rindenschälung bei Fichte und Eichen. Forstwiss. Centbl. 67: 129–164.

HUBER, B., E. SCHMIDT, and H. JAHNEL. 1937. Untersuchungen über den Assimilatstrom. I. Tharandter Forstl. Jahrb. 88: 1017–1050.

JACOBS, W. P. 1954. Acropetal auxin transport and xylem regeneration: A quantitative study. Amer. Nat. 88: 327–337.

JACOBS, W. P., and I. B. MORROW. 1957. A quantitative study of xylem development in the vegetative shoot apex of *Coleus*. Amer. Jour. Bot. 44: 823–842.

JACQUIOT, C. 1950. Contribution à l'étude des facteurs déterminant le cycle d'activité du cambium chez quelques arbres forestiers. Rev. Forst. Franç. 2: 605–610.

JOST, L. 1891. Über Dickenwachstum und Jahresringbildung. Bot. Ztg. 49: 482–499, 501–510, 522–531, 541–547, 557–563, 573–579, 589–595, 605–611, 625–627.

———. 1893. Über die Beziehungen zwischen der Blattentwickelung und der Gefässbildung in der Pflanze. Bot. Ztg. 51: 89–138.

———. 1907. Lectures on Plant Physiology. Oxford University Press, Oxford. Translated by R. J. H. GIBSON.

JOST, L., and E. REISS. 1936. Zur Physiologie der Wuchsstoffe. II. Einfluss des Heteroauxins auf Längen- und Dickenwachstum. Z. Bot. 30: 335–376.

KASTENS, E. 1924. Beiträge zur Kenntnis der Funktion der Siebröhren. Mitt. Inst. Allg. Bot. Hamburg 6: 33–70.

KIENHOLZ, R. 1934. Leader, needle, cambial, and root growth of certain conifers and their interrelations. Bot. Gaz. 96: 73–91.

KLEBS, G. 1914. Über das Trieben der einheimischen Bäume, speziell der Buche. Heidelberg. Akad. der Wiss., Math. -Nat. Kl. Abhandl. 3. Reviewed in Forestry Quart. 14: 83–85. 1916.

KORIBA, K. 1958. On the periodicity of tree-growth in the tropics, with reference to the mode of branching, the leaf fall, and the formation of the resting bud. Gard. Bull. Straits Settlements 17: 11–81.

LADEFOGED, K. 1952. The periodicity of wood formation. Kgl. Danske Vidensk. Selsk. Biol. Skr. 7(3).

LODEWICK, J. E. 1928. Seasonal activity of the cambium in some northeastern trees. Bull. N. Y. State Col. Forestry, Syracuse Univ. Tech. Pub. 23: 1–87.

MacDOUGAL, D. T. 1930. Lengthened growth periods and continuous growth. Proc. Amer. Phil. Soc. 69: 329–345.

MIROV, N. T. 1941. Distribution of growth hormone in shoots of two species of pines. Jour. Forestry 39: 457–464.

MÜNCH, E. 1938. Untersuchungen über die Harmonie der Baumgestalt. Jahrb. f. Wiss. Bot. 86: 581–673.

PAULEY, S. S., and T. O. PERRY. 1954. Ecotypic variation of the photoperiodic response in populus. Jour. Arnold Arboretum 35: 167–188.

PRESTON, J. F., and F. J. PHILLIPS. 1911. Seasonal variation in the food reserves of trees. Forestry Quart. 9: 232–243.

PRIESTLEY, J. H. 1930. Studies in the physiology of cambial activity. III. Seasonal activity. New Phytol. 29: 316–351.

PRIESTLEY, J. H., and L. I. SCOTT. 1936. A note upon summer wood production in the tree. Proc. Leeds Phil. and Lit. Soc. Sci. Sect. 3: 235–248.

PRIESTLEY, J. H., L. I. SCOTT, and M. E. MALINS. 1933. A new method of studying cambial activity. Proc. Leeds Phil. and Lit. Soc. Sci. Sect. 2: 365–374.

REED, H. S. 1928. Intra-seasonal cycles of growth. Proc. Natl. Acad. Sci. U.S. 14: 221–229.

REED, H. S., and D. T. MacDOUGAL. 1937. Periodicity in the growth of the orange tree. Growth 1: 371–373.

RICHARDS, R. W. 1942. The Tropical Rain Forest. Cambridge University Press, London.

SNOW, R. 1933. The nature of the cambial stimulus. New Phytol. 32: 288–296.

———. 1935. Activation of cambial growth by pure hormone. New Phytol. 34: 347–360.

SÖDING, H. 1936. Über den Einfluss von Wuchsstoff auf das Dickenwachstum der Bäume. Ber. Deut. Bot. Ges. 54: 291–304.

———. 1937. Wuchsstoff und Kambiumtätigkeit. Jahrb. f. Wiss. Bot. 84: 639–670.

————. 1940. Weitere Untersuchungen über die Wuchsstoffregulation der Kambiumtätigkeit. Z. Bot. 36: 113–141.

STEWARD, F. C., and E. M. SHANTZ. 1959. The chemical regulation of growth: Some substances and extracts which induce growth and morphogenesis. Ann. Rev. Plant Physiol. 10: 379–404.

SUSSEX, I. M., and M. E. CLUTTER. 1959. Seasonal growth periodicity of tissue explants from woody perennial plants in vitro. Sci. 129: 386–387.

SWARBRICK, T. 1927. Studies in the physiology of fruit trees. I. The seasonal starch content and cambial activity in one- to five-year-old apple branches. Jour. Pomol. and Hort. Sci. 6: 137–156.

TITMAN, P. W., and R. H. WETMORE. 1955. The growth of long and short shoots of Cercidiphyllum. Amer. Jour. Bot. 42: 364–372.

TORREY, J. G. 1953. The effect of certain metabolic inhibitors on vascular tissue differentiation in isolated pea roots. Amer. Jour. Bot. 40: 525–533.

TURESSON, G. 1922. The species and the variety as ecological units. Hereditas 3: 100–113, 211–350.

VAARTAJA, O. 1954. Photoperiodic ecotypes of trees. Can. Jour. Bot. 32: 392–399.

WAREING, P. F. 1951. Growth studies in woody species. IV. The initiation of cambial activity in ring-porous species. Physiol. Plant. 4: 546–562.

————. 1958. Interaction between indoleacetic acid and gibberellic acid in cambial activity. Nature (London) 181: 1744–1745.

WAREING, P. F., and D. L. ROBERTS. 1956. Photoperiodic control of cambial activity in Robinia pseudacacia L. New Phytol. 55: 289–388.

WENT, F. W. 1928. Wuchsstoff und Wachstum. Rec. des Trav. Bot. Néerland. 25: 1–116.

WIGHT, W. 1933. Radial growth of the xylem and the starch reserves of Pinus sylvestris: A preliminary survey. New Phytol. 32: 77–95.

WILCOX, H., F. J. CZABATOR, G. GIROLAMI, D. E. MORELAND, and R. F. SMITH. 1956. Chemical debarking of some pulpwood species. Tech. Pub. N. Y. State Col. Forestry, Syracuse Univ. 77.

ZIMMERMANN, W. A. 1936. Untersuchungen über die räumliche und zeitliche Verteilung des Wuchsstoffes bei Bäumen. Z. Bot. 30: 209–252.

4

Physiology of Cambial Activity

D. J. Wort

When plant physiological investigations of a few decades ago are compared with those of the present, the transition from descriptive to biochemical content is very evident. This change from morphological-anatomical interest to a demand for metabolic explanation is likewise evident in the literature concerning the cambium and its place in wood formation. Wilcox's paper underlines this need for information concerning the *modus operandi* of plant-growth regulators particularly.

This paper will focus attention on some of the physical, chemical, and biochemical changes which occur in the cambial region from the initiation of cambial activity in the spring until dormancy in the autumn. The paucity of papers and lack of information on these subjects, coupled with their great practical importance emphasize the need for fundamental research in this field.

Initial Cambial Activity

Rhythmical behavior is characteristic of all living matter. Even in a constant environment the endogenous rhythms of a plant manifest themselves. Within a biological system, the concentration of reactants, enzymes, or cofactors may build up slowly and reach the level required for a reaction. Then the reaction occurs, the reactants are used up or decreased in concentration, and the cycle begins again. Wilcox has drawn attention to several of these rhythmical or periodical phenomena.

During dormancy of a tree, the cells of the cambium are rectangular in cross-section and the walls are sharply and distinctly outlined. The radial and tangential walls are relatively thick and in tangential section the radial walls often have a beaded appearance.

In the spring (March, April), the walls become semitransparent and more plastic and the protoplasm changes from a gel to a sol state. The radial walls extend and the cambial ring increases in width. This increase, which occurs before the start of cell division, often almost doubles the cambium width. The bark will now "slip," and its inner portion becomes sensitive to frost (Ladefoged, 1952).

The onset of cambial activity is climatically controlled, but the date of readiness for cambial activity is determined genetically. The preliminary change occurs when the temperature rises and buds begin to swell, and usually begins first in the 2-year-old branches and spreads basipetally.

Stage of Division

The transition between the preliminary change and cell division occurs gradually, often occupying 1 to 4 weeks. The clear-cut division between the cambium and lignified cells, seen during dormancy, is no longer evident. A series of partially differentiated xylem elements stretches between the thin-walled cambium and fully lignified wood tissue.

Ladefoged (1952), in Denmark, Fraser (1958), from his observations on Canadian hardwoods, and Wareing (1958), in England, state that cambial division begins first in the twigs immediately below the swelling buds and spreads to the bases of the branches, and thence downwards. Cell division spreads more quickly in a basipetal direction in ring-porous species than in diffuse-porous hardwoods and conifers. Exceptions to the basipetal activation have been noted, however (Brown, 1912; Stewart, 1957).

A two-stage process is involved in the succession of cell divisions. An initial cell in each radial file of elements gives rise to tissue mother cells on either side (xylem and phloem), which in turn divide to produce the wood and bast components. Increase of girth is achieved by semitransverse multiplication division of the cambial initials. These divisions occur relatively frequently with a consequent potential of overproduction of new cambial cells. In the resulting intracambial competition, the initials which are the longest and have the most extensive contacts with the vascular rays survive to continue the cyclic process of growth and multiplication, whereas the less favored cells fail. The cambium is thus in a state of flux with a ceaseless alteration in cell pattern and continual renewal of initials (Bannan, 1957).

Wilcox has pointed out that even if we assume that "auxin" is a complex of indoleacetic acid, kinetin, and gibberellins, and that its transport is through the procambium and cambium or through the phloem, it is apparent that, in some way, this auxin is responsible for the initiation of cell division in the cambium. And, too, auxin may be involved in xylem differentiation. This is suggested by xylem differentiation in wound healing and root-culture work. The production of an annual ring by treatment of ash and apricot shoots with gibberellin is suggestive but not conclusive evidence of the participation of gibberellin *in natura*. Söding's demonstration that auxin collected from the active cambium of *Acer circinatum* was able to stimulate more cambial activity in *Helianthus* than a comparable amount of indoleacetic acid strongly suggests the presence of a hormone complex or cofactors.

The fact that the dormant cambium in many timber species, cultivated in vitro, resumes its activity when exposed to a temperature of about 25° C. in the absence of any added growth-promoting substance suggests that tissues adjoining the cambium contain a reserve of auxin, and an increase in temperature triggers the liberation of free auxin from these stores of inactive hormone. It is possible that the departure from the usual basipetal spread of cell division may be explained in a similar way.

The correlation found in many diffuse-porous trees between the durations of cambial activity and of extension growth can be understood in terms of the auxin hypothesis. When extension growth ceases, the production of auxin falls and in many cases cambial division ceases (horsechestnut, apple). In those cases where cambium activity continues after extension growth has stopped (pines, ash) it may be that mature leaves produce small amounts of auxin which are able to allow production of latewood (Wareing, 1958).

Earlywood and Latewood

It has been known for some time that auxins affect cell division and that their influence on growth results from increased cell enlargement. This effect on enlargement, plus the fact that auxins do not induce any growth response in organisms without cellulose cell walls, favors the view that auxins alter the cellulose cell walls in such a way as to lead to cell enlargement. Another *modus operandi* is the participation, direct or indirect, in the reactions whereby cellulose molecules are deposited within the wall. This may be but an end expression of auxin-regulated processes.

The addition of indoleacetic acid (IAA) to *Avena* coleoptile sections may result in an increase in their oxygen consumption and growth rate. Arsenate inhibits both growth and increase in respiration induced by IAA, but is without effect on the basal metabolism of the coleoptile sections. While causing an actual increase in the rate of respiration, 2,4-dinitrophenol may inhibit growth almost completely. Both these inhibitory chemicals are believed to work by uncoupling the link between the oxidative breakdown of carbohydrates and the phosphorylative process, that is, they prevent the synthesis of adenosine triphosphate (ATP) which is known to power so many constructive metabolic processes. Indoleacetic acid produces its growth effects when ATP synthesis can occur, and cannot do so when this synthesis is prevented. This suggests that IAA may well be active at the ATP-synthesizing points in respiration and in this way can regulate the flow of energy to other reactions in the plant. It may influence metabolism through this key or master controlling reaction.

Of all the changes during auxin-induced growth the most spectacular is that concerned with water uptake. The dependency of growth upon respiration seems to lie in a requirement for ATP. Thus the effect of auxin could be directly on the process of water intake or upon the linkage of ATP to this process (Bonner and Bandurski, 1952). Kramer (1956), however, has emphasized that the relationship of respiration and water uptake may be an indirect one, since energy may influence the permeability of the living cell membrane and the concentration of solutes in the xylem.

The ability of auxin to increase salt intake suggests that the direct water uptake force is an osmotic one. However Van Overbeek (1944) and others have shown that the osmotic pressure actually decreased during response to auxin, and that auxin effects can be obtained with tissues immersed in pure water. These findings, coupled with the discovery that IAA increases the activity of pectin methylesterase and through this increases the plasticity of the primary wall, have led Van Overbeek to the conclusion that a dual effect of indoleacetic acid exists: (1) a decrease in wall pressure by a breakdown of protopectins which reduces tensile strength of the young primary wall while the wall is stretched by the turgor pressure produced by water intake (DPD = OP -- WP), and (2) an acceleration of active (metabolic) water absorption (Bonner and Bandurski, 1952). A third effect may be an auxin-induced increase in permeability of the cell membrane (Brauner and Hasman, 1952).

To suggest an answer to the question "Why does the change from earlywood to latewood occur?" two phases of auxin activity may be selected: (1) its effect on cell expansion and (2) its effect, or lack of effect, on cellulose deposition. That the expansion of the cell may be dependent on a relatively high auxin concentration while a relatively low concentration will permit cellulose deposition is suggested by the situation in Siberian larch and in Douglas-fir (Kennedy, 1960). Measurements of cell and lumen diameters of wood cells produced in linear sequence during the entire growth season revealed that the difference between the area of the entire cross-section of the individual cells and the area of the lumen is quite constant. This means that the cross-sectional area of the wall, formed in both earlywood and latewood, varies but little. The diameter of the lumen, and of the cell, changes very abruptly, giving a distinct line of demarcation between earlywood and latewood. This suggests that a sharp, critical level of auxin for earlywood formation exists in these species, but that the deposition of secondary cell wall material continues unabated, even at low auxin concentrations.

The change from the production of earlywood to latewood may thus be a response to a changed level of auxin reaching the cambium, coupled with a specific response to a diminishing hormone supply. Ring-porous species may have a high auxin production during the formation of earlywood and a sharp threshold level which gives an abrupt transition to latewood when the supply of active auxin falls to, and below, this threshold. Other species, e.g., western hemlock, may possess a mechanism that does not have a sharp threshold value, and they respond to a falling auxin supply by a gradual transition to latewood. The supply of active auxin is the sum of the auxin from the apices and younger leaves, the smaller amounts from mature leaves, and that stored in the neighborhood of the cambium (Stewart, 1957).

Biochemical and Chemical Mechanisms

Gerola and Barbesion (1956) used a tetrazolum staining technique to detect seasonal changes of dehydrogenase activity in the cambium and phloem of branches of *Corylus, Populus,* and *Prunus.* Maximum activity occurred in the spring and autumn, coinciding with maximum cambial cell activity and maximum accumulation of reserves, respectively. A gradient of activity was found along the branch, reaching a maximum at the apex.

The chemistry of the transformations from cambium to wood has been the subject of much speculation but few attempts at experimental analysis. As Sultze (1957) pointed out, our knowledge of cambial chemistry is based on the pioneering work of a very few individuals, and with very few exceptions (black spruce, aspen poplar) this has been limited to Australian and European woods.

Sultze summarizes the analyses by saying that cambial tissues, including the cambium proper with its immediate derivatives, are characterized by high nitrogen and uronic anhydride values, and low hexosan, pentosan, and lignin contents. High nitrogen and low uronic anhydride indicate that cambial material is rich in protein and pectin, a condition typical of all embryonic tissues. The low hexosan, pentosan, and lignin values suggest that the materials of the cell wall are laid down as the tissues develop.

Cambial saps are rich in sucrose. Sucrose may comprise 33 per cent of the dry material of the cambial zone (*Picea mariana*) and 80 per cent of total solids (*Quercus* spp). Glucose and fructose are present in much smaller amounts, e.g., glucose 2.6 per cent, fructose 1.1 per cent (*Quercus*). Coniferin, quaiacol, and vanillin, any of which may be a lignin precursor, have also been detected.

Since the cambial cell wall becomes the primary wall of a mature wood cell, the carbohydrates correspond to the carbohydrates in the compound middle lamella (middle lamella + primary wall) of mature wood. This tissue in aspen gave negative Mäule and Wiesner tests and yielded neither vanillin nor syringaldehyde upon oxidation with alkaline nitrobenzene. These results indicate that, in the aspen, start of lignification is coincident with commencement of secondary wall formation (Shultz, 1957). Sultze's findings with respect to hemicelluloses agree with those of other workers in that hemicellulose represents half or more of the carbohydrate material in the outer wall of spruce and birch and only 10 to 20 per cent of the carbohydrate material around the lumen. His data also suggest that pectic substances are deposited completely in the tissue representing the cambium and its immediate derivatives.

The extent of secondary growth is dependent upon the rate of production of raw materials, especially sucrose. Provided the tree has an ample supply of light, water, inorganic materials, and carbon dioxide, the rate of production is largely dependent on the temperature. The net rate is a resultant of photosynthesis-respiration ratios. In seedlings of *Pinus taeda* and *Pinus resinosa* the ratio of photosynthesis to respiration was 13 at 20° C., 7 at 30°, and 3 at 40° (Decker, 1944). It follows that there is an optimum temperature for the rate of secondary growth of any species.

The formation of the components of wood substance is dependent upon numerous enzymatic reactions, the free energy being supplied by catabolic reactions such as those occurring during respiration. Phosphorylative reactions do not necessarily occur if sucrose is the normal basic material. The relatively large amounts of energy required for the formation of glucosidic linkages are furnished in the photosynthesizing cells during the synthesis of monosaccharide phosphates. This energy is retained in sucrose formed from glucose-1-phosphate and fructose-6-phosphate with the assistance of uridine diphosphate. Monosaccharides must be present as phosphates or be accompanied by sufficient adenosine phosphates to provide the free energy for polymerization to polysaccharides.

One may conclude by quoting Stewart (1957): "Very few investigations have been concerned directly with the chemistry of the cambium. The use of modern techniques such as ion exchange, absorption and partition chromatography, and electrophoresis should prove of value in elucidating the composition and the fluctuations in composition of the cambial zone constituents."

LITERATURE CITED

BANNAN, M. W. 1957. The structure and growth of the cambium. Tappi 40: 220–225.

BONNER, J., and R. S. BANDURSKI. 1952. Studies of the physiology, pharmacology and biochemistry of the auxins. Ann. Rev. Plant Physiol. 3: 59–86.

BRAUNER, L., and M. HASMAN. 1952. Weitere Untersuchungan über den Wirkungsmechanismus des Heteroauxins bei der Wasseraufnahme von Pflanzenparenchymen. Protoplasma 41: 302–326.

BROWN, H. P. 1912. Growth studies in forest trees. I. *Pinus rigida* mill. Bot. Gaz. 54: 386–402.

DECKER, J. P. 1944. Effect of temperature on photosynthesis and respiration in red and loblolly pines. Plant Physiol. 19: 679–688.

FRASER, D. A. 1958. Growth mechanisms in hardwoods. Pulp and Paper Mag. Canada 59: 202–209.

GEROLA, F. M., and M. BARBESION. 1956. The dehydrogenase activity of the cambium at different seasons of the year in *Corylus, Populus* and *Prunus*. Nuovo Gior. Bot. Ital., n.s., 63: 37–45. In Italian.

KENNEDY, R. W. 1960. Faculty of Forestry, University of British Columbia, Vancouver. Personal communication.

KRAMER, P. J. 1956. Permeability in relation to respiration. In: Encyclopedia of Plant Physiology. Vol. II. Pp. 358–368.

LADEFOGED, K. 1952. The periodicity of wood formation. Kgl. Danske Vidensk. Selsk. Biol. Skr. 7: 1–98.

OVERBEEK, J. VAN. 1944. Auxin, water uptake and osmotic pressure in potato tissue. Amer. Jour. Bot. 31: 265–269.

STEWART, C. M. 1957. Status of Cambial chemistry. Tappi 40: 244–256.

SULTZE, R. F. 1957. A study of the developing tissues of aspenwood. Tappi 40: 985–994.

WAREING, P. F. 1958. The physiology of cambial activity. Jour. Inst. Wood Sci. 1: 34–42.

5

Auxin Gradients and the Regulation of Cambial Activity

PHILIP R. LARSON

The auxins are among the most widely discussed but least understood of all plant constituents. Yet these substances are known to be intimately involved in a host of plant responses, including the initiation and control of cambial activity and the morphogenetic development of the diverse cambial products. For the most part, research workers have emphasized the role of auxin with respect to a specific phase of cambial activity or to a particular aspect of cellular organization and growth. No attempt has been made to follow the cambium and its derivatives through a seasonal cycle with reference to an ever changing auxin gradient and to formulate a cohesive theory of ontogenetic development.

Once initiated, the formation and differentiation of xylem normally proceed uninterruptedly throughout the seasonal course of development, and thus each of the xylem elements is intimately related to contiguous elements in both time and function. It is logical to assume that these elements should also be intimately related with respect to their physiological development. The objective of this paper is to show that one phase of cambial physiology, the regulation of cell size, may be directly influenced by auxin gradients. Although it is recognized that cambial activity and xylem development are more or less continuous processes in nature, it is nevertheless convenient, for purposes of discussion, to consider the progression and the consequences of radial growth as three separate problems, namely:

1. The initiation of cambial activity
2. The formation of the annual ring
3. The regulation of stem form

97

No attempt will be made to review all the extensive literature on these individual problems, but rather to synthesize pertinent facts into a unified concept. For simplicity of presentation, the discussion will be limited primarily to conifers, particularly the pines, although it is believed that with only slight modifications the conclusions may be equally applicable to the hardwoods. For this reason, data and references concerning these species have been included for supporting evidence. In synthesizing these data, generalizations will also be made with respect to certain phases of growth and development while fully recognizing the many subtle variations that occur in nature.

The Initiation of Cambial Activity Following Dormancy

The cambia of Temperate Zone trees are dormant in the winter and during this time no auxin activity can be found (Zimmermann, 1936; Avery *et al.*, 1937; Gunckel and Thimann, 1949). With the advent of warm weather in the spring the buds begin to swell and the first indications of auxin activity can be detected in the bud tissues. Shortly thereafter, cambial activation can be observed beneath each developing bud. For the most part, cambial activity originating in the buds is strictly basipetal but a slight acropetal transport of the stimulus has been noted (Esau, 1948). As the buds continue to expand and the new leaves unfold, the wave of cambial activity progresses down the main stem and branches and eventually envelops the entire bole.

The simplicity of the foregoing illustration is by no means universal; often very subtle variations in the time and nature of cambial reactivation have been found to exist between trees of different vigor classes, habits of growth, and species. This subject has been thoroughly covered in previous reviews (Wareing, 1951b; Ladefoged, 1952; Stewart, 1957), and it suffices to note that the widely accepted view is that the initiation of cambial activity following the break of dormancy (Gouwentak and Maas, 1940; Gouwentak, 1941; Samish, 1954) is an auxin phenomenon originating in the newly developing buds. The exact nature of the auxin stimulus and its mode of action have yet to be discovered.

The Formation of the Annual Ring

The initiation of cambial activity is a process quite distinct from the initial swelling of the cambial zone, for it involves the beginning of cambial division and the vacuolation and redivision of the xylem mother cells (Ladefoged, 1952; Bannan, 1955). This phase of cambial activity grades imperceptibly into the succeeding phase, the formation of the annual ring.

In past years many investigators have attempted to clarify the processes involved in annual-ring formation and a number of theories have been proposed (Grossenbacher, 1915; Büsgen and Münch, 1929; Priestley, 1930; Ladefoged, 1952). As tree physiology became more advanced, however, it became increasingly clear that the changes in cell size which accounted for the formation of annual rings were to some extent auxin controlled (Oppenheimer, 1945; Mašková, 1948; Megli, 1955; Wareing, 1958). The relationships involved can be most readily illustrated by summarizing the results of some recent studies.

In these studies (Larson, 1960, and unpublished data) photoperiod was used as a research tool to control the terminal growth [*] in 5-year-old red pine (*Pinus resinosa* Ait.) trees. It was found that, under long days (18 hours), terminal activity was prolonged and cells of the earlywood type continued to be produced. Auxin bioassay showed that this period of high meristematic activity was also a time of high auxin synthesis (Fig. 5–1). When long-day plants were shifted to short-day conditions (8 hours), terminal elongation ceased and meristematic activity was drastically curtailed. Accompanying the cessation of terminal growth were a parallel decrease in auxin synthesis and a transition to the production of cells of the latewood type.

If a series of short days was interposed in the long-day cycle, a false ring could be produced; the false ring so formed consisted of earlywood–latewood–earlywood laid down during the periods of long-day–short-day–long-day, respectively (Fig. 5–2). The false ring, however, could not be induced to form without an active bud; young trees decapitated during the short-day period failed to respond to subsequent long-day exposure and continued to produce latewood cells. The effects of both the active bud and the long-day stimulus could be replaced by exogenous applications of synthetic growth hormones. When indoleacetic acid (IAA) was placed on the decapitated tips of short-day plants, a new zone of earlywood-like cells was induced to form resulting in a very pronounced false ring, despite the lack of a long-day stimulus (Fig. 5–3).

The briefly summarized results of the foregoing studies suggest that cambial activity, including xylem development, is regulated by

[*] Throughout this paper, the general terms *terminal growth* and *terminal activity* will refer to the foliar organs as well as the buds and elongating apices with regard to probable sites of auxin synthesis.

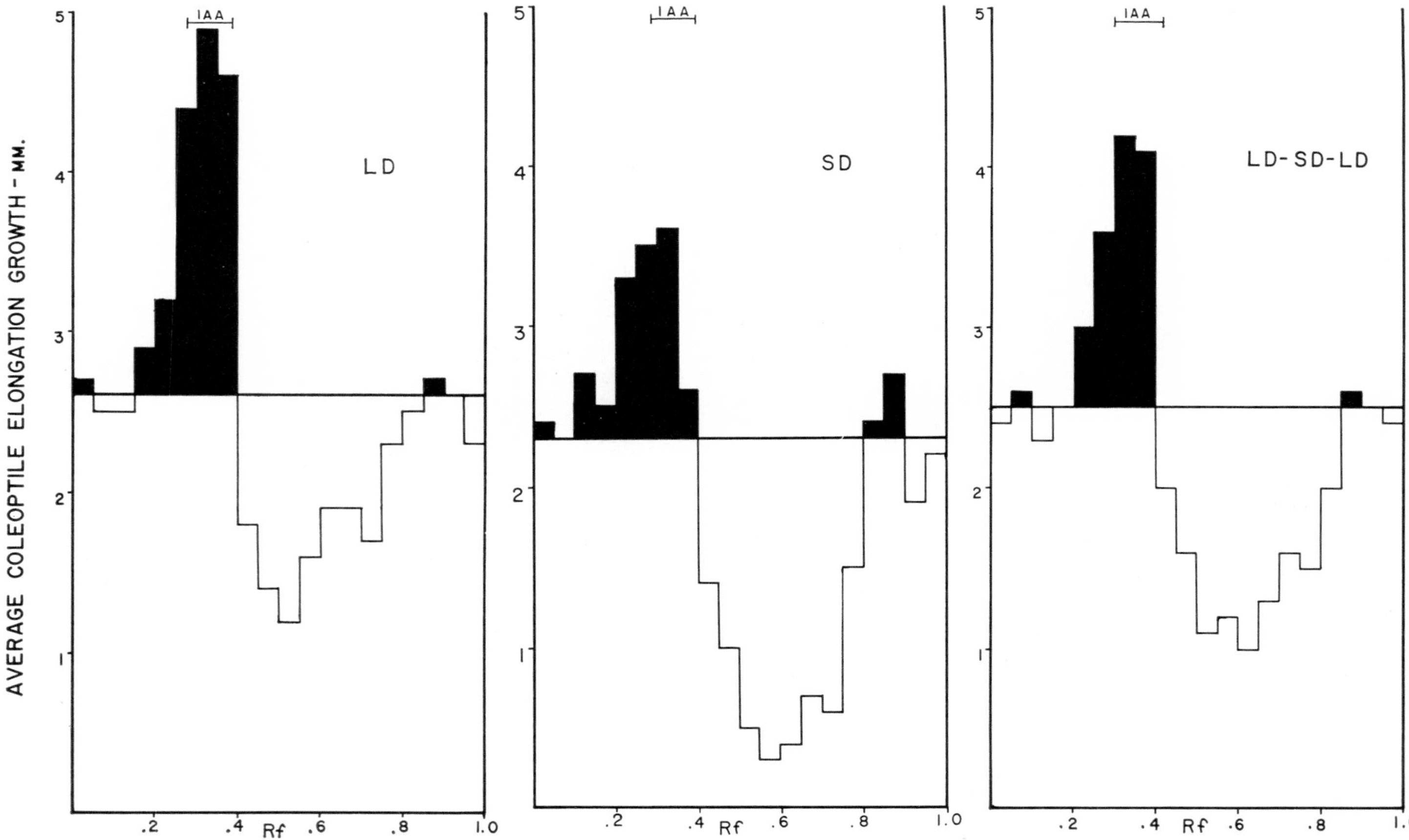

Fig. 5–1. Influence of daylength on growth-substance content of red pine terminals. The histograms indicate the growth-promoting (shaded) and growth-inhibiting zones on paper chromatograms of tissue extracts. Left: Long days (18 hrs.). Center: Long days followed by 2 weeks of short days (8 hrs.). Right: Long days followed by 2 weeks of short days and then retransferred to 2 weeks of long days. The central horizontal bars indicate the growth of the control *Avena* coleoptiles.

an auxin system controlled directly by the activity of the terminal meristems. In the following sections the interrelationships of these growth processes and the lines of evidence supporting the auxin theory of cambial growth regulation will be considered in greater detail.

PHOTOPERIODIC STUDIES. Numerous investigations have suggested that a correlation exists between the termination of elongation

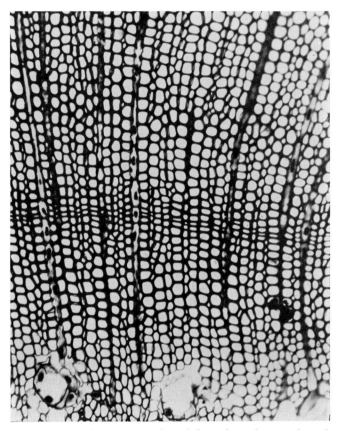

FIG. 5–2. Young red pines transferred from long-day to short-day conditions cease elongation growth and revert to the production of narrow-diameter cells. The false ring shown above was produced by a 3-week short-day treatment followed by a long-day treatment; the latter brought about a renewal of apical activity and large-diameter cell production.

growth and the initiation of latewood in natural-growing trees of the Temperate Zone. For example, studies involving sequential sampling have shown a remarkable similarity in the activity curves of terminal and radial growth (Kienholz, 1934) as well as a marked pause in the mid-season radial growth pattern. This growth pause has been interpreted as an indication of the transition period between earlywood and latewood formation (Friedrich, 1897; Lodewick, 1925; Chalk, 1927; Kienholz, 1934). Decisive proof of a direct correlation between these growth processes, however, has been difficult to obtain under field conditions.

By employing photoperiod, fairly rigorous control of terminal growth can be attained and the effect of the terminal meristems on cambial activity readily studied. The determinate buds of red pine, as well as other conifers (Wareing, 1951a; Hellmers, 1959; Vaartaja,

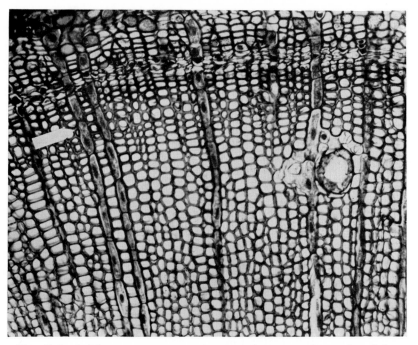

Fig. 5–3. A false ring consisting of narrow-diameter cells produced during 2 weeks of short-day exposure, followed by large-diameter cells (arrow) produced by 100 micrograms of IAA applied to the decapitated stem tip. The effect of the IAA was temporary, and narrow-diameter short-day cells are again evident near the periphery of the xylem.

1959), with their preformed needle primordia, elongate at the beginning of the growing period regardless of photoperiod, providing other growth conditions are favorable. But, exposure to short days suppresses internode and needle elongation and shortens the period of apical growth activity, whereas exposure to long days stimulates internode and needle elongation and greatly increases the period of apical growth activity. These photoperiodic effects are well known and have been extensively covered in the literature (Gustafson, 1938; Langlet, 1943; Wareing, 1949, 1951a; Wassink and Wiersma, 1955; Downs and Borthwick, 1956; Downs and Piringer, 1958).

When studying cambial activity of young red pines raised under varying photoperiodic regimes, it becomes clearly evident that latewood is initiated at the termination of height growth. Thus latewood cells can be observed in trees that have ceased elongation growth following exposure to short days. On the contrary, red pines grown on long days continue to produce earlywood cells as long as active growth continues in the apical meristems.

The effect of daylength is complicated by the fact that young pines maintained on long days for extended periods of time continue to produce earlywood-like cells, known as long-day latewood, even though internode elongation has ceased. In this case, the stimulus for the production of these large-lumened cells can be traced to the prolonged meristematic activity of the needles and the apical bud. The growing point, under the influence of continued exposure to long days, fails to set a compact resting bud but, instead, forms a large tufted-appearing bud from which the basal needles begin to emerge as soon as primordia develop. New needles appear acropetally along the elongated bud axis as additional primordia develop until a brushlike shoot is formed. The needles of this second shoot, as well as those of the previous shoot, continue elongating while a new bud is developing. In some trees, long-day exposure promoted several flushes of growth all of which developed in the aforementioned manner. Examination of the xylem of these trees revealed bands of varying cell size that could be correlated with the periodic phases of growth (Fig. 5–4). Although none of the cells could be classified as true latewood, those produced during the growth pauses were decidedly narrower in radial diameter than those produced during the growth flushes.

Measurable terminal growth cannot be maintained even under continued exposure to 18-hour days and, as terminal activity decreases, cell size decreases accordingly. Eventually, cambial activity ceases but, just prior to dormancy, a band of true latewood cells forms. There is evidence, as Wareing (1951a) has pointed out for *Pinus sylvestris*, that cambial activity can continue for some time after apparent terminal activity has ceased, possibly through photoperiodic perception within the mature as well as the maturing needles. Under such conditions, however, only narrow-lumened cells of the latewood-type are produced.

AUXIN STUDIES. In considering auxin gradients associated with the changing pattern of terminal development, reliance must be

placed on the indirect evidence provided by bioassay and the exogenous applications of growth substances. Without going into great
detail, the numerous investigations that have dealt with auxin distribution in woody species can be summarized by stating that all
exhibit a general similarity in the pattern of seasonal and spatial
distribution (Czaja, 1934; Zimmermann, 1936; Avery *et al.*, 1937;
Söding, 1937; Mirov, 1941; Gunckel and Thimann, 1949).

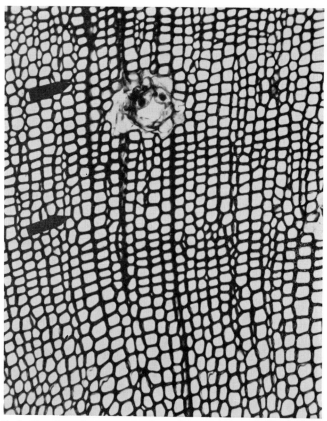

FIG. 5–4. Continued exposure to long days causes periodic flushes of growth
which can be correlated with the production of larger-diameter cells (arrows).
During the growth pauses, cell diameter decreases.

Auxin is first detectable at or slightly before bud break, depending upon the species and vigor of the trees examined, and increases
as terminal elongation proceeds. Since auxin activity closely coincides with terminal activity, both processes reach a maximum during early summer and decrease thereafter.

The spatial distribution of auxin also changes, and the site from
which the greatest quantity of auxin may be obtained gradually

shifts from the bud toward the base of the current internode as both the season and terminal activity progress (Avery *et al.*, 1937; Mirov, 1941; Gunckel and Thimann, 1949; Gregory and Hancock, 1955; Brown and Wetmore, 1959; Hatcher, 1959). From the data available, it is not possible to say conclusively whether this pattern represents the true locus of auxin synthesis or merely a translocatory center. Nevertheless, on the basis of this shift in auxin distribution and other evidence, the tentative conclusion has been reached that the rapidly expanding internodes and foliage organs may gradually either replace the buds as the primary sites of auxin synthesis or become new centers for the conversion of precursors (Hatcher, 1948; Gunckel and Thimann, 1949; Gordon, 1953). The significance of the various organs as contributors of auxin will be considered later, but for the current discussion it need only be recognized that the terminal meristem, including all its auxin-producing tissues, is the physiological source of auxin for the differentiating cambial derivatives of the tree. Although none of the investigations of auxin distribution has been specifically concerned with the early-wood-latewood transition, they have shown nonetheless that auxin is dependent upon terminal activity and that radial growth, per se, is dependent upon auxin.

Additional evidence may be obtained by utilizing the more recent auxin test employing chromatography in conjunction with a bioassay. By means of this technique, it has been demonstrated that woody plants grown on long days possess a high content of growth-promoting and a low content of growth-inhibiting substances, whereas plants transferred to short days possess a low content of growth-promoting and a high content of growth-inhibiting substances (Nitsch, 1957; Kawase and Nitsch, 1958, 1959; Larson, unpublished). This effect can, in turn, be partially reversed in red pine by again shifting plants from short-day to long-day conditions, but this can be done only when the short-day exposure is not of sufficient duration to induce a state of deep rest in the buds (Fig. 5–1).

Changes in auxin content detected by tests of this nature can be closely associated with both terminal activity and the attendant changes in cambial activity as previously described in the photoperiodic experiments. The significance of the variations in growth inhibitors under the influence of changing photoperiods can only be surmised at this time. It may be argued that they are intimately involved in latewood initiation, since they do occur simultaneously with the cessation of terminal growth activity. Yet, the equally cogent argument may be advanced that these inhibitors are involved in no way with cambial activity but are merely concerned with bud dormancy since this stage of bud development has also been shown to be intimately related to growth-inhibiting substances (Hemberg, 1949; Wareing, 1951a; Doorenbos, 1953; Samish, 1954; Phillips and Wareing, 1958).

A more direct line of evidence implicating auxin with the regulation of cambial growth comes from studies in which growth substances have been exogenously applied to woody plants. Many attempts have been made to study the effects of artificial preparations, such as indoleacetic acid (IAA) on various phases of cambial activity, but, for the most part, such trials have resulted in the production of abnormal cells suggestive of compression wood (Gouwentak, 1936; Wershing and Bailey, 1942; Fraser, 1949; Wardrop, 1957). In a few instances, cells resembling true earlywood have followed the applications of relatively low concentrations of these substances (Gouwentak, 1936; Söding, 1936; Brown and Cormack, 1937; Fraser, 1949), but the tests involved were not specifically concerned with finding a solution to the earlywood-latewood transition. The results of these investigations were nevertheless vital in formulating the basic hypotheses of the regulation of cambial activity, because they suggested that cell size was directly controlled by growth hormones.

The fact that IAA may simulate the effect of auxin emanating from the terminal bud may be demonstrated by using red pine grown under controlled photoperiods. Thus, when IAA is applied to a decapitated short-day plant, a new zone of earlywood cells will be produced following the normal short-day latewood (Fig. 5–3). The false ring so formed suggests that IAA has effectively replaced both the apical bud and the long-day stimulus. The effect of such applications, however, varies with the stage of development and the condition of the trees at the time of treatment. For example, earlywood formation can be prolonged by low concentrations of IAA applied to decapitated plants transferred to short-day conditions, whereas the same concentrations applied to long-day plants are generally ineffective. High concentrations of IAA, however, can induce increased cell size in seedlings with active cambia at all stages of development, but, invariably, the cells produced are either undifferentiated callus or of the compression-wood type (Fig. 5–5).

THE ROLE OF AUXIN IN ANNUAL-RING FORMATION. The evidence presented so far indicates that cambial activity may be regulated through an auxin-mediated system originating in the terminal meristems. It was pointed out that the terminal shoot goes through a definite pattern of development and that the activity curve of auxin closely parallels that of the apex. The primary role of auxin in differentiating xylem appears to be as a determinant of cell size.

Large-diameter cells of the earlywood type will therefore be produced during periods of active terminal growth when auxin synthesis is high, and the transition to narrow-diameter latewood cells will occur when terminal activity and auxin synthesis decline. From this, one might conclude that the radial diameter of the cell produced will be dependent upon the quantity of auxin reaching that cell, other conditions being normal. Many points of evidence could be cited to support this conclusion, but, on the basis of our work with red pine, one generalization prevails: A decreasing gradient of cell size parallels the decreasing auxin gradient regardless of

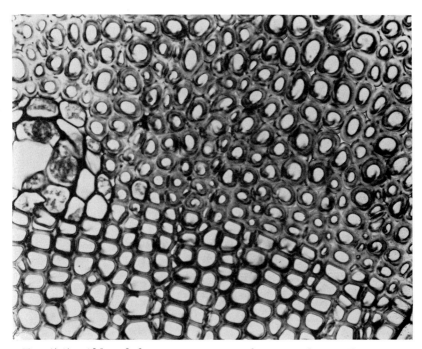

FIG. 5–5. Although low concentrations of IAA produce cells resembling typical earlywood, high concentrations produce cells resembling compression wood. The compression wood shown in this photomicrograph was formed in response to an application of 1,000 micrograms of IAA.

whether this gradient originates from endogenously produced auxins or exogenously applied growth substances.

Assuming the correctness of this interpretation, the following explanation of annual-ring formation may now be proposed on the basis of auxin gradients: In the spring, the first flush of growth in normally developed trees is rapid and the resulting high auxin synthesis stimulates production of a zone of earlywood cells throughout the cambial region of the tree. As the season advances, terminal elongation growth ceases, auxin synthesis declines, and latewood formation is initiated. This point is one of the seemingly anomalous aspects of the auxin hypothesis, for latewood is not initiated uniformly throughout the tree. Nevertheless, this anomaly can also be explained in terms of auxin gradients.

It has been pointed out that needle elongation and limited meristematic activity continue long after terminal elongation growth ceases and that these growth processes, together with the mature needles (Onaka, 1950b), continue to produce limited quantities of auxin. Since large-diameter cell production is dependent upon relatively high auxin concentrations, earlywood formation continues in the vicinity of the auxin-synthesizing tissues. Hence, in the current season's growth and the internodes immediately beneath it, so-called juvenile wood will form; this type of wood is characterized by a number of atypical features but primarily by its lack of true latewood. With increasing distance down the stem, cell size gradually decreases, and at lower internodes true latewood is produced as the auxin stimulus emanating from the terminal meristems becomes more limiting. As the growth period advances, auxin synthesis continues to decline and latewood cells can be found at higher and higher internodes in the tree.

Although from the anatomical viewpoint, latewood initiation may be considered as originating independently in the lower stem, it must be recognized that physiologically latewood is initiated at the stem apices, for it is here that the regulatory auxin gradients originate. This can be verified by reversing the auxin gradient, for example, by decapitation of young red pines growing on short days but prior to normal latewood formation. Then, latewood initiation can be observed first at the apex following the abrupt removal of the auxin source. In both cases, however, vertical gradations in cell size occur between true earlywood and true latewood, but in opposite directions. These gradations are very similar to the normal cessation of cambial activity which also occurs first at the apex (Chalk, 1927; Brown, 1937), as does the disappearance of auxin (Onaka, 1950b).

An attempt has been made to account for the continued activity of the cambium at points far removed from the apex by postulating a cambial-produced auxin (Söding, 1937; Münch, 1938; Jost, 1940). This view has been further modified by proposing that this auxin was, in a sense, adaptively formed and required stimulation from the auxin originating in the terminal meristem (Gouwentak, 1936). Although active cambia have been found to contain auxin (Söding, 1937; Söding, 1941; Mirov, 1941), it is believed that diffuse meristems, such as the cambium, are almost wholly dependent upon external sources (Loomis, 1953; Gunckel, 1957). This latter view is supported, in part, by the diverse patterns of annual-ring formation produced by trees of varying growth habits. Many factors tend to vary these ring patterns as well as the relative distribution of the earlywood and latewood components of the annual ring along the bole. These factors will be considered shortly under the discussion of stem form, but first the formation of false rings should be brought into proper perspective.

FORMATION OF FALSE RINGS. The occurrence of false or double rings provides some of the most convincing evidence in favor of the auxin hypothesis. False rings produced by photoperiodic control of terminal activity and by exogenous applications of growth substances have already been discussed. From experiments such as these it has been noted that in young red pine a second flush of growth following a growth pause invariably produces a false ring. Failure to note a correlation between multiple growth flushes and false ring formation generally results from sampling the base of the tree, for, quite unlike the vernal surge of growth, second flushes are usually limited in both duration and over-all growth. Thus, the auxin stimulus emanating from this region of renewed growth is of limited intensity and will reach the stem base only under exceptionally favorable conditions. Examination of the upper stem region will usually reveal a false ring, providing the second flush was preceded by a growth pause of sufficient duration so that an intervening zone of latewood cells could be laid down. This latter qualification must be invoked, for in certain precocious individuals or biotypes summer buds frequently flush while earlywood formation is still in progress within the crown and the wide-lumened cells produced by the two growth flushes are indistinguishable. Such a condition has been observed in young red pine trees that have been induced to renew height growth under long-day conditions, while a similar, natural-occurring phenomenon has been alluded to by a number of European workers (Jost, 1893; Späth, 1912; Grudzinskaja, 1957).

False rings occur in nature under a variety of conditions, but all can be associated with a temporary cessation of terminal growth followed by growth resumption as in the case of second flushes (Späth, 1912; Hine, 1922; Cameron and Schroeder, 1945; Sokolov and Artyushenko, 1957). Mid-season defoliations by insects, storms, or other factors are also commonly recognized natural causes of false ring formation (Hartig, 1895; Harper, 1913; Bailey, 1925). In these cases, an additional zone of earlywood cells can be associated with the renewal of apical activity brought about by bud development and refoliation; this has been confirmed by artificial defoliation experiments (Jost, 1893; Kühns, 1910).

Droughts occurring during the period of active elongation growth can also result in the temporary growth suspension necessary for false ring formation (Ladefoged, 1952; Foote, 1954). That this is dependent upon auxin gradients is suggested by the work of Hatcher (1959), who noted an auxin minimum occurring during a drought followed by a new auxin peak when growth resumed during more favorable conditions.

Although many examples of the conditions contributing to false ring formation could be cited, the pattern of development appears to be quite similar in all cases. It might therefore be concluded that, when any factor causing a temporary cessation of terminal activity and a concomitant decrease in auxin synthesis is followed by conditions favoring renewed terminal growth and high auxin synthesis, the physiological requirements for false ring formation have been satisfied. Under these conditions, a visually evident structure falling within the confines of the anatomical definition will be produced only if two further requirements have been satisfied. First, the growth suspension must be of sufficient duration so that the diminishing auxin gradient can bring about production of cells with narrow diameters. Second, and conversely, the growth resumption must be sufficiently intense that a high auxin gradient can stimulate production of cells with large diameters. As in the case of second flushes, the auxin gradient originating from any slight growth resumption may produce new earlywood cells visible only in the upper reaches of the crown, or, conceivably, these larger cells may fail to progress beyond the zone of juvenile wood and thus may remain indistinguishable. Failure to satisfy any of these requirements may account for the absence of false rings, reported by many investigators, following renewed apical activity (Guard and Postlethwait, 1958; Rose, 1958).

The Regulation of Stem Form

Regulation of stem form concerns the distribution of radial growth along the main stem axis of the tree, and the possible role of auxin in regulating this distribution. An attempt has been made to confirm by various means the fact that the patterns of xylem cell size reflect the auxin gradients in the stem. Since, however, the auxin source lies within portions of the growing crown, the supply is not equally available to all parts of the stem below. Therefore, these auxin gradients occurring within a tree must be considered as concurrent functions of time and space.

To do this, the annual increments may be visualized as a sheath of wood encircling the tree. Then, the time factor may be considered as the normal seasonal transition from earlywood to latewood across the ring. The distance factor will then be the variation in cell size within the annual increment down the stem and away from the auxin supply of the crown. Thus the annual rings comprising the juvenile wood of the upper stem will be composed almost entirely of earlywood-type cells. In this region of juvenile wood, the seasonal decrease in auxin synthesis will be partially offset by proximity to the apical bud and elongating needles as some auxin continues to be released by these organs. With increasing distance down the stem, however, a gradual divergence into recognizable earlywood and latewood components will occur until, in the lower stem positions, the time and distance factors culminate and true, narrow-diameter latewood cells will be produced.

As was mentioned previously, many factors tend to vary the seasonal distribution of radial growth along the bole and to influence the size and proportion of the wood elements comprising the annual ring. Foremost among these factors are crown size and the distribution of the branches within the crown. Numerous studies of stem form have shown that trees with long, vigorous crowns produce strongly tapering stems with a rather high proportion of earlywood to latewood. As the crown recedes, owing either to advancing age, stand closure, or artificial pruning, the stem becomes more cylindrical and the proportion of earlywood to latewood decreases. If the hypothesis is accepted that auxin gradients regulate the size of the wood elements within an annual ring, then it is not illogical to extend this hypothesis to include an auxin-regulating influence over increment distribution as well (see also, Münch, 1938).

Beginning with bud break, cambial initiation has been shown to begin earlier (Chalk, 1927, 1930) and to proceed more rapidly (Priestley, 1932; Ladefoged, 1952) down the stems of long-crowned, open-grown trees than down those of trees with small crowns growing under more restricted conditions. Once initiated, cambial activity proceeds more vigorously, and the period of earlywood formation extends for a longer time, in the larger-crowned individuals (Chalk, 1927). In attempting to relate these differences to auxin gradients, it can be shown that auxin synthesis parallels bud development throughout the tree. Thus, auxin content of the buds increases from the basal branches toward the apex (Zimmermann, 1936; Onaka, 1950a; Gregory and Hancock, 1955), and within any one branch the terminal bud contains more auxin than the whorl buds (Zimmermann, 1936; Mirov, 1941). Furthermore, a greater disparity in auxin content has been found between the terminal and lateral buds of small-crowned trees than between comparable buds of larger-crowned individuals (Mirov, 1941).

Because of these differences in auxin synthesis, each lateral branch acts, in a sense, as an independent structure with regard to cambial activity. The pattern of development of the main stem is repeated in each branch under the influence of the auxin produced by its own buds. As one would expect, the lateral branches nearest the stem apex are the most vigorous and contribute the greatest quantity of auxin to the main stem. Proceeding downward, bud vigor and auxin synthesis not only decrease but the branch distance over which the stimulus must be translocated to the main stem increases so that the lower branches contribute less and less auxin to the supply of the main axis. In the lowermost branches of stand-grown trees, the cambial stimulus fails to reach the branch base or it may be visibly expressed only in the form of latewood. Under extreme conditions of branch suppression, cambial activity barely reaches beyond the bud and indicates the incipient stages of branch death. Obviously, such branches contribute nothing to the auxin supply of the stem. That the more vigorous branches do contribute auxin has been confirmed by the work of Onaka (1950a), who found that removal of a lateral branch reduced the auxin content in the stem section lying below.

With this information, an explanation of the differences in stem form and the earlywood-latewood distributions in trees of varying crown size may be attempted. Trees with long, vigorous crowns not only have the potential for high auxin production but also possess the advantageous distribution of these auxin-contributing branches over most of their bole length. These more favorable auxin relations not only lead to a high quantitative production of earlywood but also to a high proportion of earlywood in the lower bole. The ratio of earlywood to latewood gradually reverses as crown length recedes owing to increasing senescence or competition. In trees with high-setting crowns, the effects of decreased auxin synthesis and fewer contributing branches are further accentuated by the greater distance over which the limited stimulus must be translocated to reach the stem base. Such trees, therefore, produce lower proportions of earlywood in the bole and greater proportionate quantities of low auxin-requiring latewood. In fact, trees suffering from extreme conditions of suppression may fail to produce earlywood over large sectors of the lower bole or the circumference may be completely devoid of earlywood cells (Rubner, 1910; Lakari, 1915; Harris, 1952; Larson, 1956). As in the case of suppressed branches, the culmination of severe crown suppression is the complete disappearance of cambial activity in the lower bole, and eventual death of the tree.

From the foregoing discussion, one might expect the greatest growth to occur in the vicinity of the auxin-producing crown. Stem analyses have, indeed, confirmed this supposition and have shown that maximum radial growth occurs in the general vicinity of the live crown base (Shreve, 1924; Young and Kramer, 1952; Labyak and Schumacher, 1954; Duff and Nolan, 1957). Therefore, the point of maximum ring width may be found low in the bole of a long-crowned tree and a gradual upward shift parallels crown recession. Seasonal effects may be superimposed on this pattern, and, within any one tree, the maximum is displaced downward during favorable growth periods and upward as a result of critical growth conditions that reduce tree vigor (Duff and Nolan, 1953). The net result of this upward displacement of radial growth is to make the small-crowned trees more cylindrical as opposed to the strongly tapered stems of trees with long, vigorous crowns.

Crown size also exerts an influence on the abruptness of the earlywood-latewood transition. Because of the greater auxin supply to the lower bole of the long-crowned trees, the distance factor is less obligate; hence, the annual rings display a very gradual transition from earlywood to latewood. On the other hand, in the small-crowned trees with long, clear boles, the distance factor predominates and the earlywood-latewood transition is extremely abrupt.

It appears, therefore, that the distribution of radial growth along the bole may also be controlled by auxin gradients. Since, however, it is only possible to discuss the effects of auxin gradients in generalities, the response of any individual tree in terms of stem form must be judged upon its own inherent qualities and conditions of growth.

Conclusion

Throughout this paper, the impression has no doubt been conveyed that all cambial activity is dependent solely upon auxin. Concentration upon auxin synthesis was intentional in order to emphasize the decisive role of auxins in cambial growth, although the contribution of other cell constituents is fully recognized. This omission has no doubt been particularly evident in the discussion of latewood formation, as no mention was made of the cell-wall thickening that accompanies transition to this cell type. Evidence is available, however, which indicates that the secondary thickening of latewood cell walls is not necessarily causally correlated with the auxin-controlled change in cell dimensions (Larson, unpublished). In this respect, stress has also been given to the singular influence of auxin on cell size. Nevertheless, one must recognize auxin as a probable metabolic participant in cell division (Gautheret, 1955; Gunckel, 1957), differentiation (Jacobs, 1954; Wetmore and Sorokin, 1955; Klein, 1957), lignification (Jensen, 1955; Siegel, 1956; Solberg and Higinbotham, 1957), and perhaps other phases of xylem and, possibly, phloem development.

The evidence presented strongly suggests that gradations in cell size will parallel the auxin gradients as they vary both temporally and spatially within the tree. When the effects are considered strictly in terms of cell size, earlywood and latewood can be recognized, and, when the distribution of these xylem elements is considered, stem form can be recognized. Occasionally, conditions of growth result in the preferential development of supraoptimal auxin gradients. When these occur, the formation of reaction wood can be recognized (Onaka, 1949; Necesany, 1958). The significance of this latter auxin action has just begun to be appreciated. In time, perhaps, it may be possible to explain all phases of cambial activity by means of a single regulatory influence, for it is logical to assume that these are all closely integrated processes. It is believed that auxin may provide this regulatory stimulus.

LITERATURE CITED

AVERY, G. S., JR., P. R. BURKHOLDER, and H. B. CREIGHTON. 1937. Production and distribution of growth hormone in shoots of *Aesculus* and *Malus,* and its probable role in stimulating cambial activity. Amer. Jour. Bot. 24: 51–58.

BAILEY, I. W. 1925. Notes on the "spruce budworm" biocoenose II. Structural abnormalities in *Abies balsamea.* Bot. Gaz. 80: 300–310.

BANNAN, M. W. 1955. The vascular cambium and radial growth in *Thuja occidentalis* L. Can. Jour. Bot. 33: 113–138.

BROWN, A. B. 1937. Activity of the vascular cambium in relation to wounding in the balsam poplar, *Populus balsamifera* L. Can. Jour. Res. Sect. C, Bot. Sci. 15: 7–31.

BROWN, A. B., and R. G. H. CORMACK. 1937. Stimulation of cambial activity, locally in the region of application and at a distance in relation to a wound, by means of heteroauxin. Can. Jour. Res. Sect. C, Bot. Sci. 15: 433–441.

BROWN, C. L., and R. H. WETMORE. 1959. Auxin transport in the long shoots of pine. Amer. Jour. Bot. 46: 586–590.

BÜSGEN, M., and E. MÜNCH. 1929. The structure and life of forest trees. Translated from German by T. THOMSON. John Wiley & Sons, Inc., New York.

CAMERON, S. H., and C. A. SCHROEDER. 1945. Cambial activity and starch cycle in bearing orange trees. Proc. Amer. Soc. Hort. Sci. 46: 55–59.

CHALK, L. 1927. The growth of the wood of ash (*Fraxinus excelsior* L. and *F. oxycarpa* Willd.), and Douglas fir (*Pseudotsuga Douglasii* Carr.). Quart. Jour. Forestry 21: 102–122.

―――. 1930. The formation of spring and summer wood in ash and Douglas fir. Oxford Forestry Mem. 10. 48 pp.

CZAJA, A. T. 1934. Der Nachweis des Wuchsstoffes bei Holzpflanzen. Ber. Deut. Bot. Gesell. 52: 267–271.

DOORENBOS, J. 1953. Review of the literature on dormancy in buds of woody plants. Meded. Landbouwhoogesch. (Wageningen) 53: 1–24.

DOWNS, R. J., and H. A. BORTHWICK. 1956. Effects of photoperiod on growth of trees. Bot. Gaz. 117: 310–326.

DOWNS, R. J., and A. A. PIRINGER, JR. 1958. Effects of photoperiod and kind of supplemental light on vegetative growth of pines. Forest Sci. 4: 185–195.

DUFF, G. H., and N. J. NOLAN. 1953. Growth and morphogenesis in the Canadian forest species. I. The controls of cambial and apical activity in *Pinus resinosa* Ait. Can. Jour. Bot. 31: 471–513.

——— and ———. 1957. Growth and morphogenesis in the Canadian forest species. II. Specific increments and their relation to the quantity and activity of growth in *Pinus resinosa* Ait. Can. Jour. Bot. 35: 527–572.

ESAU, K. 1948. Phloem structure in the grapevine, and its seasonal changes. Hilgardia 18: 217–296.

FOOTE, T. K. 1954. False rings in larch, *Larix decidua* Mill. Jour. Oxford Univ. Forest Soc. Ser. 4 No. 2: 5–8.

FRASER, D. A. 1949. Production of spring wood with β-indole acetic acid (heteroauxin). Nature (London) 164: 542.

FRIEDRICH, J. 1897. Einfluss der Witterung auf den Baumzuwachs. Centbl. f. das gesam. Forstw. 23: 1–27.

GAUTHERET, R. J. 1955. The nutrition of plant tissue cultures. Ann. Rev. Plant Physiol. 6: 433–484.

GORDON, S. A. 1953. In: Growth and Differentiation in Plants. W. E. LOOMIS (ed.). Iowa State College Press, Ames, Iowa.

GOUWENTAK, C. A. 1936. Kambiumtätigkeit und Wuchsstoff. I. Meded. Landbouwhoogesch. (Wageningen) 40: 1–23.

———. 1941. Cambial activity as dependent on the presence of growth hormone and the non-resting condition of stems. Proc. Amsterdam Acad. Sci. 44: 654–663.

GOUWENTAK, C. A., and A. L. MAAS. 1940. Kambiumtätigkeit und Wuchsstoff. II. Meded. Landbouwhoogesch. (Wageningen) 44: 1–16.

GREGORY, F. G., and C. R. HANCOCK. 1955. The rate of transport of natural auxin in woody shoots. Ann. Bot. 19: 451–465.

GROSSENBACHER, J. G. 1915. The periodicity and distribution of radial growth in trees and their relation to the development of "annual rings." Trans. Wis. Acad. Sci. 18: 1–77.

GRUDZINSKAJA, I. A. 1957. The influence of lammas shoots on the formation of false rings in oak. Dok. Akad. Nauk S.S.S.R. 115: 392–395. English Translation AIBS Dok., Bot. Sci. Sect. 1958.

GUARD, A. T., and S. N. POSTLETHWAIT. 1958. Relation of the formation of annual rings to multiple flushes of growth in several species of *Quercus*. Proc. Ind. Acad. Sci. 67: 104–106.

GUNCKEL, J. E. 1957. The effects of ionizing radiation on plants: Morphological effects. Quart. Rev. Biol. 32: 46–56.

GUNCKEL, J. E., and K. V. THIMANN. 1949. Studies of development in long shoots and short shoots of *Ginkgo biloba* L. III. Auxin production in shoot growth. Amer. Jour. Bot. 36: 145–151.

GUSTAFSON, F. G. 1938. Influence of the length of day on the dormancy of tree seedlings. Plant Physiol. 13: 655–658.

HARPER, A. G. 1913. Defoliation: Its effects upon the growth and structure of the wood of *Larix*. Ann. Bot. 27: 621–642.

HARRIS, J. M. 1952. Discontinuous growth layers in *Pinus radiata*. New Zeal. Forest Prod. Res. Notes 1(4):1–10.

HARTIG, R. 1895. Doppelringe als Folge von Spätfrost. Forstl. Naturw. Ztschr. 4: 1–8.

HATCHER, E. S. J. 1948. The study of auxin in shoots of apple and plum. East Malling (Kent) Res. Sta. Ann. Rpt. for 1947: 113–116.

————. 1959. Auxin relations of the woody shoot. Ann. Bot. 23: 409–423.

HELLMERS, H. 1959. Photoperiodic control of bud development in Coulter pine and bigcone Douglas-fir. Forest Sci. 5: 138–141.

HEMBERG, T. 1949. Growth-inhibiting substances in terminal buds of *Fraxinus*. Physiol. Plant. 2: 37–44.

HINE, W. R. 1922. Fine points in ring counting. U.S. Forest Serv. Bull. 6(30):1–2.

JACOBS, W. P. 1954. Acropetal auxin transport and xylem regeneration: A quantitative study. Amer. Nat. 88: 327–337.

JENSEN, W. A. 1955. The histological localization of peroxidase in roots and its induction by IAA. Plant Physiol. 30: 426–432.

JOST, L. 1893. Über Beziehungen zwischen der Blättentwicklung und der Gefässbildung in der Pflanze. Bot. Ztg. 51: 89–138.

————. 1940. Zur Physiologie der Gefässbildung. Ztschr. f. Bot. 34: 114–150.

KAWASE, M., and J. P. NITSCH. 1958. Growth substances and the photoperiodic control of growth in *Betula pubescens*. Plant Physiol. 33(Sup.): xix.

———— and ————. 1959. Growth substances and the photoperiodic control of growth in *Betula pubescens* and *B. lutea*. Plant Physiol. 34(Sup.): iv.

KIENHOLZ, R. 1934. Leader, needle, cambial and root growth of certain conifers and their inter-relations. Bot. Gaz. 96: 73–92.

KLEIN, R. M. 1957. In: Rhythmic and Synthetic Processes in Growth. D. RUDNICK (ed.). Princeton University Press, Princeton, N. J.

KÜHNS, R. 1910. Die Verdoppelung des Jahresringes durch künstliche Entlaubung. Biblioth. Bot. 15: 1–53.

LABYAK, L. F., and F. X. SCHUMACHER. 1954. The contribution of its branches to the main stem growth of loblolly pine. Jour. Forestry 52: 333–337.

LADEFOGED, K. 1952. The periodicity of wood formation. Kgl. Danske Vidensk. Selsk. Biol. Skr. 7: 1–98.

LAKARI, O. J. 1915. Studien über die Samenjahre und Altersklassenverhältnisse der Kiefernwälder auf dem Nordfinnischen Heideboden. Acta Forest. Fenn. 5: 1–211.

LANGLET, O. 1943. Photoperiodismus und Provenienz bei der gemeinen Kiefer (*Pinus silvestris* L.). Meddel. från Statens Skogsforsoksanstalt 33: 294–330.

LARSON, P. R. 1956. Discontinuous growth rings in suppressed slash pine. Trop. Woods 104: 80–99.

————. 1960. A physiological consideration of the springwood-summerwood transition in red pine. Forest Sci. 6: 110–122.

————. Unpublished data.

LODEWICK, J. E. 1925. Growth studies in forest trees. III. Experiments with the dendrograph on *Fraxinus americana*. Bot. Gaz. 89: 311–323.

LOOMIS, W. E. 1953. In: Growth and Differentiation in Plants. W. E. LOOMIS (ed.). Iowa State College Press, Ames, Iowa.

MAŠKOVÁ, J. 1948. Annual rings from the point of view of the hormone theory (a review). Lesnická Práce 27(2/3): 55–59, 88–99. Czech with English summary.

MEGLI, V. 1955. Experiments in disbudding of *Prunus persica* and their effects on growth-ring formation. Nuovo Gior. Bot. Ital. 62: 41–74. Original not seen; cited from Forestry Abs. 18: 2073. 1957.

MIROV, N. T. 1941. Distribution of growth hormone in shoots of two species of pine. Jour. Forestry 39: 457–464.

MÜNCH, E. 1938. Untersuchungen über die Harmonie der Baumgestalt. Jahrb. f. Wiss. Bot. 86: 581–673.

NECESANY, V. 1958. Effect of β-indoleacetic acid on the formation of reaction wood. Phyton 11: 117–127.

NITSCH, J. P. 1957. Growth responses of woody plants to photoperiodic stimuli. Proc. Amer. Soc. Hort. Sci. 70: 512–525.

ONAKA, F. 1949. Studies on compression and tension wood. Bull. Wood Res. Inst. Kyoto University 1: 1–88. Japanese with English summary.

————. 1950a. The longitudinal distribution of radial increments in trees. Bull. Kyoto Univ. Forests 18: 1–53. Japanese with English summary.

————. 1950b. The effects of defoliation, disbudding, girdling and other treatments upon growth, especially radial growth in evergreen conifers. Bull. Kyoto Univ. Forests 18: 55–95.

OPPENHEIMER, H. R. 1945. Cambial wood production in stems of *Pinus halepensis*. Palestine Jour. Bot. and Hort. Sci. 5: 22–51.

PHILLIPS, I. D. J., and P. F. WAREING. 1958. Studies in dormancy of sycamore. I. Seasonal changes in the growth-substance content of the shoot. Jour. Expt. Bot. 9: 350–364.

PRIESTLEY, J. H. 1930. Studies in the physiology of cambial activity. III. The seasonal activity of the cambium. New Phytol. 29: 316–354.

————. 1932. The growing tree. Forestry 6: 105–112.

ROSE, A. H. 1958. The effect of defoliation on foliage production and radial growth of quaking aspen. Forest Sci. 4: 335–342.

RUBNER, K. 1910. Das Hungern des Cambiums und das Aussetzen der Jahrringe. Naturw. Ztschr. f. Forst- und Landw. 8: 212–262.

SAMISH, R. M. 1954. Dormancy in woody plants. Ann. Rev. Plant Physiol. 5: 183–204.

SHREVE, F. 1924. The growth record in trees. Carnegie Inst. Wash. Pub. 350. Pp. 89–116.

SIEGEL, S. M. 1956. The chemistry and physiology of lignin formation. Quart. Rev. Biol. 31: 1–18.

SÖDING, H. 1936. Über den Einfluss von Wuchsstoff anf das Dickenwachstum der Bäume. Ber. Deut. Bot. Gesell. 54: 291–304.

————. 1937. Wuchsstoff und Kambiumtätigkeit der Bäume. Jahrb. f. Wiss. Bot. 84: 639–670.

————. 1941. Weitere Untersuchungen über die Wuchsstoffregulation der Kambiumtätigkeit. Ztschr. f. Bot. 36: 113–141.

SOKOLOV, S. Y., and Z. T. ARTYUSHENKO. 1957. Ivanov shoots in the pine. Botaniceskij Zurnal 42: 741–745. Original not seen; cited from Translation JPRS(NY) Rpt. No. 783. Forestry. 1958.

SOLBERG, R. A., and N. HIGINBOTHAM. 1957. The effects of indoleacetic acid, sucrose, and eugenol on differentiation in segments of etiolated pea epicotyls. Amer. Jour. Bot. 44: 769–778.

SPÄTH, H. 1912. Der Johannistrieb: Ein Beitrag zur Kenntniss der Periodizität und Jahresringbildung sommergrüner Holzgewachse. Paul Parey, Berlin.

STEWART, C. M. 1957. Status of cambial activity. Tappi 40: 244–256.

VAARTAJA, O. 1959. Evidence of photoperiodic ecotypes in trees. Ecol. Monog. 29: 91–111.

WARDROP, A. B. 1957. The phase of lignification in the differentiation of wood fibers. Tappi 40: 225–243.

WAREING, P. F. 1949. Photoperiodic control of leaf growth and cambial activity in *Pinus sylvestris*. Nature (London) 163: 770–771.

————. 1951a. Growth studies in woody species. III. Further photoperiodic effects in *Pinus silvestris*. Physiol. Plant. 4: 41–56.

————. 1951b. Growth studies in woody species. IV. The initiation of cambial activity in ring-porous species. Physiol. Plant. 4: 546–562.

————. 1958. The physiology of cambial activity. Jour. Inst. Wood Sci. 1: 34–42.

WASSINK, E. C., and J. H. WIERSMA. 1955. Daylength responses of some forest trees. Acta Bot. Néerland. 4: 657–670.

WERSHING, H. F., and I. W. BAILEY. 1942. Seedlings as experimental material in the study of "redwood" in conifers. Jour. Forestry 40: 411–414.

WETMORE, R. H., and S. SOROKIN. 1955. On the differentiation of xylem. Jour. Arnold Arboretum 36: 305–317.

YOUNG, H. E., and P. J. KRAMER. 1952. The effect of pruning on the height and diameter growth of loblolly pine. Jour. Forestry 50: 474–479.

ZIMMERMANN, W. A. 1936. Untersuchungen über die räumliche und zeitliche Verteilung des Wuchsstoffes bei Bäumen. Ztschr. f. Bot. 30: 209–252.

6

Development of Tree-Ring Dating as an Archeological Aid

J. L. GIDDINGS

Tree-ring dating is the application of a principle and a set of techniques. A description of how and why it works can be so deceptively simple that the student who hears about it for the first time is tempted to saw down trees and try for himself. The simplicity of tree-ring dating is real enough, yet the process did not and could not materialize for its originator all at once. The techniques, most of them, came first. Only then were added, one at a time, the applications that have led scientists and laymen all over the world to study, criticize and admire the work of A. E. Douglass. The dendrochronology that will be discussed mainly in its botanical setting has been synthesized from several disciplines in a scientific manner. This is to say, Douglass began with an idea which had been shared and tentatively tested by others. Yet he alone proceeded inductively and imaginatively to follow the first observations in whatever direction they might take, while at the same time measuring and experimenting without rest to hold the exciting promises under control.

Neither botany nor archeology can take much credit for the first and basic development of dendrochronology. The triumph was Douglass' own. An idea entered his mind and he brought the mathematical and technical training of an astronomer to the invention of a method for its testing. The cross-dating principle had occurred to several men, most of whom entertained it, as Douglass may at first have done, without knowledge that it had been entertained by others before.* The synthesis began for Douglass uniquely when, in 1901, he recognized in the pines and junipers of northern Arizona

* Accounts of some other applications of ring counting and early cross-dating are given in Campbell (1949), Heizer (1956), and Studhalter (1956).

119

a special dependence upon the year's always limited moisture supply.* Thinking as an astronomer, he wondered whether or not solar cycles might be more permanently registered in these long-lived trees than in other forms of local vegetation. It was in 1904 when, by chance, the lingering idea could be somewhat casually tested on the stumps of a cutover forest. The crucial observation made one day came not as a stroke of luck so much as the long-deferred test of a guess that the variation in ring growth of one tree might be repeated in others. The cross-dating that Douglass saw was in the form of sets of compact patterns of ring variation duplicated from one tree stump to the next with such clarity as to be easily recognized without a ring count. The next step was to identify the patterns with the cutting dates of the trees. Another 7 years went by, however, before the full significance of the cross-dating principle and a range of possible applications became clear through the further study of forest trees.

The Cross-dating Principle

The validity of the cross-dating principle and the simple usability of the first techniques of Douglass' tree-ring analysis have stood the test of time remarkably well. Criticisms that have appeared now and then in print, many of them based on inadequate or unrelated studies, were often anticipated and pretested by Douglass and his students in the course of measuring the rings of hundreds of trees and analyzing the results. Perhaps it is fortunate that the challenges of archeological dating waited until the techniques of dendrochronology were a going concern.

The cross-dating principle (Douglass, 1941b) has it simply that the observed repetition of ring-growth patterns from tree to tree across miles of space, and consistently back through time, is caused by a close dependence upon the aspects of climate which all the trees have held in common. It begins with the concrete and moves toward the abstract.

Cross-dating (Fig. 6–1) cannot be taken for granted. But if it is shown to exist in the trees of a region, there is then occasion to search the environment and climate for its causes. The dendrochronologist is greatly aided in his search for material by the many general and specific reasons why his trees cross-date, yet it would be entirely possible for him to apply limited cross-dating to archeol-

---

* The notes on the early development of tree-ring dating by Douglass are compiled mainly from Douglass (1919, 1928, 1935, and 1937), and from notes by Neil M. Judd in Douglass (1935).

ogy if he knew none of the explanations of the processes with which he worked.

The student who consistently finds cross-dating in wood specimens that show considerable variation in ring widths has, in this cross-dating, all the proof that he needs of identity between the trees. In order to achieve cross-dating in long series of rings he has been obliged first to master a few techniques. Certain microscopic

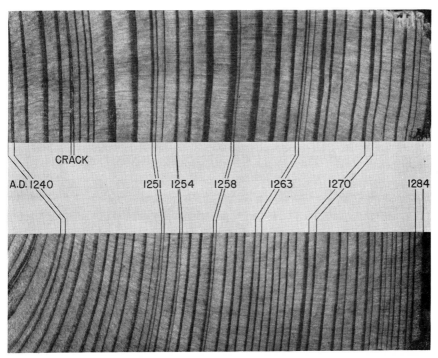

FIG. 6–1. Cross-dating between archeological beams from widely separated sites in northern Arizona—from Betatakin ruin in Tsegi Canyon (top), and from Mummy Cave in Canyon del Muerto, 75 miles away (bottom). Both pieces are Douglas-fir, the outside ring on the bottom one being from A.D. 1284. Both photographs are greatly enlarged. (Courtesy Dr. Bryant Bannister and the Laboratory of Tree-Ring Research, Tucson, Ariz.)

or faint ring boundaries may be determined only after the wood is planed in such a way as to outline each cell wall with as little distortion as possible. The sharper the microtome and the more precise the angle of reflected light against the concave inner surfaces of cell walls, the more opportunity there is to achieve precision in ring identification and measurement. The experiments between 1911 and the present day in the Tree-Ring Laboratory at Tucson and elsewhere have been extremely wide-ranging. While other methods of preparing surfaces may have a growing applicability, none has entirely replaced the diagonal cut by a microtome at an angle of 35 to 40 degrees from the grain of the wood. This cut, together with a carefully trained light source, makes possible the measuring and photographing of as minuscule rings as have yet been demonstrated in stress-area conifers. Charcoal is surfaced by other means. *

Cross-dating cannot be achieved by any student if he does not take into consideration the locally absent rings and false annual rings in his material (Schulman, 1945a, pp. 19–23; Douglass, 1946, pp. 10–16). The recognition of those rings, and the careful and unending study of them, is vital to success, especially in the Southwest.

Another essential technique is the retention of a mental image of ring patterns while two or more specimens are being tested. An unusual individual can hold in mind hundreds of years of relative thicknesses with all the limited patterns, the "signatures," intact. He thus cross-dates quickly by eye and cross-compares rings with assurance. Others, and the skilled memorizer as well, may rely upon a shorthand method of cross-comparison, however. The "skeleton plot," as Douglass (1936, p. 22) first used it, is a remarkable tool. It is a temporary and often a personal guide, yet it standardizes for quick visual acuity in a way that no formal curve can do. Various experiments, both in the Laboratory of Tree-Ring Research and elsewhere, have shown that the skeleton plot can carry as much or as little information as its user requires. The more crowded the plot, however, the less effective it is likely to become as a quick guide to cross-identification. One may plot only the thinnest of thin rings relative to one another, as is the usual practice, noting in pencil special features of other outstanding rings, or he may plot only the thickest of the thick rings. Since the microscopic rings at the lower limits of measurability offer the sharpest visual markers of cross-identity, however, the original Douglass skeleton plot will be found by most students the practical one for their purposes. While the dendrochronologist, as a technician doing the endless work which is cross-dating, needs no more than his memory, and perhaps skeleton plots, in his first day-to-day working out of chronology, he is obliged to make a permanent record for himself and others in the form of tables and curves of measures. Parenthetically, a published curve of measures can be skeleton plotted almost as effectively as can the rings, themselves, of a section of wood.

---

* These techniques of tree-ring dating are detailed in Douglass (1919, 1928, 1935, 1940, 1941a, 1941c, 1943a, 1943b), Giddings (1941, pp. 8–10), Glock (1937, pp. 1–7), Hall (1939, 1946), Hawley (1941), and Scantling (1946).

Another essential of tree-ring dating may be mentioned in passing. The ring record must have "circuit" or "pattern" uniformity. The remarkable uniformity of the most readily datable trees in the Southwest has been amply illustrated by Douglass (1937, p. 16), Glock (1937, pp. 35–62), and others. Uniformity in the ring record is also an essential of dendrochronology at the northern tree line (Giddings, 1941, pp. 51–52).

Archeological Dating in the Southwest

The dendrochronologist may thus operate strictly as a technician independently of other disciplines. On the other hand, if he is to collect the wood for cross-dating and if he wishes to apply the results of his work in a practical way, he is obliged to work within limited areas of plant ecology, climatology, and archeology, and perhaps in other fields such as paleontology and oceanography. Archeology deserves first consideration because through this agency tree-ring dating has received its most impressive and enduring application. The many questions brought up in the course of archeological dating have given encouragement to the other studies with which this volume is mainly concerned.

The dating of southwestern ruins that so dramatically altered archeological time scales in the 1920's seems in retrospect to have been almost explosive. The truth is, however, that more than 10 years passed between the time of first recognition of tree-ring dating as an effective archeological tool and the acceptance of an exact chronology that was to affect the interpretation of even the remotest archeological sites in America. During this decade the students who worked with Douglass developed an enthusiasm and an intensity such as archeology has seldom seen. Among those who mastered the precisions of dating technique and became experienced collaborators with Douglass can be mentioned L. L. Hargrave, E. W. Haury, H. T. Getty, and, somewhat later, W. S. Stallings, J. C. McGregor, G. Willey, Florence Hawley, G. C. Baldwin, E. T. Hall, F. H. Scantling, R. Lassetter, and this writer. While none of these individuals is now primarily engaged in dating archeological wood, it is revealing to note that they collectively are responsible for an impressive amount of the recent and current writing on North American anthropology.

Douglass himself, during the years between 1937 and 1942, seemed to have attained an almost professional view of southwestern archeology. Yet his early inducements to interrupt the studies of climatic cycles, particularly those in long sequoia records, took effect with painful slowness. Clark Wissler, 3 years before he published his definitive study of American culture areas in *The American Indian*, offered Douglass in 1914 samples of prehistoric wood for him to examine and try to date. The offer was accepted, but the sections from ruins of northwestern New Mexico did not arrive until 1916. An archeologist, Earl H. Morris, contributed six beam sections from his excavation at Aztec Ruin in 1919, and these specimens were immediately cross-dated to form the initial "floating chronology," a sequence of dates not identified with the Christian calendar. During the following year, Neil M. Judd contributed samples from the huge masonry village ruin of Pueblo Bonito. Interest in tree-ring dating as an archeological tool reached a fever pitch with the knowledge that log by log and room by room of the multicelled open-air villages and the cliff dwellings could be cross-dated on a relative basis. Even today one reads the account of dating one set of beams after another, between the years 1922 and 1929, as though it were a detective story. The climax came, of course, in the finding of a set of charred beams that dramatically closed the gap between a relative chronology and the actually dated calendar derived from living trees and inhabited Indian villages. Overnight it had become possible to assign to, not only the villages, but family rooms of the Pueblo Indians of the Southwest the precise Christian dates of their construction.

We need not recount the separate triumphs of this archeological dating that was sped along with the aid of such veteran archeologists as Fewkes, Kidder, and Colton. While archeologists demanded precision and proofs from Douglass and his students, there is little doubt that this very precision and methodology of tree-ring dating contributed in return toward the refinement of archeological practice. The archeologist was now obliged to treat his charcoal and beams as though they were artifacts, cleaning them carefully and determining their possible cultural meanings. Wood fragments and charcoal had acquired significance not unlike that of manuscripts from an Egyptian tomb. The archeological dating which depended on the most detailed accuracy, judgment, and measurement thus brought about not only improvements in the techniques of tree-ring dating but new evidence toward a climatic interpretation of cross-dating.

Douglass' unflagging interest in relating solar activity to climate through life forms insured the analysis of ring sequences past the needs of simply cross-dating beams. Out of the archeological dating emerged a recognition of the close relation of cross-dating to dry sites, and in particular to the relative supply of rainfall upon which the growth of a season might draw. The lower forest border was envisioned as a stress area for those trees carrying the most sensitive ring record, and close correlations were noted between the annual measurements of ring growth and the local indices of rainfall and river runoff. Archeologists soon learned which species of conifers provided the best cross-dating, but they have not yet been given the full reason for this selectivity.

Between 1934 and 1939, the Tree-Ring Laboratory was provided with a resident botanist, Waldo S. Glock, who made a detailed study of some of the assumptions which had grown inductively out of the archeological dating and climatic study. Among other contributions, Glock and his assistants undertook the dissection of an entire ponderosa pine and were able to show that a high degree of uniformity in this tree, which possessed high cross-dating qualities, was present not only in the stem but also in the branches and roots. This, and further studies, demonstrated the fundamental correctness of Douglass' assumptions about rings missing in parts of the stem and rings missing entirely in isolated trees in a stand (Glock, 1937, p. 62). Archeologists were thus doubly assured that their interpretation of rings absent in limited wood segments was correct. Archeological verification was first sought out, of course, wherever it could be found by tracing the locally absent rings to several parts of timbers from which the limited samples had been cut. Other scientists who were especially helpful in promoting the environmental studies of tree-ring dating were E. Antevs, R. W. Chaney, F. Shreve, F. E. Clements, and G. A. Pearson.

Tree Growth and Climate

Nearly all of Douglass' associates who had fully mastered the techniques of tree-ring dating moved on into the anthropological fields that their work was helping to illuminate. It may be noted in passing that, with some exceptions (Haury, 1935; McGregor, 1941; Stallings, 1949; Bell, 1952; Bannister and Smiley, 1955), little has been written by them to impress upon other archeologists the vital distinction between amateur and professional tree-ring work. Only one of Douglass' close collaborators, Edmund Schulman, persisted in the basic studies of the meaning of cross-dating at the Tree-Ring Laboratory. The indefatigable and scholarly attention of Schulman to the meanings of ring variations has been reported by him over a period of 2 decades in a series of articles and monographs culminating, shortly before his untimely death, in the book *Dendroclimatic Changes in Semiarid America.** This volume does two things: It places on record the precise measures and curves derived from many parts of North America and the Patagonian Andes, and it furnishes extraordinary proof that the refinement of tree-ring material through exhaustive sampling bears out the theory that stress-area trees are sensitive recorders of climate. A recent appraisal in *Geographical Review* (Glock, 1957) of Schulman's major work, surprisingly enough, contains little analysis of the content but consists almost entirely of critical remarks, most of them quite tangential to the subject matter. The one-third million tree-rings measured, and statistically treated in Schulman's volume, offer remarkable clarification of many aspects of tree-ring dating.

Nearly all of the assumptions implicit in the work of Douglass and others are subjected to field and laboratory tests of far-reaching geographical significance. It might be stressed that the book records, in some areas for the first time, that cross-dating of quality suitable for archeology exists at the lower forest border in the following areas of western North America: Fraser River Basin, Saskatchewan River Basin, Columbia River Basin, Clark Fork River Basin, Snake River Basin, Missouri–Yellowstone river basins, Big Horn–Platte–Arkansas river basins, the Eastern Great Basin, Colorado River Basin, Gila River Basin, Rio Grande Basin, California and the Western Great Basin, and west-central Mexico. Statistics and graphs are presented for each area. When Indian sites are found along the lower forest border in the archeologically untapped parts of these regions, any tree-ring material included in the sites can be expected to carry adequate to excellent cross-dating records. The longest series of continuous ring records that are statistically well based are those of the Colorado Basin, 2,009 years; the Snake River Basin, 1,494 years; and the Missouri Basin, 973 years. All who have traversed the many miles necessary to select the trees that will result in a representative mean curve can appreciate the magnitude of Schulman's contribution. Records such as his, together with their lucid evaluation based on years of study of climatic and other tree-ring principles, make *Dendroclimatic Changes*

---

* Schulman's extensive bibliography is to be found in his bibliographic compilation of tree-ring publications (1940), in the index to the Tree-Ring Bulletin, Vol. 20, Nos. 3–4, 1954, and in the subject volume. Some major contributions are "Centuries-Long Tree Indices of Precipitation in the Southwest" (1942a), "Dendrochronology in Pines of Arkansas" (1942b), "Tree-Ring Hydrology of the Colorado River Basin" (1945a), "Root-Growth Rings and Chronology" (1945b), "Tree-Ring Hydrology in Southern California" (1947), and "Tree-Ring Evidence for Climatic Changes" (1953).

in Semiarid America an invaluable contribution to all those interested in dendrochronology, whatever their special fields.

Areal Extensions

Tree-ring dating has been attempted in several parts of the world other than the North American West, with varying degrees of success. The odds are against sensitive dating in short sequences of tree-rings wherever the trees grow far from either an upper or a lower tree line of climatic stress. Nevertheless, investigators have found passable cross-dating in the hemlocks of New England (Lyon, 1946), the pines of Arkansas (Schulman, 1942b) and the Tennessee Valley (Hawley, 1937; Lassetter, 1938), the trees of parts of the Mississippi Valley (Hawley, 1941; Bell, 1952), and trees of the Middle East (Gindel, 1944). No doubt there exist many regions in which local environmental stresses may affect trees to such an extent as to make limited dating possible. The archeological dividends, in those regions where the dating is difficult, are so slight as to encourage little experimentation. Noteworthy local successes have been achieved, however, in the central and southeastern states by Florence Hawley, Roy Lassetter, Gordon Willey, and Robert E. Bell. Cedar, and even hardwoods, have been used with some success in these regions. The most satisfactory demonstration that this dating can be applied to archeology comes from the Kincaid site in southern Illinois, for which Bell (1952) reports on 500 years of dendroclimatic record in a cultural deposit. The possibilities at lower forest borders in other dry regions in the world than the American West have hardly been explored. Douglass early determined that the cedar of Lebanon, in specimens used by ancient Egyptians, carried a clear and apparently datable record. Only recently, the writer had the opportunity to examine a limited number of samples of what proved to be junipers from the eleventh century B.C. tomb of the Phrygian King Gordius. Although one wood section held some 600 rings and another was nearly as long, the two samples failed to cross-date. The records looked promising enough, however, to suggest that cross-dating can be worked out when more samples from the tomb are available. The archeological possibilities of tree-ring dating in the Middle East appear very good indeed for an ambitious investigator who has cut his teeth in the American Southwest. Some isolated studies of local structures in Bronze Age and neolithic sites of Europe have been carried out (Huber and von Jazewitsch, 1956), and old buildings have been cross-dated with living trees in the Trondheim and Kongsberg areas of Norway (Høeg, 1956, p. 14).

The Arctic Tree Line as a Special Area

Our dendrochronological studies in Alaska have been applied with considerable success to correlations with climate (Giddings, 1941, 1943), the tracing of sea currents (Giddings, 1952b; Van-Stone, 1958), and archeology (Giddings, 1942, 1952a; Oswalt, 1950, 1952; VanStone, 1953). Cross-dating quality in the American Arctic

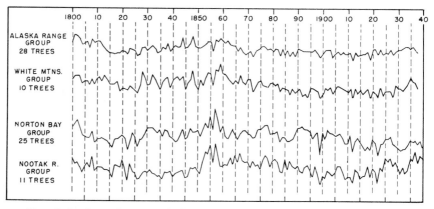

Fig. 6–2. Cross-dating and climatic relationships between widely separated forest-edge sites in Alaska. The upper two curves are from about 3,000 feet elevation at an interval of 200 miles north and south; the lower two are from the forest edge at sea level in the northern Bering Sea and Chuckchee Sea areas, also about 200 miles apart north and south. An agreement in trend appears to reflect closely the temperature of the growing season. From Giddings (1941).

closely parallels fluctuations in temperature of the early part of the growing season. The soil maintains sufficient moisture throughout the year, because of ground frost in most of this region. The coniferous trees of swampy muskeg may even be limited by insufficient nutrition where their roots lie in or upon the frozen ground during a good part of the growing season. They, as well as the better nourished but more marginal trees near the uppermost or northernmost forest border, respond to temperature stress. Lines of cross-dating have been shown to follow very closely isotherms of midsummer temperatures and to move from 3,000 feet in the interior of Alaska to sea level at the outer edges of forest to the west and north (Fig. 6–2). The changing records along the two large rivers, Yukon and Mackenzie, have made possible the tracing of driftwood by cross-dating to the point of origin into the Bering Sea and thence northward through Bering Strait on the one hand (Giddings, 1952b) and into the Arctic Sea and westward toward Point Barrow on the other (Giddings, 1947).

Cross-dating over a 500-year span has been achieved in Eskimo sites far from the nearest growing timber by means of driftwood reflecting three different climatic records. The earlier coastal sites may some day be included by extension of the three separate chronologies. While archeological dating would clearly be possible wherever wood is preserved in the interior of Alaska and northern Canada, there is as yet only one inland region in which sites have been discovered of sufficient age and in a good enough state of preservation for the building of a chronology. This is the Kobuk-Noatak-Selawik drainage system at or above the Arctic Circle in western Alaska. Five major sites and several isolated house pits are now dated in this chronology, which spans a thousand years. Scandinavian investigators across the polar basin have since 1936 continued to accumulate proof of the close relationship between the growth of Arctic conifers and temperature of the growing season, yet their chronologies do not seem to have been lengthened enough to assist in archeological dating.*

If truly long ring records are to be achieved through the dating of archeological or paleontological sites in parts of the Arctic other than Alaska, this will most likely be done by those who ignore the normal trees and search out the exceptional ones that have grown under stress. The Scandinavian dendrochronologists appear to be all botanists and foresters. Not even Ilmari Hustich, who not long ago visited the Tree-Ring Laboratory, seems to have broken away from the average forest stand in a determined search for long-lived stress trees that carry, in the American part of the Arctic, at any rate, the ring record most closely related to climate. It has been the writer's experience in following the tree line for hundreds of miles in northern Alaska and the Hudson Bay regions of Canada that the oldest trees invariably exist at the very forest edge. One finds, for example, that trees growing along the banks of the Yukon River have grown rapidly with a considerable age curve and have seldom achieved more than 150 or 200 years of age. A climb up the mountainsides to the timber lines brings one quickly, however, to the stress trees from 300 to 500 years old, the growth of which is uniform but sensitive in ring record. The sensitivity there is to

---

* Scandinavian tree-ring work has been summarized by Schulman (1944), and more recently outlined by Høeg, Mikola, Eklund, and Holmsgaard in the Tree-Ring Bulletin, Vol. 21. See especially Hustich (1948).

mean June–July temperature. Again, toward the mouth of the Mackenzie River in northwestern Canada, one begins to reach stress trees within a hundred miles of the forest edge. Longevity rapidly increases, accompanied by considerable twist in the trunk and branches of the trees, until almost at the edge itself, well above the Arctic Circle, are found spruces nearly 1,000 years old. Douglass, Schulman, and others have repeatedly made the point that trees growing on extreme sites at the lower forest border in the Southwest are both the most ancient and the most amenable to dating (Douglass, 1941b, p. 825-b; 1946, pp. 5–7; and Schulman, 1942a, pp. 150–151, 205; 1956, pp. 7–10, 68–69). Schulman (1958) dramatically made this point in searching out the 4,000-year-old bristlecone pines in the White Mountains of California.

The Outlook for Dendrochronology

The future of dendrochronology seems to be limited only by the enthusiasm of those who have the patience to learn its fascination. The challenges in applications to climatic studies remain unchanged. Some think radiocarbon dating is about to replace the tree-ring method, just as automobiles replaced the horse and buggy. The assumption is doubtful. Tree-ring dating insists upon the absolute dating to a specific year. Its results stand unshaken by any other method, regardless of conflict of dates. Even if radiocarbon dating becomes less expensive and more precisely focused, tree-ring dates will still be needed both to verify the general dating and to pinpoint the specific. The backlog of documented archeological specimens for which dates are needed is still great in spite of the determined efforts of Smiley (1951), Ferguson (1949), Bannister (1951), Stokes and others at the Tree-Ring Laboratory to reduce the wood to sets of statistics, and to meet the continuing demands of Southwestern archeology.* The only shortage appears to be within this field of accomplished workers who are willing and able to carry on the work of the Tree-Ring Laboratory. Archeological tree-ring dating is further insured by our awareness of areas for which Schulman and others have published chronologies before there has been an archeological demand. An immediate need, it would seem, is for more researchers with the scientific bent of Douglass and Schulman who can continue to observe, induce, and experiment with the almost endless possibilities of climatic and archeological interpretation. If these students are encouraged as they continue to appear, the future of dendrochronology and of the Tree-Ring Laboratory is assured for the decades to come.

---

* Major archeological contributions are to be found also in Smiley, Stubbs, and Bannister (1953) and Bannister (1959).

LITERATURE CITED

BANNISTER, B. 1951. Tree-ring dates for the Gallina area, New Mexico. Tree-Ring Bull. 17(3): 21–22.

————. 1959. Tree-ring dating of archaeological sites in the Chaco Canyon Region, New Mexico. Ph.D. dissertation. University of Arizona, Tucson.

BANNISTER, B., and TERAH L. SMILEY. 1955. Dendrochronology. In: Geochronology. TERAH L. SMILEY (ed.). Univ. Ariz. Bull. Ser. 26(2): Phys. Sci. Bull. No. 2. Pp. 177–195.

BELL, R. E. 1952. Dendrochronology in the Mississippi Valley. In: Archeology of Eastern United States. J. B. GRIFFIN (ed.). University of Chicago Press, Chicago. Pp. 345–351.

CAMPBELL, T. N. 1949. The pioneer tree-ring work of Jacob Kuechler. Tree-Ring Bull. 15(3): 16–20.

DOUGLASS, A. E. 1919. Climatic cycles and tree growth. Pub. 289, Vol. I. Carnegie Inst. Wash.

————. 1928. Climatic cycles and tree growth. Pub. 289, Vol. II. Carnegie Inst. Wash.

————. 1935. Dating Pueblo Bonito and other ruins of the Southwest. Natl. Geog. Soc., Contributed Tech. Papers, Pueblo Bonito Ser. No. 1. Wash.

————. 1936. Climatic cycles and tree growth. Pub. 289, Vol. III. Carnegie Inst. Wash.

————. 1937. Tree rings and chronology. Univ. Ariz. Bull. 8(4); Phys. Sci. Bull. No. 1.

————. 1940. Notes on the technique of tree-ring analysis. I. Tree-Ring Bull. 7(1): 2–8.

————. 1941a. Notes on the technique of tree-ring analysis. II. Tree-Ring Bull. 7(4): 29–34.

————. 1941b. Crossdating in dendrochronology. Jour. Forestry 39(10): 825–31.

————. 1941c. Notes on the technique of tree-ring analysis. III. Tree-Ring Bull. 8(2): 10–16.

————. 1943a. Notes on the technique of tree-ring analysis. IV. Practical instruments. Tree-Ring Bull. 10(1): 2–8.

————. 1943b. Notes on the technique of tree-ring analysis. V. Practical instruments. Tree-Ring Bull. 10(2): 10–16.

————. 1946. Precision of ring dating in tree-ring chronologies. Univ. Ariz. Bull. 17(3); Lab. Tree-Ring Res. Bull. No. 3.

FERGUSON, C. W., JR. 1949. Additional dates of Nine-Mile Canyon, northeastern Utah. Tree-Ring Bull. 16(2): 10–11.

GIDDINGS, J. L., JR. 1941. Dendrochronology in northern Alaska. Univ. Ariz. Bull. 12(4); Univ. Alaska Pub. No. 4.

————. 1942. Dated sites on the Kobuk River, Alaska. Tree-Ring Bull. 9(1): 2–8.

————. 1943. Some climatic aspects of tree growth in Alaska. Tree-Ring Bull. 9(4): 26–32.

————. 1947. Mackenzie River Delta chronology. Tree-Ring Bull. 13(4): 26–29.

————. 1952a. The Arctic woodland culture of the Kobuk River. Mus. Monog., Univ. Mus. Philadelphia.

————. 1952b. Driftwood and problems of Arctic Sea currents. Proc. Amer. Phil. Soc. 96(2): 129–142.

GINDEL, J. 1944. Aleppo pine as a medium for tree-ring analysis. Tree-Ring Bull. 11(1): 6–8.

GLOCK, W. S. 1937. Principles and methods of tree-ring analysis. Pub. 486, Carnegie Inst. Wash.

————. 1957. Review of Edmund Schulman's Dendroclimatic changes in semiarid America. Geog. Rev. 47(4): 606–608.

HALL, E. T., JR. 1939. A method for obtaining a plane surface on charcoal. Tree-Ring Bull. 5(4): 31.

————. 1946. Preserving and surfacing rotted wood and charcoal. Tree-Ring Bull. 12(4): 26–27.

HAURY, E. W. 1935. Tree-rings: The Archaeologist's Timepiece. Amer. Antiquity 1: 98–108.

HAWLEY, FLORENCE. 1937. Relationship of southern cedar growth to precipitation and run-off. Ecol. 18(3): 398–405.

————. 1941. Tree-ring analysis and dating in the Mississippi drainage. Univ. Chicago Publs. Anthrop., Occas. Papers No. 2. The University of Chicago Press, Chicago.

HEIZER, R. F. 1956. The first dendrochronologist. Amer. Antiquity 22(2) Part 1: 186–188.

HØEG, O. A. 1956. Growth-ring research in Norway. Tree-Ring Bull. 21(1–4): 2–15.

HUBER, B., and W. VON JAZEWITSCH. 1956. Tree-ring studies of the forestry-botany institutes of Tharandt and Munich. Tree-Ring Bull. 21(1–4): 28–30.

HUSTICH, I. 1948. The Scotch pine in northernmost Finland and its dependence on the climate in the last decades. Acta Bot. Fenn. 42. Helsinki.

LASSETTER, R. 1938. The value of tree-ring analysis in engineering. Tree-Ring Bull. 5(2): 13–15.

LYON, C. J. 1946. Hemlock chronology in New England. Tree-Ring Bull. 13(1): 1–4.

McGREGOR, J. C. 1941. Southwestern Archaeology. New York.

OSWALT, W. H. 1950. Spruce borings from the lower Yukon River, Alaska. Tree-Ring Bull. 16(4): 26–30.

————. 1952. Spruce samples from the Copper River drainage, Alaska. Tree-Ring Bull. 19(1): 5–10.

SCANTLING, F. H. 1946. Photography of charcoal. Tree-Ring Bull. 12(4): 27–32.

SCHULMAN, E. 1940. A bibliography of tree-ring analysis. Tree-Ring Bull. 6(4): 27–39.

————. 1942a. Centuries-long tree indices of precipitation in the Southwest. Bull. Amer. Met. Soc. 23: 148–161, 204–217, April, May.

————. 1942b. Dendrochronology in pines of Arkansas. Ecol. 23(3): 309–18.

————. 1944. Tree-ring work in Scandinavia. Tree-Ring Bull. 11(1): 2–6.

————. 1945a. Tree-ring hydrology of the Colorado River Basin. Univ. Ariz. Bull. 16(4); Lab. Tree-Ring Res. Bull. No. 2.

————. 1945b. Root growth-rings and chronology. Tree-Ring Bull. 12(1): 2–5.

————. 1947. Tree-ring hydrology in southern California. Univ. Ariz. Bull. 18(3); Lab. Tree-Ring Res. Bull. No. 4.

————. 1953. Tree-ring evidence for climatic changes. In: Climatic Change. H. SHAPLEY (ed.). Harvard University Press, Cambridge, Mass.

————. 1956. Dendroclimatic changes in semiarid America. University of Arizona Press, Tucson.

————. 1958. Bristlecone pine, oldest known living thing. Natl. Geog. Mag. March, 1958.

SMILEY, TERAH L. 1951. A summary of tree-ring dates from some southwestern archaeological sites. Univ. of Ariz. Bull. 22(4); Lab. Tree-Ring Res. Bull. No. 5.

SMILEY, TERAH L., S. A. STUBBS, and B. BANNISTER. 1953. A foundation for the dating of some late archaeological sites in the Rio Grande area, New Mexico: Based on studies in tree-ring methods and pottery analyses. Univ. Ariz. Bull.; Lab. Tree-Ring Res. Bull. No. 6.

STALLINGS, W. S., JR. 1949. Dating prehistoric ruins by tree-rings. Rev. ed. Lab. Anthrop. Bull. 8, 1939. Tucson.

STUDHALTER, R. A. 1956. Early history of cross-dating. Tree-Ring Bull. 21(1–4): 31–35.

VANSTONE, J. W. 1953. Notes on Kotzebue dating. Tree-Ring Bull. 20(1): 6–8.

————. 1958. The origin of driftwood on Nunivak Island, Alaska. Tree-Ring Bull. 22(1–4): 12–15.

7

Photocontrol of Growth and Dormancy in Woody Plants

ROBERT JACK DOWNS

Introduction

Photocontrol of growth and dormancy in woody plants results from a photoreaction that also controls flowering of photoperiodically sensitive plants (Downs, 1956), elongation of internodes (Borthwick *et al.*, 1951; Downs *et al.*, 1957), coloration of fruits (Piringer and Heinze, 1954; Siegelman and Hendricks, 1957), and germination of light-sensitive seeds (Borthwick *et al.*, 1952; Toole *et al.*, 1958). This discussion will deal primarily with this photoreaction and will be based largely on work at Beltsville, Maryland, because time and space do not allow a complete review of all the facets of the regulatory effects of light on woody plants.

Studies of the photoperiodic responses of woody plants began about 1923, when Garner and Allard (1923) reported that *Liriodendron tulipifera* L., *Rhus glabra* L., and *Hibiscus moscheutos* L. continued to grow when the light period was lengthened with artificial light, and "ceased upward growth" when the days were short. As a result of the many descriptive studies made since that time (reviewed by Nitsch, 1957b; and Wareing, 1956), it is possible to proceed into more fundamental investigations because the behavior of many plants under a particular set of conditions can be predicted with reasonable accuracy. It also is known that several kinds of dormancies are induced by short days (Downs and Borthwick, 1956a and b; Nitsch, 1957a; Downs and Piringer, 1958), that different species may exhibit a wide range of response (Downs and Borthwick, 1956b; Nitsch, 1957a and b), and that seeds of different geographic origin may produce plants that react differently to photoperiod (Olson *et al.*, 1959; Pauley and Perry, 1954; Vaartaja, 1954, 1959).

The Reversible Photoreaction

The diverse responses of plants to light, such as flowering, elongation, fruit coloration, and germination, were shown to be subject to the same causal photocontrol by means of response or action spectra. For example, germination of lettuce (*Lactuca sativa* var. Grand Rapids) seeds is promoted by visible radiation. The principle of the action spectra is to measure germination of seeds placed across the spectrum in terms of incident energy. The result is a maximum effectiveness for promotion of germination between 600 and 700 millimicrons, with a peak at about 650 millimicrons.

Germination of Grand Rapids lettuce seeds is inhibited by radiant energy with wavelengths longer than 700 millimicrons. The action spectrum for inhibition is measured by promoting maximum germination with red radiant energy and then placing the seeds across the spectrum and irradiating them for various periods. The result is a maximum effectiveness between 700 and 800 millimicrons, with a peak at about 735 millimicrons.

Action spectra obtained from several plant responses (Borthwick *et al.*, 1951, 1952; Downs, 1956) were the same and showed that the pigment controlling growth, flowering, and germination absorbs in the red and far-red regions of the spectrum. The wide scope of activity of this particular pigment is illustrated by the different plant responses to an irradiation with red radiant energy. Red radiant energy inhibits flowering of short-day plants and promotes flowering of long-day ones (Downs, 1956). It promotes seed germination (Borthwick *et al.*, 1952), cuticle coloration of tomato fruits (Piringer and Heinze, 1954), and anthocyanin formation (Siegelman and Hendricks, 1957), and inhibits internode elongation (Downs *et al.*, 1957). Far-red radiant energy applied immediately after the exposure to red will reverse these effects. Moreover, most of the responses are repeatedly reversible by red and far-red energy, so the ultimate response of the plants is governed by the kind of radiant energy used last (Borthwick *et al.*, 1952; Downs, 1956; Downs *et al.*, 1957).

Red and far-red radiant energies can be obtained in pure form by using a spectrograph. The spectrograph at Beltsville (Borthwick *et al.*, 1951, 1952) is a two-prism instrument that provides a spectrum 10 cm. broad and nearly 2 m. long with a dispersion of 1.6 mμ cm.$^{-1}$ at 500 mμ and 7.5 mμ cm.$^{-1}$ at 750 mμ. The source is a carbon-arc lamp operating at 150 amps, which produces an energy of about 0.1×10^{-3} joules cm.$^{-2}$ sec. More simply, relatively pure red and far red can be obtained from ordinary lamps fitted with inexpensive filters. Use of filtered light sources allows irradiation of larger areas than a spectrograph, and, although the purity of the radiant energy is less, it usually is adequate.

Red radiant energy can be obtained from fluorescent lamps by using a filter made of two layers of red cellophane. The red cellophane removes most of the visible radiant energy at the red end of the spectrum, and, since the fluorescent lamps emit almost no far red, the result is relatively pure red radiant energy. Moreover, filtering the light emitted by the fluorescent lamps is not really necessary, because the radiation absorbed by the filter has only a very slight influence on the phenomenon. Therefore, unfiltered light from fluorescent lamps would be expected to produce the red effect in plants nearly as well as a relatively pure form of red radiant energy.

Far-red energy must be obtained from a light source that emits a considerable quantity of far red, so the sun or incandescent-filament lamps are suitable. These sources are used in conjunction with a filter made of two layers of red and two layers of dark-blue cellophane, which removes most of the visible radiation. Heat can be removed with a water filter, although heating has not produced measurable effects during the brief periods of irradiation.

When plants respond to light, they do so because the light is absorbed by a pigment system in the plant. The repeated reversal of germination (Borthwick *et al.*, 1952) and other plant responses (Downs, 1956; Downs *et al.*, 1957) by red and far-red radiation indicates that only a single reaction is involved. This means that the pigment exists in two forms, a red-absorbing form and a far-red–absorbing one. When the red-absorbing form of the pigment is irradiated with red radiant energy, it is changed into a form that absorbs far red. When the far-red–absorbing form is irradiated with far red, it reverts to the red-absorbing form.

The same reversible pigment system that controls flowering (Downs, 1956), growth (Downs *et al.*, 1957), germination (Borthwick *et al.*, 1952), and coloration of herbaceous plants (Piringer and Heinze, 1954; Siegelman and Hendricks, 1957) also controls growth and dormancy, germination, and coloration of woody plants. This pigment is now called "phytochrome." The characteristics of the system are the red, far-red reversibility, saturation in either direction by low energies, and a slow drift in darkness from the far-red– to the red-absorbing form of the pigment.

Internodes of many kinds of plants elongate markedly when a brief irradiation with far-red radiation follows each daily period of high-intensity light. The potential effect of the far red is reversed by a subsequent exposure to red radiant energy (Downs *et al.*, 1957). Since the pigment is present and functionable at the close of the light period, it must be stable and not photooxidized.

Growth of internodes of albino barley plants responds to light in the same way as growth of internodes of green barley plants (Borthwick *et al.*, 1951). Therefore, the pigment system is present and operating in albino plants, but the concentration of the pigment is too low to impart visible color. Because the pigment absorbs red energy, it would be expected that a blue color would be seen if the pigment was concentrated enough.

Thus, a pigment concentration too low to impart visible color is activated by relatively low energies to produce a large effect. These considerations imply that the pigment or one of its immediate products has the characteristics of an enzyme.

Effect of Short Days

In general, woody plants stop shoot growth on short days. Leaves usually become darker green and the fascicular leaves of pines stop elongating. Under our experimental conditions many deciduous species, larch (Fig. 7-1), and many southern pines stop growth on daylengths of 12 hours or less. Sitka spruce (*Picea sitchensis* [Bong.] Carr.), however, stopped growth on photoperiods of 14 hours or less, and Norway spruce (*P. abies* [L.] Karst.) and white spruce (*P. glauca* [Moench.] Voss) (Fig. 7-2) stopped growth on photoperiods of 16 hours or less (Table 7-1).

As the elongation of stems of plants on short days slows, shorter and shorter internodes are produced until growth finally stops. Stems of *Catalpa bignonioides* Walt. become black just below the terminal, and the terminal meristem is then abscised. Tulip poplar (*Liriodendron tulipifera* L.), Asian white birch (*Betula mandshurica* [Regel] Nakai), and alder (*Alnus rugosa* [Du Roi] Spreng.) stop expansion of leaves and internodes and form a pseudobud in which the stipules function as bud scales. Other woody plants such as red maple (*Acer rubrum* L.) and sweetgum (*Liquidambar styraciflua* L.) stop differentiating leaves and produce true bud scales.

Woody plants from the tropics, such as coffee (*Coffea arabica* L.) (Piringer and Borthwick, 1955), *Rauvolfia vomitoria* Afzel (Piringer *et al.*, 1958), and cacao (*Theobroma cacao* L.) (Piringer and Downs, 1960) are as responsive to daylength as many of the

FIG. 7–1. Growth of Japanese larch (*Larix leptolepis* Sieb. and Zucc.) after 4 months on photoperiods of 10, 12, 14, 16, and 24 hrs., left to right.

FIG. 7–2. Growth of white spruce (*Picea glauca* [Moench.] Voss) after 4 months on photoperiods of 12, 14, 16, and 24 hrs., left to right.

TABLE 7-1

Effect of Photoperiod on Several Species in the Pinaceae.

Species	Total Growth (Centimeters) on Indicated Photoperiods (Hours)							Fresh Weight (Grams) on Indicated Photoperiods (Hours)							Duration of Experiment (Months)
	8	12	14	16	20	24	LSD$_{05}$*	8	12	14	16	20	24	LSD$_{05}$*	
Pinus radiata	66	71	78	77	—	121	10	26.9	32.8	33.5	29.6	—	49.3	9.7	7
P. elliottii	10	23	29	31	—	56	5	4.2	11.0	15.1	14.1	—	25.3	3.1	8.5
P. rigida	8	12	26	23	—	39	9	0.7	1.3	4.3	4.2	—	8.3	2.2	8.5
P. banksiana	3	5	10	14	—	25	6	0.3	0.8	2.8	6.3	—	7.2	1.6	8.5
P. strobus	1	4	4	7	—	31	6	0.2	0.5	2.2	3.6	—	15.4	2.0	15
P. resinosa	1	3	6	8	—	15	2	0.2	0.5	1.2	4.5	—	13.6	1.1	12
P. aristata†	2	4	6	10	—	19	1	0.2	0.6	1.9	3.4	—	9.2	0.9	15
Larix occidentalis	—	7	—	30	48	57	19	—	0.8	—	3.1	4.3	5.3	1.5	4
L. leptolepis	—	8	42	59	66	95	13	—	1.5	6.3	5.9	7.1	8.9	1.1	4
Picea glauca	—	4	5	9	16	32	4	—	0.2	0.3	0.5	0.9	1.8	0.8	4
P. abies	2	2	2	11	—	144	28	0.1	0.1	0.2	1.3	—	15.2	0.4	11
P. sitchensis	—	21	27	117	—	156	31	—	1.2	1.7	6.0	—	8.5	1.8	17
Sequoia gigantea†	—	15	—	25	37	42	4	—	14.6	—	28.5	54.0	55.3	8.4	12
S. sempervirens†	—	60	73	78	70	60	Not sig.	—	59.4	76.2	87.7	81.2	69.1	13.7	12

*Least Significant Difference—5% Level.
†Length of the main axis only.

Temperate Zone plants, except that these tropical plants do not completely stop shoot elongation and set dormant buds as do many of the Temperate Zone woody plants. Plants such as the California redwood (*Sequoia sempervirens* [D. Don] Endl.) and Monterey pine (*Pinus radiata* D. Don) react much like the Tropical Zone plants (Table 7–1).

At the close of the light period more than 70 per cent of the phytochrome pigment is in the far-red–absorbing form. During the following dark period the pigment slowly drifts back into the red-absorbing form, and, if the dark period is adequately long, less than 10 per cent remains in the far-red–absorbing form (Table 7–2).

TABLE 7–2

EFFECT OF VARIOUS KINDS OF LIGHT ON THE PER CENT OF THE PIGMENT IN THE FAR-RED-ABSORBING FORM.*

Light Condition	Pigment in Far-Red-Absorbing Form (Per Cent)
Fluorescent	> 90
Incandescent or sunlight	> 70
Incandescent plus red and blue cellophane.......	< 10
Darkness.....................................	< 10

*Data from spectrophotometric measurements of pigment extract communicated by S. B. Hendricks.

If the pigment remains predominantly in the red-absorbing form for an appreciable time during each dark period, woody plants stop growth and become dormant, because the amount of the active form of the pigment, the far-red–absorbing form, is inadequate.

Effect of Long Days

Many kinds of woody plants can be kept in a state of continuous growth if the days are long enough (Tables 7–1 and 7–3). Long-day effects can be obtained by supplementing natural light with low-intensity artificial light or by interrupting a long dark period with low-intensity artificial light. The growth of woody plants that receive the dark-period interruption is usually equivalent to that obtained from a continuous daily period of light in excess of 16 hours (Table 7–3). The minimum duration and intensity of the dark-period interruption have not been determined for many woody plants, although effective interruptions were reported for several species (Zahner, 1955; Wareing, 1956; Vaartaja, 1959). Figure 7–3 shows the effect of a 1-hour interruption with 40 foot-candles near the middle of a 12-hour dark period on the growth of Douglas-fir (*Pseudotsuga menziesii* [*Mirb.*] Franco).

TABLE 7–3

EFFECT OF PHOTOPERIOD ON GROWTH OF DOUGLAS-FIR.

| Photo-period (Hours) | Length | | | Branches (Number) | Buds (Number) | Fresh Weight (Grams) |
	Main Axis (Centimeters)	Branches (Centimeters)	Total Growth (Centimeters)			
10	8.4	0.7	9.2	1.9	1.2	–
12	9.4	2.8	12.2	3.2	1.6	0.9
12 + 1*	41.7	176.0	217.7	23.0	2.1	15.0
14	19.7	9.6	29.3	3.8	2.5	5.3
16	38.9	91.2	140.4	16.0	1.7	19.3
20	47.9	227.1	274.9	29.5	2.0	17.9
24	52.9	190.3	243.2	24.2	2.7	23.2
LSD$_{05}$ †	7.7	77.0	81.5	8.3	0.8	10.4

*A 1-hour interruption near the middle of the dark period, using an illuminance of 40 foot candles from incandescent-filament lamps.
†Least significant difference—5% level.

When the dark periods are short, the pigment does not remain in the red-absorbing form, because, as soon as the light period begins, the pigment is driven into the far-red–absorbing form. Thus, the pigment is predominantly in the far-red–absorbing form for an appreciable time and the plants continue to grow. Interrupting a long dark period with a brief exposure to light drives the pigment back to where 90 per cent of it is in the far-red–absorbing form (Table 7–2), thus having the same effect as a short dark period.

Catalpa and Acer rubrum require photoperiods of 16 hours or more for continuous growth. Other species may require longer photoperiods, and still others form terminal buds even on continuous light. In plants such as pine and oak, terminal buds form and undergo a period of quiescence during which the buds enlarge. Then the buds break and produce a new flush of growth. Another terminal bud is set and the process is repeated. Pines apparently continue to flush in this way as long as they remain on long photoperiods. Oaks, however, after several flushes, finally set a more permanent terminal bud that does not break under long-day conditions. *Quercus rubra* L. produced about six flushes before such a permanent bud was formed.

Douglas-fir and spruce flush in much the same manner as the pines except that, when the days are as long as 20 hours or more, the formation of buds is so infrequent as to make the growth ap-

FIG. 7–3. Growth of Douglas-fir (*Pseudotsuga menziesii* [Mirb.] Franco) after 12 months on photoperiods of 12 hrs., 12 hrs. plus a 1-hr. interruption near the middle of the dark period, and 20 hrs., left to right.

pear continuous. For example, Douglas-fir on 20-hour photoperiods grew for about 1 year and produced a main axis more than 1 m. long before setting the first bud. This bud broke soon after it was formed and infrequent flushing occurred thereafter. Under certain daylength conditions the flushing habit may be changed or discontinued. For example, slash pine (*Pinus elliottii* Englem.) grew continuously without flushing on 14-hour photoperiods (Fig. 7–4).

In experiments that cover a complete year, maximum growth of most of the woody plants investigated was made under continuous light. These plants included several deciduous species, 11 species of pines, 2 of larch, 4 of spruce, 2 of *Sequoia*, Douglas-fir, and several tropical species. The only exceptions were cacao (Piringer and Downs, 1960) and *Sequoia sempervirens*, to which continuous light seemed to be detrimental.

Resumption of Growth

Catalpa made dormant by short photoperiods resumes growth if placed on long days soon after the loss of the terminal meristem. If the shift to long days is delayed, the new growth appears much later, and, finally, if the shift is delayed for several weeks, long days do not break the short-day–induced dormancy. During this short-day period the catalpas develop a chilling requirement that must be fulfilled before growth will resume.

Red oak and sweetgum set terminal buds even under continuous light. Defoliation causes the buds to resume growth and the flushing process starts again, especially if the plants receive long days. After several more flushes, however, the oak sets another permanent bud and defoliation a second time has no effect.

Asian white birch is an example of a species that resumes growth at any time it is returned to long-day conditions. Even after as much as a year on short photoperiods, Asian white birch resumes growth promptly under long-day conditions. Usually, however, this growth is from axillary buds, not from the terminal.

Flowering

Information on the effect of photoperiod on the flowering of woody plants is rare. The most quoted example is perhaps from early work of Garner and Allard (1923), in which they reported that *Hibiscus moscheutos* L. is a long-day plant for flowering. More detailed studies on *H. syriacus* L. showed that on short days *Hibiscus* stops elongation, becomes dormant, and, of course, does not develop flowers. On long photoperiods it continues to grow and finally produces flowers. However, flowers can be produced at a lower node by manipulating the photoperiods. The plants are grown on long days until they produce about 15 nodes; then they

FIG. 7–4 (left). Growth of slash pine (*Pinus elliottii* Engelm.) after 15 months on photoperiods of 12, 14, and 16 hrs., left to right.

FIG. 7–5 (right). Growth of slash pine (*Pinus elliottii* Engelm.) after 15 months on photoperiods of 12 hrs., 16 hrs. with fluorescent supplemental light, and 16 hrs. with incandescent supplemental light, left to right.

are placed on short days until growth stops. As soon as growth stops the plants are returned to long days and, upon resumption of growth, flowering occurs.

Flowering of *Paulownia tomentosa* (Thunb.) Sieb. and Zucc. also was induced by the same methods. On short days growth stops and does not resume, whereas on long days growth continues. No flowering occurs under either condition. However, if the plants from the long-day treatment are placed on short days until growth stops and then returned to long days, growth resumes and is often accompanied by flowering.

Germination

Some kinds of light-sensitive seeds, such as those of Grand Rapids lettuce and *Lepidium virginicum* L., require only a single brief exposure to light to induce maximum germination. Germination of seeds of other species such as those of *Paulownia tomentosa* seems to require long periods of light (Toole *et al.*, 1958). Seeds of *Paulownia* germinated after about 48 hours of light. However, continuous light during this 48-hour period was not necessary for germination. For example, a 1-hour irradiation at the beginning, the middle, and the end of the 48-hour period resulted in 87 per cent germination, and continuous light throughout the 48 hours resulted in 85 per cent germination. Other light conditions during this 48-hour period did not improve the germination. *Paulownia* seeds seem to have a time-measuring device that apparently results from the promotive effect of the irradiation being slowly lost during the dark period following the irradiation as the pigment slowly drifts from the far-red–to the red-absorbing form. Thus, after about 24 hours of darkness another promotive boost must be given.

Light Quality

The extension of a short day of natural light may be conveniently done with either incandescent or fluorescent lamps. Usually either kind of lamp is effective in maintaining growth, but plants receiving their supplemental light from the incandescent lamps become appreciably taller and weigh more than ones receiving the fluorescent supplemental light (Fig. 7–5). This increased height of deciduous species is often a result of longer internodes, but coniferous species receiving the incandescent light produce both a greater number of nodes and longer internodes.

The difference in effectiveness of the two light sources is a result of the different quality of the light emitted by the lamps. Thus catalpa, pines, and other woody plants respond differently to supplemental light from incandescent or fluorescent lamps, because of the different amounts of red and far-red radiation emitted by the two kinds of lamps. A predominance of red (from fluorescent lamps) shifts the pigment predominantly into the far-red–absorbing form and inhibits internode elongation. A predominance of far red (from incandescent lamps) leaves more of the pigment in the red-absorbing form and promotes internode elongation (Table 7–1).

Photoperiod-Temperature Interaction

In studies of photocontrol of plant growth the temperature factor is of special interest when it interacts with the photoreaction. Preliminary experiments with woody plants indicate that temperature and light operate independently. However, low night temperatures may prevent the long-day effect from being exhibited. For example, catalpa plants on 16-hour days grow larger with 80° F. nights than they do with 60° ones. On 8-hour photoperiods catalpas stop growth sooner with 60° than with 80° nights. With 40° nights growth is equally slow on both 8- and 16-hour photoperiods. Loblolly pine (*Pinus taeda* L.), on the other hand, continues to grow with long days and 40° nights but stops growth on 8-hour days and 40° nights. With 80° or 60° nights loblolly pines act like catalpas.

Detection and Extraction of Pigment

The red–far red reversibility was described by Borthwick *et al.* (1952). Using this reversibility as an assay, attempts were made to detect the pigment in vivo by physical means. Ordinary spectrophotometers, however, lacked the necessary sensitivity, so physical detection of the pigment was not possible.

About a year ago agricultural engineers of the Agricultural Marketing Service, U.S. Department of Agriculture, perfected a double-beam, bichromatic spectrophotometer for detecting ripeness of various fruits and discoloration of potatoes. This instrument was used to demonstrate the pigment physically. (Butler *et al.*, 1959) (Fig. 7–6). The low concentration, the red–far red reversibility, and the wavelength maxima confirm that the pigment detected

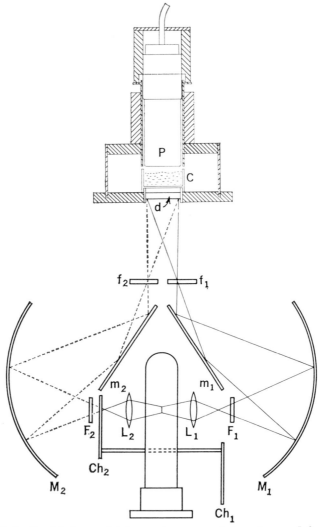

FIG. 7–6. Double-beam, bichromatic spectrophotometer used for assay of the reversible pigment *in vivo* or in solution. Ch_1, Ch_2 chopper blades; F_1, F_2 wedge interference filters; f_1, f_2 auxiliary filters to improve spectral purity; C sample holder; P end-window photomultiplier tube; and d diffusing disc. From Butler *et al.* (1959).

by the spectrophotometer is the same as the pigment responsible for the numerous photoresponses of plants.

After the pigment was detected in many kinds of plant tissue including catalpa seedlings, extraction procedures were begun. Six-day-old, dark-grown corn seedlings were frozen, harvested, and extracted with an aqueous alkaline buffer solution. The pigment was precipitated at 33 per cent saturation of ammonium sulfate for about a sixfold purification. An additional twofold purification was obtained by reprecipitation with ammonium sulfate at low protein concentration.

The pigment is precipitated by protein precipitants and it is heat-labile and non-dialysable. Thus, the pigment probably is a protein, but no information is available at this time on its probable structure.

Conclusion

Studies of the photoperiodic mechanism are by no means completed. Continuation of these studies will add to our understanding of how light regulates growth and lead to a better understanding of dormancy and tree physiology in general. Results of these studies can already be put to use as a tool for investigations of other problems involving mineral uptake, nutrition, pathology, and breeding.

LITERATURE CITED

BORTHWICK, H. A., S. B. HENDRICKS, and M. W. PARKER. 1951. Action spectrum for inhibition of stem growth in dark-grown seedlings of albino and nonalbino barley. Bot. Gaz. 113: 95–105.

BORTHWICK, H. A., S. B. HENDRICKS, M. W. PARKER, E. H. TOOLE, and V. K. TOOLE. 1952. A reversible photoreaction controlling seed germination. Proc. Nat. Acad. Sci. 38: 662–666.

BUTLER, W. L., K. H. NORRIS, H. W. SIEGELMAN, and S. B. HENDRICKS. 1959. Detection, assay and preliminary purification of the pigment controlling photoresponsive development of plants. Proc. Nat. Acad. Sci. 45: 1703–1708.

DOWNS, R. J. 1956. Photoreversibility of flower initiation. Plant Physiol. 31: 279–284.

DOWNS, R. J., and H. A. BORTHWICK. 1956a. Effect of photoperiod upon the vegetative growth of Weigela florida var. variegata. Proc. Amer. Soc. Hort. Sci. 68: 518–521.

———— and ————. 1956b. Effects of photoperiod on the growth of trees. Bot. Gaz. 117: 310–326.

DOWNS, R. J., H. A. BORTHWICK, and A. A. PIRINGER. 1958. Comparison of incandescent and fluorescent lamps for lengthening photoperiods. Proc. Amer. Soc. Hort. Sci. 71: 568–578.

DOWNS, R. J., S. B. HENDRICKS, and H. A. BORTHWICK. 1957. Photoreversible control of elongation of pinto beans and other plants under normal conditions of growth. Bot. Gaz. 118: 199–208.

DOWNS, R. J., and A. A. PIRINGER. 1958. Effects of photoperiod and kind of supplemental light on vegetative growth of pines. Forest Sci. 4: 185–195.

GARNER, W. W., and H. A. ALLARD. 1923. Further studies in photoperiodism: The response of the plant to relative lengths of day and night. Jour. Agr. Res. 23: 871–920.

NITSCH, J. P. 1957a. Growth responses of woody plants to photoperiodic stimuli. Proc. Amer. Soc. Hort. Sci. 70: 512–525.

————. 1957b. Photoperiodism in woody plants. Proc. Amer. Soc. Hort. Sci. 70: 526–544.

OLSON, J. S., F. W. STEARNS, and H. NIENSTAEDT. 1959. Eastern hemlock seeds and seedlings. Conn. Agr. Expt. Sta. Bull. 620.

PAULEY, S. S., and T. O. PERRY. 1954. Ecotypic variations of the photoperiodic response in *Populus.* Jour. Arnold Arboretum 35: 167–188.

PIRINGER, A. A., and H. A. BORTHWICK. 1955. Photoperiodic responses of coffee. Turrialba 5: 72–77.

PIRINGER, A. A. and R. J. DOWNS. 1960. Effects of photoperiod and kind of supplemental light on the growth of *Theobroma cacao.* Proc. 8th Inter-Amer. Cacao Conf. (in press).

PIRINGER, A. A., R. J. DOWNS, and H. A. BORTHWICK. 1958. Effects of photoperiod on *Rauvolfia.* Amer. Jour. Bot. 45: 323–326.

PIRINGER, A. A., and P. H. HEINZE. 1954. Effect of light on the formation of a pigment in the tomato fruit cuticle. Plant Physical. 29: 467–472.

SIEGELMAN, H. W., and S. B. HENDRICKS. 1957. Photocontrol of anthocyanin formation in turnip and red cabbage seedlings. Plant Physiol. 32: 393–398.

TOOLE, E. H., V. K. TOOLE, H. A. BORTHWICK, S. B. HENDRICKS, and R. J. DOWNS. 1958. Action of light on germination of seeds of *Paulownia tomentosa.* Plant Physiol. Sup. 33: xxiii.

VAARTAJA, O. 1954. Photoperiodic ecotypes of trees. Can. Jour. Bot. 32: 392–399.

————. 1959. Evidence of photoperiodic ecotypes in trees. Ecol. Monog. 29: 91–111.

WAREING, P. F. 1956. Photoperiodism in woody plants. Ann. Rev. Plant Physiol. 7: 191–214.

ZAHNER, R. 1955. Effect of interrupted dark period on height growth of two tree species. Forest Sci. 1: 193–195.

8

Photosynthesis, Climate, and Tree Growth

THEODORE T. KOZLOWSKI

Successful growth of trees results from internal correlations involving carbohydrates, hormones, water, and minerals. Hormones and water are discussed in other papers of this volume. This paper emphasizes the importance of carbohydrates to tree growth.

It is well known that carbohydrates comprise the major portion of the bulk of woody plants. Since the raw materials and energy required for wood formation ultimately are derived from reduction of carbon dioxide, photosynthesis is considered the major physiological process in tree growth. The amount of growth depends on the relative rates of photosynthesis and use of food. Thus, development of a tree involves important regulatory mechanisms of food conversion in addition to food synthesis.

The food economy of a tree might be considered in terms of a budget consisting of "income," or food manufactured in photosynthesis; "expenditures," or food used in assimilation and respiration; and a "balance," or food accumulated and used as a metabolic substrate at a later date (Kramer and Kozlowski, 1960). Since trees shed leaves, roots, branches, fruits, and other parts, the dry weight of an old tree represents only a fraction of the total photosynthate which it produced during its lifetime. Polster (1950) has estimated that 25 to 45 per cent of the carbohydrate produced in photosynthesis goes into the production of usable wood.

A large part of the total photosynthate is consumed in respiration, but the amount varies with species and age of trees. Heinicke and Childers (1937) estimated that respiration used up about a third of the carbohydrate produced by an 8-year-old apple tree. Respiration in forest trees has been estimated to consume up to half the carbohydrate manufactured in photosynthesis (Möller *et al.*, 1954; Pisek and Tranquillini, 1954). Möller *et al.* concluded that 40 per cent of the total photosynthate was used in respiration by 25-year-old beech trees but the amount increased to 50 per cent in 85-year-old trees. This apparently occurred because the ratio of respiring surface to leaf area increased with age.

Height Growth

Both stored and currently produced carbohydrates are utilized in producing new tissues, but the amounts of each vary with the type of tissues produced. There is considerable evidence that height growth of many trees is made primarily at the expense of stored carbohydrates rather than products of current photosynthesis (Kozlowski, 1958). In many species, height growth starts early in the season, often before the frost-free season begins, and much or all of it is completed before the leaves are fully grown and before the tree has developed an effective photosynthetic mechanism (Kramer, 1943). In Temperate Zone deciduous species, carbohydrate reserves reach a maximum in the autumn, decrease slightly in late winter, and decrease very rapidly with spring growth. In the south and in the tropics carbohydrate reserves decrease with each flush of growth (Kramer and Kozlowski, 1960).

In Connecticut, maples, red oak, white ash, beech, and white, red, Scots and jack pines completed 90 per cent of their height growth in approximately 30 days. Growth of these species was completed before the end of June (Kienholz, 1941). Other species including gray and white birch and aspen completed 90 per cent of their seasonal height growth in about 60 days. An unusually short growing season was reported by Johnston (1941), who found three species of oak in Missouri to complete practically all their height growth in only 19 days. Several other investigators have reported that the season for height growth is relatively short and occupies only the early part of the frost-free season (Baldwin, 1931; Cook, 1941; Kramer, 1943; Kozlowski, 1955; Kozlowski and Ward, 1957a, 1957b; Husch, 1959). Nevertheless, growth patterns vary considerably with species and those with unusually long growing seasons may use current photosynthate for at least the latter part of their height growth. It should also be remembered that the length of the growing season of different trees of the same species varies with vigor of the individual tree and it varies with tree age. Merrill and Kilby (1952) found that reduced competition increased the length of the growing season. Some variations in the lengths of growing seasons of nursery-grown gymnosperms and angiosperms are given in Table 8–1.

In England, Rutter (1957) showed that shoot extension of 2- to 5-year-old *Pinus sylvestris* seedlings was virtually completed by mid-June. By May 26 about half the annual shoot growth was completed, but total dry weight of the plants decreased up to this date. During the period of bud expansion, when photosynthesis was only

TABLE 8–1

HEIGHT-GROWTH DATA FOR NURSERY-GROWN SEEDLINGS DURING THE GROWING SEASON OF 1954 IN CENTRAL MASSACHUSETTS. (FROM KOZLOWSKI AND WARD, 1957A AND 1957B.)

Species	Approximate Date Growth Started	Days to Complete 90 Per Cent of Growth
GYMNOSPERMS		
Picea abies	April 15	57
P. glauca	April 20	99
Pinus resinosa	April 20	103
Abies balsamea	April 15	82
Tsuga canadensis	April 15	93
ANGIOSPERMS		
Acer saccharum	May 1	75
A. saccharinum...............	April 24	80
Castanea mollissimma..........	April 24	91
Gymnocladus dioicus..........	April 19	36
Sorbus americana	April 19	39
Betula papyrifera.............	April 19	98
Hamamelis virginiana	April 24	84
Cornus florida	April 24	95
Oxydendrum arboreum.........	April 24	89
Aesculus hippocastanum........	April 19	91

sufficient to balance respiration, the old needles showed a significant decrease in dry weight which approximately equaled the gain in weight of the elongating shoots. This suggested that height growth was made at the expense of carbohydrates stored in the old needles but reserve carbohydrates in the twigs probably were important also. Recently Newirth (1959) found that at the beginning of shoot growth of young *Picea abies, Pseudotsuga taxifolia,* and *Pinus sylvestris* seedlings respiration exceeded photosynthesis, so the carbon dioxide balance was negative, further stressing the importance of stored carbohydrates for shoot elongation. Newirth concluded that a full complement of the old needles was necessary for normal flushing. If the old needles were removed, growth of the young shoots was suppressed. Apparently this is due to a considerable extent to the use of reserves in the old needles (Rutter, 1957).

The expanding buds and growing shoots are centers of intense respiration and consume considerable carbohydrate reserve at the time of year when carbohydrate production is negligible in hardwoods and very low in conifers. As may be seen in Fig. 8–1, there is a large increase in respiration of buds with loss of dormancy (Kozlowski and Gentile, 1958). According to Clark (1956), the new needles of balsam fir release carbon dioxide in respiration in greater quantity than they utilize it in photosynthesis early in the season (Fig. 8–2). Thus shoot growth of conifers must depend on food reserves in stem tissues and old needles, carbohydrates currently produced by old needles, or all of these sources. Late in the summer the new needles produce more carbohydrates than old needles, but by that time height growth is completed.

Linzon (1958) has shown that early removal of the new foliage of white pine saplings decreased height growth during the same year. Linzon used only two test trees per treatment. The test trees were 5 feet high and the control trees more than 7.5 feet high. Furthermore, injury to the newly developing shoots may have increased respiration. However, he did find large differences in height growth of test and control trees. Since carbohydrates from the new foliage probably did not contribute to early height growth, possibly the latter part of height growth of white pine utilized currently produced carbohydrates. In addition, the new leaves were undoubtedly an important auxin source. Thus the possibility of conifers utilizing first the terminal bud as an auxin source and later the new leaves as an auxin source while carbohydrates are translocated into the developing shoot from old leaves and stem tissues should be examined further.

Some species with unusually long growing seasons probably begin height growth with reserve carbohydrates but later utilize current photosynthate for shoot elongation. In contrast to northern pines, southern pines such as loblolly, slash, and shortleaf make measurable growth in March and then distribute most of their height growth over a 5-month period. According to Kramer (1943) these three species made 15–20 per cent of the seasonal height growth in every month from April to August. McGregor (1958) has shown that a significant excess of photosynthesis over respiration for loblolly pine does not occur until April and it is low during that month. The excess of photosynthesis over respiration then

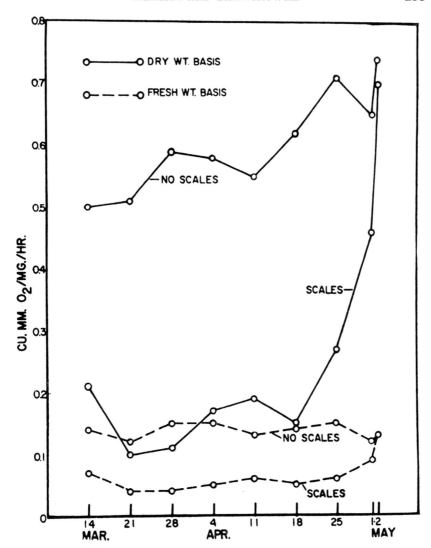

FIG. 8–1. Change in respiration rates of buds of eastern white pine from several weeks before until just after bud break. Respiration rates are given for intact buds and for buds which had bud scales removed. After Kozlowski and Gentile (1958).

accelerates rapidly and reaches high levels during July, August, September, and October. Loblolly pine, with its long growing season, undoubtedly uses current photosynthesis for much of its height growth (Table 8–2).

It has been demonstrated in several conifers that the formation of a terminal shoot is a process which requires 2 years. This two-

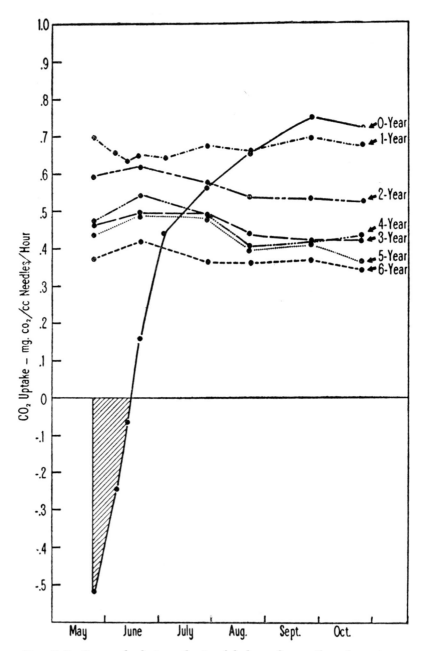

Fig. 8–2. Seasonal photosynthesis of balsam fir needles of varying age. After Clark (1956).

stage process is affected by environmental conditions of both years, but in many areas those of the first year are of paramount importance in determining the amount of seasonal height growth. In the first stage, which is differentiative, the bud which contains primordia of the next year's growth is formed. Sacher (1954) emphasized that the winter buds of pines are compound structures with unextended internodes that contain all the primordia of the following

TABLE 8–2

SEASONAL CHANGES IN RATES OF PHOTOSYNTHESIS AND RESPIRATION OF LOBLOLLY PINE AND WHITE PINE. THE LOBLOLLY PINE SEEDLINGS WERE IN THEIR SECOND SEASON AND THE WHITE PINE SEEDLINGS IN THEIR FOURTH SEASON. (FROM MCGREGOR, 1958.)

Monthly Excess of Photosynthesis over Respiration in Grams of CO_2 per Plant

Month	Loblolly Pine	White Pine
January	−0.596	−0.356
February	−0.564	−0.514
March	0.525	0.366
April	1.679	1.757
May	8.837	8.011
June	14.282	12.170
July	24.920	15.419
August	32.249	17.179
September	34.604	20.224
October	31.527	11.614
November	19.755	5.147
December	7.443	0.976

season's growth. During the second year the parts already laid down in the bud expand into a terminal shoot. If the environment is unusually favorable during the year of bud formation, a large amount of shoot growth usually occurs the following year, unless very severe environmental stresses occur during the period of height growth. However, the distribution of seasonal growth is sensitive to large air temperature variations. Farnsworth (1955) showed that low temperatures in May inhibited height growth during that month and caused the bulk of leader growth to occur in the next month. The controlling effect of temperature on growth is shown by the fact that although more height growth usually occurs during the night than during the day, the reverse often is true on unusually cold nights. Furthermore, during a cold spring the inception of height growth often is delayed. After the cold spring of 1922, Sitka spruce began growth nearly a month later than in 1921 (Hiley and Cunliffe, 1923). These inhibiting effects of low temperature on growth are exerted at a time when food supplies are abundant.

A number of studies show that the total amount of seasonal height growth is correlated with the size of the terminal bud and is better related to environment of the previous season than to environment of the current season (Tolsky, 1913; Perry, 1921; Burger, 1926; Motley, 1949). For example, Motley (1949) found that in *Pinus resinosa* increases or decreases in shoot growth occurred in the growing season of the calendar year following that in which marked increases or decreases in May–November rainfall occurred. Rainfall slumps in May–November of 1940 and 1944 were followed by decreases in height growth in 1941 and 1945. Increases in rainfall during a particular year were reflected in increased growth the following year. The period of May–November, 1945, had an increase in rainfall of over 100 per cent over the previous year, and this was followed by more than a 100 per cent increase in shoot growth in 1946 over that of 1945. It should not be inferred from such observations that height growth is insensitive to moisture deficiency but, rather, that over large areas height growth occurs early in the frost-free season and often is completed before severe summer droughts occur. In dry areas or in local situations in which severe moisture stresses develop in the spring, height growth may be correlated with current-season rainfall.

Pearson (1918) emphasized that in northern Arizona western yellow pine made its height growth during the time of year when the least precipitation occurred. During this period the trees depended almost entirely on moisture stored in the soil during the preceding winter and spring. Normally most, and in some years all, of this moisture was stored during the winter months, December–March. If winter rain constituted the entire supply available, height growth of trees was small. However, if winter rains were supplemented by at least 2 inches of rain in April and May, height growth was stimulated. Pearson added that there probably were sites within the range of western yellow pine on which current rainfall did not influence height growth materially. Tryon *et al.* (1957) showed that height growth of yellow poplar on a well-drained hillside in West Virginia was related to May–June precipitation of the current year, although the relationship was poorer than for diameter growth. Thus it appears, as emphasized by Hustich (1948), that, in areas with abundant soil moisture in the spring, the amount of height growth of many species is largely controlled by weather of the previous growing season. In contrast, in areas with low total rainfall and severe soil moisture deficiency in the spring, height growth can be correlated with current-year rainfall.

Diameter Growth

In contrast to height growth, diameter growth depends primarily on current photosynthesis, although some reserve carbohydrates may be used for diameter growth very early in the season. Diameter growth of the lower stem usually starts later and lasts longer than height growth of the same tree. This relationship appears to be most pronounced in diffuse-porous trees. However, in ring-porous trees and conifers a cambial growth wave moves rather rapidly down the tree from the expanding buds. Reimer (1949) found that Norway and sugar maples completed height growth in May but diameter growth of the lower stem did not begin until well into June and then continued into August. According to Cockerham (1930), as long as 10 weeks may elapse between the beginning of xylem formation in the twigs and in the roots of trees in some species. Friesner (1942) and Wareing (1958) also reported differences in the time of beginning of radial growth in ring-porous and diffuse-porous species. In contrast, Young and Kramer (1952) found diameter growth of loblolly pine to begin at about the same time as height growth.

During the long period of diameter growth, trees are subjected to a variety of environmental stresses which height growth usually escapes by virtue of its relatively short duration. Diameter growth responds readily to fluctuations in environmental factors, especially soil moisture, light intensity, and temperature. Using a dendrograph, Fritts (1958) found rapid diameter responses of trees to the passage of a cold front. During the growing season there may be shifts from one controlling external factor to another. Fritts (1958) found that, while both temperature and soil moisture affected diameter growth of beech, temperature exerted a greater effect in the spring while soil moisture was more important in late summer when droughts occurred.

Diameter growth involves addition of xylem cells, but such actual growth often is masked by hydration changes. Tree trunks usually undergo a small, but measurable, amount of shrinkage in the afternoon, because of stem dehydration caused by excess of transpiration over water absorption. During the night the reverse is true and tree diameters increase as trees tend to fill up with water. There also may be seasonal shrinkage or swelling of stems which is traceable to hydration changes. Many small but rapid diameter changes are of this type and complicate the problem of determining the factors responsible for actual growth of tissues.

It is well known that both photosynthesis and diameter growth are checked by water deficiency. Stomates close earlier in the day for trees in dry soil than for those growing in well-watered soil (Kramer, 1944). During the growing season, soil moisture remains at critically low levels for extended periods (Kozlowski, 1958).

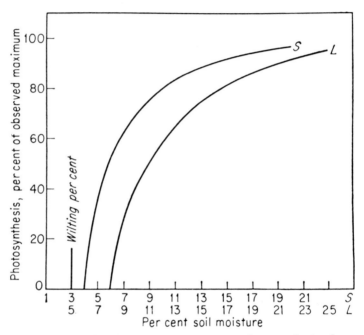

FIG. 8–3. Effect of soil moisture on apparent photosynthesis of sweetgum (S) and loblolly pine (L). (Used by permission from Kramer and Kozlowski, *Physiology of Trees*, 1960, McGraw-Hill Book Co., Inc. Sweetgum data are from Bormann [1953]; loblolly pine data from Kozlowski [1949].)

Fritts (1956), for example, found in Ohio that soil moisture actually stayed below the wilting percentage from mid-July to mid-August. As may be seen in Fig. 8–3, there is considerable evidence that photosynthesis decreases before wilting occurs (Loustalot, 1945; Kozlowski, 1949; Bormann, 1953; Negisi and Satoo, 1954). It has also been demonstrated that both growth and carbohydrate reserves of herbaceous plants are greater if soil moisture is maintained close to field capacity than if it is allowed to fluctuate between the field capacity and wilting percentage (Woodhams and

Kozlowski, 1954). Despite the decrease of photosynthesis in response to late summer droughts, the accompanying inhibition of growth often is not caused directly by lack of food, because trees usually have a substantial carbohydrate reserve when this occurs. Kramer (1958b) has pointed out that even under conditions of adequate light, water, and minerals loblolly pine seedlings do not grow continuously. Furthermore, trees show greatly increased growth with longer photoperiods even when the added light is of exceedingly low intensity. This suggests that food supply often is adequate but growth is checked because utilization of food is not always readily accomplished. It appears that both water deficiency and auxin deficiency often play decisive roles in growth inhibition when carbohydrate supplies are adequate.

In other circumstances there is evidence that carbohydrate deficiency may be involved in growth control. An important feature of the physiology of reproduction is a diversion of carbohydrates from vegetative tissues to reproductive organs. Heinicke (1937) estimated that in apple trees about 35 per cent of the total carbohydrate went into fruit production. This was approximately as much as went into the formation of structural tissues. Tingley (1936) observed that two rings formed in red Astrachan apple trees in years of heavy fruiting, probably because of carbohydrate deficiency, but only one in off years. Diversion of carbohydrates for fruiting is greater in orchard trees than in forest trees, but heavy seeding also seriously depletes carbohydrate reserves of forest trees. The most narrow annual rings of beech occurred during the years of heavy seed crops (Huber and von Jazewitsch, 1956). The view has long been held that lack of regular seed years in forest trees is traceable to the difficulty of building up carbohydrates to a necessary threshold for seed production except over a period of years. Gäumann (1935) stated that during heavy seed years the carbohydrate requirements of flowering and fruiting exceeded the needs of branches by 40 to 1. In Canada heavy flower production by balsam fir was always accompanied by a large reduction in quantity and size of current season foliage. Morris (1951) noted that heavy crops of seeds and flowers usually occurred in alternate years. In 1947, a heavy flowering year, the weight of new foliage of mature balsam fir trees was only 27 per cent of that produced in 1946, while for non-flowering trees it was 84 per cent. Such a decrease in leaf area may reduce carbohydrate production sufficiently to affect growth eventually. Mott et al. (1957) demonstrated a depressing effect of flower production on diameter growth of balsam fir. Bilan (1960) has shown that crown release caused increased growth and greatly increased seed production in loblolly pine. However, carbohydrate reserves in twigs were less in the released trees than in controls. This probably reflects a large diversion of carbohydrates into increased seed production.

Several studies suggest that sprouting from cut stumps is related to available carbohydrates. Seasonal cycles in carbohydrate reserves are correlated with sprouting vigor (Aldous, 1929). Stumps often sprout for several years after cutting, but they usually sprout best the first year after cutting. It has been suggested that as carbohydrate reserves are exhausted the ability to sprout declines. However, hormones probably also are involved in control of sprouting vigor (Wenger, 1953).

In a stratified forest understory, trees commonly are subjected to severe environmental stresses which may limit photosynthesis to only a fraction of its capacity. In a dense understory, intolerant species are maintained at a sustained low level of carbohydrate supply. Furthermore, trees are subject to catastrophes such as severe insect defoliation which may eliminate most or all of the photosynthetic mechanism for long periods of time. When repeated defoliation occurs, carbohydrate deficiency is translated into decreased growth. In well-exposed, vigorous trees the rate of photosynthesis fluctuates regularly with variations in light, temperature, soil moisture, carbon dioxide supply, and other factors (Kramer, 1958a), but, since such trees contain considerable carbohydrate reserves, growth inhibition, when it occurs rapidly, is often caused by a deficiency of something other than food. Since growth is physiologically ordered in the individual tree, available carbohydrates are more crucial for growth in some trees than in others.

Severe pruning removes part of the photosynthetic mechanism and eventually influences available carbohydrate supply. Pruning also removes auxin-supplying tissues. Removal of lower branches has little effect on growth, because such branches produce little auxin and little carbohydrate. Furthermore, lower branches have high respiration rates because of their large amount of exposed branch surface relative to their small leaf area. This suggests a certain degree of correlation between auxin supply and carbohydrate supply, both of which are required for growth. Furthermore, as pointed out by Larson (1956), low levels of photosynthesis may decrease auxin availability in growing tree stems. There is considerable evidence that translocatable carbohydrates are required for downward movement of growth hormones. There also is a relation between moisture stress and auxin deficiency, with less auxin available for growth during droughts. This is discussed further by Larson in this volume.

Root Growth

Forest trees vary greatly in their capacity for root growth (Kozlowski and Scholtes, 1948). Since root growth depends on carbohydrates from the crown, reductions in photosynthesis often reduce growth of roots. However, there are wide variations among species in speed of root-growth response to environmental stresses. As may be seen in Table 8–3, shading reduced growth of both oak and pine seedlings but it reduced the rate of root growth of pine seedlings more than that of the oak seedlings.

TABLE 8–3

EFFECT OF SHADING ON ROOT AND SHOOT DEVELOPMENT OF LOBLOLLY PINE AND OVERCUP OAK. THE TREES WERE GROWN FOR 2 YEARS IN SUN AND SHADE. (FROM KOZLOWSKI, 1949.)

	Height (Centimeters)	O.D. Weight Roots	O.D. Weight Shoots	Root/Shoot Ratio
Loblolly Pine				
Sun	42	25.2	20.1	1.25
Shade..........	35	6.1	7.2	0.84
Overcup Oak				
Sun............	59	44.1	21.1	2.01
Shade..........	66	38.7	20.1	1.92

The nature of the response of root growth of trees to stored and currently produced carbohydrates appears to vary with species and with age. Richardson (1956) found that root growth of first year seedlings of *Acer saccharinum* was more sensitive to rates of current photosynthesis than was root growth of *Quercus borealis*. Any change in the environment of the shoot which changed the rate of photosynthesis was followed within 12 to 24 hours by a change in the rate of root growth of *Acer saccharinum* (Richardson, 1953a). However, when photosynthesis was curtailed for a period of several days the rate of root growth, which decreased rapidly at first, later gradually increased again. This suggested that root growth could change from a system which uses only currently produced carbohydrates to one which depends on reserve carbohydrates. It appeared that a hormonal stimulus was also necessary for root formation and elongation (Richardson, 1953b). By the end of the first year and during the second growing season root growth of *Acer saccharinum* seedlings was not sensitive to short time changes in photosynthesis but rather depended on the amount of reserve carbohydrates in the roots (Richardson, 1956). Richardson also reported differences in the rate of response of root growth of different species to rapid changes in photosynthesis. These observations re-emphasize the importance of photosynthesis which produces the carbohydrates that make up about three-fourths of the dry weight of a tree.

LITERATURE CITED

ALDOUS, A. E. 1929. The eradication of brush and weeds from pasture lands. Amer. Soc. Agron. Jour. 21: 660–666.

BALDWIN, H. I. 1931. The period of height growth in some northeastern conifers. Ecol. 12: 665–689.

BILAN, M. V. 1960. The stimulation of cone and seed production in pulpwood-size loblolly pine. Forest Sci. 6: 207–220.

BORMANN, F. H. 1953. Factors determining the role of loblolly pine and sweetgum in early old-field succession in the Piedmont of North Carolina. Ecol. Monog. 23: 339–358.

BURGER, H. 1926. Untersuchungen über das Hohenwachstum verschiedener Holzarten. Mitt. Schweiz. Centralanst. Versuchsw. 14: 1–158.

CLARK, J. 1956. Photosynthesis of white spruce and balsam fir. Can. Dept. Agr. Bimonthly Prog. Rpt. 12(5): 1–2.

COCKERHAM, G. 1930. Some observations on cambial activity and seasonal starch content in sycamore. Leeds Phil. and Lit. Soc. Proc. 2: 64–80.

COOK, B. B. 1941. The period of growth of some northeastern trees. Jour. Forestry 39: 957–959.

FARNSWORTH, C. E. 1955. Observations of stem elongation in certain trees in the western Adirondacks. Ecol. 36: 285–292.

FRIESNER, R. C. 1942. Dendrometer studies on five species of broadleaf trees in Indiana. Butler Univ. Bot. Studies 5: 160–172.

FRITTS, H. C. 1956. Radial growth of beech and soil moisture in a central Ohio forest during the growing season of 1952. Ohio Jour. Sci. 56: 17–28.

———. 1958. An analysis of radial growth of beech in a central Ohio forest during 1954–1955. Ecol. 39: 705–720.

GÄUMANN, E. 1935. Der Stoffhaushalt der Buche (*Fagus sylvatica* L.) in Laufe eines Jahres. Ber. Deut. Bot. Gesell. 53: 366–377.

HEINICKE, A. J. 1937. Some cultural conditions influencing the manufacture of carbohydrates by apple leaves. N. Y. Hort. Soc. Proc. 149–156.

HEINICKE, A. J., and N. F. CHILDERS. 1937. The daily rate of photosynthesis during the growing season of 1935, of a young apple tree of bearing age. Cornell Univ. Agr. Expt. Sta. Mem. 201.

HILEY, W. E., and N. CUNLIFFE. 1923. Further observations of the relation of the height growth of trees to meteorological conditions. Ann. Appl. Biol. 10: 442–452.

HUBER, B., and W. VON JAZEWITSCH. 1956. Tree-ring studies of the Forestry-Botany Institute of Tharandt and Munich. Tree-Ring Bull. 21(1–4): 28–30.

HUSCH, B. 1959. Height growth of white pine in relation to selected environmental factors on four sites in southeastern New Hampshire. N. H. Agr. Expt. Sta. Tech. Bull. 100.

HUSTICH, I. 1948. The Scotch pine in northernmost Finland and its dependence on the climate in the last decades. Acta Bot. Fenn. 42: 4–75.

JOHNSTON, J. P. 1941. Height growth periods of oak and pine reproduction in the Missouri Ozarks. Jour. Forestry 39: 67–68.

KIENHOLZ, R. 1941. Seasonal course of height growth in some hardwoods in Connecticut. Ecol. 22: 249–258.

KOZLOWSKI, T. T. 1949. Light and water in relation to growth and competition of Piedmont forest tree species. Ecol. Monog. 19: 207–231.

———. 1955. Tree growth, action and interaction of soil and other factors. Jour. Forestry 53: 508–512.

———. 1958. Water relations and growth of trees. Jour. Forestry 56: 498–502.

KOZLOWSKI, T. T., and A. C. GENTILE. 1958. Respiration of white pine buds in relation to oxygen availability and moisture content. Forest Sci. 4: 147–152.

KOZLOWSKI, T. T., and W. SCHOLTES. 1948. Growth of roots and root hairs of pine and hardwood seedlings in the Piedmont. Jour. Forestry 46: 750–754.

KOZLOWSKI, T. T., and R. C. WARD. 1957a. Seasonal height growth of conifers. Forest Sci. 3: 61–66.

KOZLOWSKI, T. T., and R. C. WARD. 1957b. Seasonal height growth of deciduous trees. Forest Sci. 3: 168–174.

KRAMER, P. J. 1943. Amount and duration of growth of various species of tree seedlings. Plant Physiol. 18: 239–251.

———. 1944. Soil moisture in relation to plant growth. Bot. Rev. 10: 525–559.

———. 1958a. Photosynthesis of trees as affected by their environment. In: The Physiology of Forest Trees. K. V. Thimann (ed.). The Ronald Press Co., New York.

———. 1958b. Thermoperiodism in trees. In: The Physiology of Forest Trees. K. V. Thimann (ed.). The Ronald Press Co., New York.

KRAMER, P. J., and T. T. KOZLOWSKI. 1960. Physiology of trees. McGraw-Hill Book Co., Inc., New York.

LARSON, P. R. 1956. Discontinuous growth rings in suppressed slash pine. Trop. Woods 104: 80–89.

LINZON, S. N. 1958. The effect of artificial defoliation of various ages of leaves upon white pine growth. Forestry Chron. 34: 51–56.

LOUSTALOT, A. J. 1945. Influence of soil moisture conditions on apparent photosynthesis and transpiration of pecan leaves. Jour. Agr. Res. 71: 519–532.

McGREGOR, W. H. D. 1958. Seasonal changes in the rates of photosynthesis and respiration of loblolly pine and white pine. Ph.D. dissertation. Duke University, Durham, North Carolina.

MERRILL, S., and W. W. KILBY. 1952. Effect of cultivation, irrigation, fertilization and other cultural treatments on growth of newly planted tung trees. Proc. Amer. Soc. Hort. Sci. 59: 69–81.

MÖLLER, C. M., M. D. MÜLLER, and J. NIELSEN. 1954. Graphic presentation of dry matter production of beech. Det forstl. Forsøgsv. i Danmark 21: 327–335.

MORRIS, R. F. 1951. The effects of flowering on the foliage production and growth of balsam fir. Forestry Chron. 27: 40–57.

MOTLEY, J. A. 1949. Correlation of elongation in white and red pine with rainfall. Butler Univ. Bot. Studies 9: 1–8.

MOTT, D. G., L. D. NAIRN, and J. A. COOK. 1957. Radial growth in forest trees and effects of insect defoliation. Forest Sci. 3: 286–304.

NEGISI, K., and T. SATOO. 1954. The effect of drying of soil on apparent photosynthesis, transpiration, carbohydrate reserves and growth of seedlings of Akamatu (Pinus densiflora Sieb. et. Zucc.) Jour. Jap. Forestry Soc. 36: 66–71.

NEWIRTH, G. 1959. Der CO₂ Stoffwechsel einiger Koniferen Während der Knospenaustriebes. Biol. Centbl. 78: 559–584.

PEARSON, G. A. 1918. The relation between spring precipitation and height growth of western yellow pine saplings in Arizona. Jour. Forestry 16: 677–689.

PERRY, W. J. 1921. Some observations on the relation of soil moisture to height growth in yellow pine seedlings. Jour. Forestry 19: 752–753.

PISEK, A., and W. TRANQUILLINI. 1954. Assimilation und Kohlenstoffhaushalt in der Krone von Fichten (Picea excelsa Link) und Rotbuchenbäumen (Fagus silvatica L.) Flora 141: 237–270.

POLSTER, H. 1950. Die physiologische Grundlagen der Stofferzeugung im Walde: Untersuchungen über Assimilation, Respiration und Transpiration unserer Hauptholzarten. Bayerischer Landwirtschaftsverlag G. m. b. h. Munich.

REIMER, C. W. 1949. Growth correlations in five species of deciduous trees. Butler Univ. Bot. Studies 9: 43–59.

RICHARDSON, S. D. 1953a. Studies of root growth in *Acer saccharinum* L. I. The relation between root growth and photosynthesis. Proc. Kon. Akad. v. Wetensch. Amesterdam C56: 185–193.

———. 1953b. Studies of root growth in *Acer saccharinum* L. II. Factors affecting root growth when photosynthesis is curtailed. Proc. Kon. Ned. Akad. v. Wetensch. Amsterdam C56: 346–353.

———. 1956. Studies of root growth in *Acer saccharinum* L. III. The influence of seedling age on the short-term relation between photosynthesis and root growth. Proc. Kon. Ned. Akad. v. Wetensch. Amsterdam C59: 416–427.

RUTTER, A. J. 1957. Studies in the growth of young plants of *Pinus sylvestris* L. I. The annual cycle of assimilation and growth. Ann. Bot. 21: 399–425.

SACHER, J. A. 1954. Structure and seasonal activity of the shoot apices of *Pinus lambertiana* and *Pinus ponderosa*. Amer. Jour. Bot. 41: 749–759.

TINGLEY, M. A. 1936. Double growth rings in red astrakan. Proc. Amer. Soc. Hort. Sci. 34: 61.

TOLSKY, A. P. 1913. Weather and height growth. Transl. Forestry Expt. Sta. Petersburg 47. (Abs. Forestry Quart. 12: 277–278. 1914).

TRYON, E. H., J. O. CANTRELL, and K. L. CARVELL. 1957. Effect of precipitation and temperature on increment of yellow poplar. Forest Sci. 3: 32–44.

WAREING, P. F. 1958. The physiology of cambial activity. Jour. Inst. Wood Sci. 1: 34–42.

WENGER, K. F. 1953. The sprouting of sweet gum in relation to season of cutting and carbohydrate content. Plant Physiol. 28: 35–49.

WOODHAMS, D. H., and T. T. KOZLOWSKI. 1954. Effects of soil moisture stress on carbohydrate development and growth in plants. Amer. Jour. Bot. 41: 316–320.

YOUNG, H. E., and P. J. KRAMER. 1952. The effect of pruning on the height and diameter growth of loblolly pine. Jour. Forestry 50: 474–479.

9

Some Photosynthetic Problems of Tree Growth

JOHN P. DECKER

Kramer (1958) has reviewed recently the major factors that control photosynthetic rates of trees. The present paper will be largely speculative and will be concerned mainly with some unsolved problems of photosynthesis and tree growth as related to forestry.

A tree is composed mostly of cellulose, that is, of transformed sugar. The sugar was made photosynthetically from carbon dioxide and water by green leaves of the tree. Some sugar was respired (converted back to carbon dioxide) by living tissues and the rest became the body of the tree. Thus, dry weight of a tree is related directly to net photosynthesis (total photosynthesis minus respiration). In fact, that moment when a molecule of buoyant carbon dioxide gas joins a stable system, e.g., a carbohydrate molecule, is exactly *the* moment of dry-weight gain.

In general, net photosynthesis measures tree yield over a very short period, and it is useful for preliminary evaluation of major effects or for detection of brief or subtle effects. Direct measurement of carbon dioxide exchange by plants has been greatly facilitated by development of the infrared gas analyzer (Huber, 1950; Decker, 1954), and investigation of the following problems is now feasible:

1. *Does a given section of forest canopy have a fixed photosynthetic capacity?* Looking down onto a dense forest from above, one sees a solid mass of green—a forest canopy made up of tree crowns, each tightly surrounded by other crowns and each restricted as to its horizontal area exposed to the sun. As a forest grows taller, the canopy layer rises because new branches develop at tree tops and

165

old lower branches die and drop off, but the horizontal area of canopy exposed to the sun remains about constant.

Many foresters have based silvicultural practices on the assumption that photosynthetic capacity of a canopy is related directly to horizontal area exposed to the sun, and that it is nearly constant throughout the life of a stand (Baker, 1950). A question of interest to a physiologist is: Can the soundness of the working assumption be demonstrated experimentally?

The assumption has not been tested by direct experiment, and no satisfactory indirect test has been made. Many attempts have been made to relate weight or area of foliage to amount of annual increment (dry weight of new wood), but Möller (1947) concluded that no simple relationship exists. His conclusion does not mean that the assumed relationship between amounts of canopy and yield has failed; it simply confirms that total weight or area of foliage is not a reliable measure of photosynthetic capacity of a canopy. An explanation for the latter fact becomes clear upon considering that lower leaves are not all shaded equally, and thus a unit area of one leaf does not necessarily produce the same amount of sugar as a unit area of any other leaf. The work of Heinicke and Hoffman (1933) and Heinicke and Childers (1937) shows that photosynthetic behavior of an individual leaf cannot be extrapolated simply into behavior of a crown. They found that an apple leaf reached maximal photosynthesis at approximately 30 per cent of full sunlight, but an entire crown reached a maximum only at full sunlight, because upper leaves shaded lower ones. Kramer and Clark (1947) found a similar situation with pine needles vs. pine shoots. Several other ecological difficulties have arisen because of attempts to use unit leaf area or weight as a common denominator in photosynthetic studies (Decker, 1955).

Investigators concerned with transpiration of stands, e.g., Gatewood et al. (1950), are faced with a similar problem in trying to measure effective size of a canopy, and no satisfactory scaling system has been devised yet. Transpiration of tamarisk shrubs was shown to be linearly related to size and density of crowns measured as area of shadow cast on the ground (Decker et al., in press), and perhaps a similar scaling system can be applied to entire canopies, but this question remains to be investigated.

Much attention has been devoted to measurement of light interception by forest canopies (Baker, 1950). If light interception can be shown to be simply related to photosynthetic yield, it could be used as a convenient index for scaling the photosynthetically effective size of a canopy.

Direct measurement of carbon dioxide uptake by a small section of intact canopy is feasible with only minor modifications of known apparatus. A section of canopy could be enclosed in a frameless inflatable tent made of transparent film and similar to that developed for transpiration studies (Decker *et al.*, in press). The tent could be ventilated continuously (Heinicke and Childers, 1937; Thomas and Hill, 1937) or intermittently (Decker, 1954). Changes of carbon dioxide concentration could be measured rapidly and accurately with an infrared gas analyzer. Mean carbon dioxide concentration within the tent could be adjusted to remain within a natural range established beforehand by the sampling methods of Huber (1958) to avoid the main objection to enclosure, that of unnatural carbon dioxide concentration. Air velocity within the tent would need to be taken into account, because photosynthetic rate is linearly related to air velocity over a leaf (Decker, 1947). Light intensity and temperature could be held constant either physically or mathematically. Thus, useful measurements of net photosynthesis of intact canopy could be made, and the problem of hypothetical constancy could be studied directly.

2. *Stagnation of dense stands.* A forest stand that is excessively stocked may stagnate, that is, growth and yield may become negligible. According to Baker (1950) the classic example was a 70-year-old stand of lodgepole pine with 101,000 trees per acre, average diameter 0.3 inch, and average height 4.0 feet. Hawley (1937) attributes reduced growth to competition among individual trees. An imbalance of respiration with respect to photosynthesis probably is involved.

Respiration of a tree trunk is confined mostly to the cambium and outer annual rings and is thus directly related to trunk circumference and surface (Möller, 1947, 1954) which become large with dense stocking. For example, a 10-inch tree has a basal area of about 78 square inches and a basal circumference of about 31 inches, whereas one hundred 1-inch trees, with a combined basal area of 78 square inches, have a total basal circumference of about 310 inches. If the small trees and the large tree are of equal height and occupy equal canopy space, the ratio of trunk respiration to photosynthesis will be about 10 times greater for the small trees than for the large ones.

3. *Flat top of old pine trees.* A pine tree that has been growing rapidly is pointed at the top. The point becomes blunter as the tree matures, and old trees are usually distinctly flat topped (Baker, 1950). This change of shape with age may be related to photosynthetic-respiratory balance.

Assuming that a crown stops enlarging after it becomes completely surrounded by closed canopy, its photosynthetic capacity will remain essentially constant while the tree trunk grows taller and larger. As the amount of sugar-consuming tissue between crown and root tips continues to increase, the amount of sugar available to root tips will diminish. In accordance with well-known physiological principles as stated by Meyer and Anderson (1952), the following sequence of events could be expected: diminished sugar supply will result in decreased proliferation of roots and therefore in decreased absorption of soil moisture; decreased availability of water for the crown will result in decreased growth of the terminal leader; arrest of the leader will decrease apical dominance, that is, will partly release lateral branches from previous hormonal suppression; increased growth of laterals with respect to leader will eventually result in flat top.

4. *Tree breeding.* One goal of tree breeders is to produce progeny that yield more than their parents. Parental combinations that produce heterotic progeny are rare, and their discovery has been fortuitous. Searching for such parents might be facilitated by photosynthetic studies.

Yield is directly proportional to the excess of photosynthesis over respiration, and a heterotic individual must show an unusually large excess. Perhaps there are phenotypically normal individuals within a species that have exceptionally rapid photosynthesis combined with exceptionally rapid respiration to give normal net gain rates. Perhaps there are other phenotypically normal individuals that have slow photosynthesis combined with slow respiration. If such individuals can be found and used as parental stock, perhaps the cross would yield progeny in which rapid photosynthesis and slow respiration were recombined for high yield. An infrared photosynthetic apparatus could be used to search for such parental stock and it could be used for rapid screening of very young progeny.

The preceding discussion was concerned with respiration as it is known from measurements made in darkness. There is now abundant evidence of photorespiration—a large transitory acceleration of carbon dioxide production accompanying photosynthesis (Decker, 1959). Much of the photosynthetic work done by a leaf is apparently canceled by photorespiration. Perhaps heterosis is sometimes a result of unusually slow photorespiration combined with normal photosynthesis.

5. *Stimulation following thinning of a stand.* Möller (1954) stated that volume increment increases temporarily following a

heavy thinning. Is this stimulation the result of increased crown exposure and photosynthesis, or is some other mechanism involved?

6. *Pruning.* In early pruning of sawtimber to increase yield of high-grade lumber, which branches can be removed without serious reduction of photosynthetic output of the crown? Do heavily shaded lower branches become actually parasitic before they die?

Summary

Modern photosynthetic apparatus permits study of dry-weight increment rates of trees, branches, or leaves on a minute by minute basis. Such apparatus is a practical tool for investigating many forestry problems that involve questions about subtle or transient effects on increment rates.

LITERATURE CITED

BAKER, F. S. 1950. Principles of silviculture. McGraw-Hill Book Co., Inc., New York. 414 pp.

DECKER, J. P. 1947. The effect of air supply on apparent photosynthesis. Plant Physiol. 22: 561–571.

———. 1954. The effect of light intensity on photosynthetic rate in Scotch pine. Plant Physiol. 29: 305–306.

———. 1955. The uncommon denominator in photosynthesis as related to tolerance. Forest Sci. 1: 88–89.

———. 1959. Some effects of temperature and carbon dioxide concentration on photosynthesis of *Mimulus.* Plant Physiol. 34: 103–106.

DECKER, J. P., F. D. COLE, and W. G. GAYLOR. A preliminary comparison of evapotranspiration from natural stands of tamarisk and Bermuda grass. Rocky Mountain Forest Range Expt. Sta. Paper. In press.

GATEWOOD, J. S., T. W. ROBINSON, B. R. COLBY, J. D. HEM, and L. C. HALPENNY. 1950. Use of water by bottom-land vegetation in lower Safford Valley, Arizona. U.S. Geol. Survey Water-Supply Paper 1103. 210 pp.

HAWLEY, R. C. 1937. The practice of silviculture. John Wiley & Sons, Inc., New York. P. 161.

HEINICKE, A. J., and N. F. CHILDERS. 1937. The daily rate of photosynthesis, during the growing season of 1935, of a young apple tree of bearing age. Cornell Univ. Agr. Expt. Sta. Mem. 201. 52 pp.

HEINICKE, A. J., and M. B. HOFFMAN. 1933. The rate of photosynthesis of apple leaves under natural conditions. Cornell Univ. Agr. Expt. Sta. Bull. 577. 32 pp.

HUBER, B. 1950. Registrierung des CO_2-Gefälles und Berechnung des CO_2-Stromes über Pflanzengesellschaften mittels Ultrarot-Absorptionsschreiber. Ber. Deut. Bot. Gesell. 63: 53–63.

———. 1958. Recording gaseous exchange under field conditions. In: The Physiology of Forest Trees. K. V. THIMANN (ed.). The Ronald Press Co., New York. Pp. 187–195.

KRAMER, P. J. 1958. Photosynthesis of trees as affected by their environment. In: The Physiology of Forest Trees. K. V. THIMANN (ed.). The Ronald Press Co. Pp. 157–186.

KRAMER, P. J., and W. S. CLARK. 1947. A comparison of photosynthesis in individual pine needles and entire seedlings at various light intensities. Plant Physiol. 22: 51–57.

MEYER, B. S., and D. B. ANDERSON. 1952. Plant Physiol. D. Van Nostrand Co., Inc., New York.

MÖLLER, C. MAR. 1947. The effect of thinning, age, and site on foliage, increment, and loss of dry matter. Jour. Forestry 45: 393:404.

———. 1954. The influence of thinning on volume increment. N. Y. State Col. Forestry, Syracuse Univ., Tech. Bull. 76: 33–44.

THOMAS, M. D., and G. R. HILL. 1937. The continuous measurement of photosynthesis, respiration, and transpiration of alfalfa and wheat growing under field conditions. Plant Physiol. 12: 285–307.

10

The Role of Water in Tree Growth

PAUL J. KRAMER

Introduction

Successful growth of trees requires adequate water and mineral nutrients, enough oxygen in the soil for roots to function effectively, enough light for photosynthesis, and a favorable temperature. The purpose of this paper is to show why water is such an important factor for tree growth. It is a basic biological principle that the only way in which an environmental factor such as soil moisture can affect plant growth is by affecting the internal physiological and biochemical processes and conditions which control growth. Therefore, to understand how water supply affects growth it is necessary to consider the physiological and biochemical functions of water in plants.

GENERAL FUNCTIONS OF WATER. Water has four important kinds of functions in plants:

1. Water is the principal constituent of protoplasm, which consists of a protein framework to which a large volume of water is bound. Water comprises about 90 per cent of the fresh weight of growing root and stem tips and other plant parts, and even a tree trunk is more than half water. Most of this water occurs in the vacuoles of living cells, but a considerable fraction is bound to the hydrophilic components of the cell walls, some exists relatively free in the microcapillaries of the walls, and an appreciable amount occurs in the cavities of the xylem elements.

2. Water is a reagent in photosynthesis and in hydrolytic processes such as starch digestion.

3. Water is the solvent in which salts and gases enter the cells of plants, and all movement of solutes from cell to cell and from tissue to tissue within the plant occurs in water solution. Practically all of the chemical reactions which occur in plant cells occur in this water solution

171

4. Water is essential for the maintenance of the cell turgidity which is necessary for cell enlargement and the maintenance of the form and the position of leaves, new shoots, and other slightly lignified structures. Turgidity also is important in the opening of stomata and in movements of leaves and flower parts.

Effects of Water Deficits on Growth

It seems probable that every process occurring in trees is more or less affected by water deficits. Many of these effects have been discussed in other papers and the pertinent literature has been cited, hence only a few general papers will be mentioned here (Richards and Wadleigh, 1952; Kozlowski, 1958; Kramer, 1959; Kramer and Kozlowski, 1960).

Tree growth is reduced by water deficits indirectly through interference with physiological processes such as photosynthesis, nitrogen metabolism, salt absorption, and translocation, and directly by the effects of reduced cell turgor on cell enlargement and other processes more directly involved in growth. The direct and indirect effects overlap to such an extent that the separation attempted in the following sections is only approximate.

Effects of Water Deficits
on Physiological and Biochemical Processes

Photosynthesis is particularly vulnerable to reduction by water deficits, because dehydration of protoplasm reduces its photosynthetic capacity and because stomatal closure reduces the supply of carbon dioxide. On sunny days many trees show a midday reduction in photosynthesis, even when growing in moist soil, usually attributed to closure of stomates. The reduced leaf area often found on trees subjected to severe water deficits also reduces the food supply by diminishing the photosynthetic surface.

Schneider and Childers (1941) found that respiration often increased while photosynthesis decreased in apple trees growing in drying soil (Fig. 10–1). The combined effects of increased respiration and decreased photosynthesis undoubtedly greatly reduce the amount of food available for growth. The effects of water deficits on photosynthesis are discussed in more detail by Kozlowski in another paper of this volume.

The nature and course of various other biochemical processes likewise are affected by water deficits, although less is known about this in trees than in herbaceous plants. One of the best known effects of water deficit is hydrolysis of starch to sugar, which has been observed in apple (Magness *et al.*, 1933) and many other plants. Nitrogen metabolism also is materially affected by water deficits. Gates and Bonner (1959) found that breakdown of ribonucleic acid is hastened by leaf water deficits, and Kessler (1959) found an inverse relationship between water stress and nucleic acid content in sunflower. Gates (1955, 1957) concluded that even small

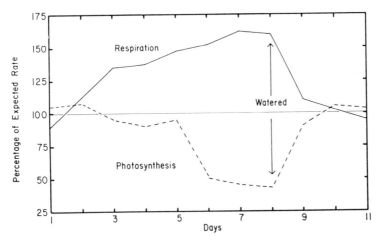

FIG. 10–1. The effects of decreasing soil moisture and increasing plant water deficit on photosynthesis and respiration of an apple tree. From Schneider and Childers (1941).

reductions in water content have significant effects on metabolism. Very moderate wilting of tomatoes caused reduced uptake of minerals and changes in leaves resembling those occurring during senescence. The premature senescence of leaves on trees subjected to drought is well known and doubtless results from disturbances in their metabolism.

Occasionally, moderate water deficits produce desirable changes in composition. For example, the rubber content of guayule plants is increased by a moderate water deficit (Wadleigh *et al.*, 1946) and the quality of apples and pears is said to be improved by water stress in the latter part of the growing season.

Presumably, most of the effects on biochemical processes are brought about by modifying enzyme activity, but little is known concerning this (Mothes, 1956). Protoplasmic properties such as permeability and viscosity also are modified by water deficits, but there is no general agreement concerning the nature or causes of these changes (Levitt, 1951, 1956). More research is needed on the effects of water stress on biochemical processes in trees.

The relations between water stress and disease are just beginning to be investigated. According to Bier (1959) development of willow bark canker is inhibited by water contents greater than 80 per cent of saturation.

DIRECT EFFECTS OF WATER DEFICITS ON GROWTH. Some of the effects of water deficits discussed in this section are direct effects while others are partly indirect effects.

The late D. T. MacDougall termed growth a constellation of activities, and it should be emphasized that it is not a single process, but the summation of a complex series of biochemical and physiological processes. In this discussion we shall concern ourselves chiefly with the processes occurring at the cellular level. In terms of cells, growth consists of cell division, cell enlargement, and cell differentiation. All of these processes are affected by water deficits and loss of turgor, but cell enlargement is affected most of all, because a certain amount of turgor is essential for cell enlargement (Heyn, 1940; Broyer, 1950; Cleland and Bonner, 1956).

Loomis (1934) and Thut and Loomis (1944) concluded that the supply of water to the growing region is the most important factor affecting the rate of growth of corn. Tree growth is equally sensitive to water deficits, and all phases of growth are reduced, including shoot and root elongation, diameter growth, and increase in size of fruits, as shown in Fig. 10–2.

Relatively small water deficits often produce significant reductions in size. Goode (1956) reported that maximum soil-moisture tensions of much less than one atmosphere reduce both vegetative and fruit growth of apple. Sands and Rutter (1959) found that a maximum soil-moisture tension of 1.5 atmospheres reduced the dry weight and stem elongation of potted Scots pine seedlings and a maximum tension of 0.5 atmosphere was sufficient to reduce leaf elongation. These effects can be attributed in part to reduced photosynthesis and mineral absorption as well as to reduced turgidity.

The diurnal and seasonal variations in diameter growth which result from internal water deficits are well known. Not only is the amount of growth reduced, but the quality usually is changed. Leaves are thicker, with additional layers of palisade cells, more supportive tissue around the vascular bundles, and vascular bundles closer together.

The effects of internal water deficits on wood structure are particularly important. Zahner, in a private communication, states that most investigators find that the large cells characteristic of spring wood are formed as long as moisture is readily available. When the

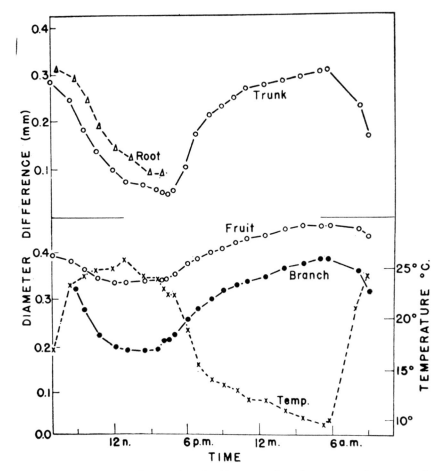

Fig. 10–2. Diurnal variations in diameter of various parts of an avocado tree. The observations were made in August on a tree growing in moist soil at Los Angeles, California. From Schroeder and Wieland (1956).

soil dries out until moisture becomes limiting the smaller cells characteristic of summer wood begin to be formed. In some of Zahner's experiments, loblolly pine trees growing in soil kept at field capacity formed spring wood from March to August, but summer wood was formed in May by trees growing in soil allowed to dry out early in the season. The amount of summer wood is dependent on water supply, growth ceasing earlier in dry summers than in summers when mid- and late-summer rainfall is abundant. In loblolly pine, once the formation of summer wood has begun, it cannot be reversed to the formation of spring wood by late-summer rains. It has been suggested that perhaps the thickness of the cell walls depends largely on the amount of photosynthate available, which in turn depends indirectly on the water supply and other environmental factors. Water deficits may also affect growth by affecting translocation of food and hormones.

Why Water Deficits Develop

It should be clear by now that the effects on tree growth which are associated with lack of rainfall and occurrence of droughts really result from the occurrence of water deficits in the tissues of trees. It therefore is necessary to consider the factors which control the occurrence of water deficits.

The water content or turgidity of a tree depends on the relative rates at which water is absorbed and lost by transpiration. Turgidity and the growth which it controls do not depend directly on either soil moisture or rainfall, but rather on the interaction of a complex of atmospheric, soil, and plant factors which modify the rates of absorption and transpiration.

The transpiration rate of well-watered plants is controlled by such plant factors as leaf area, leaf structure, and stomatal behavior, and by environmental factors such as solar radiation, temperature, humidity, and wind. The rate of water absorption depends on the rate of water loss, the extent and efficiency of root systems, and factors affecting the availability of soil moisture, such as soil-moisture tension and concentration of the soil solution. Water absorption also is affected by soil aeration and soil temperature.

Thus the water balance of trees and other plants is controlled by two different processes which in turn are at least partly controlled by different sets of factors. It therefore is not surprising that these two processes do not always keep in step. The rate of absorption always tends to lag somewhat behind the rate of transpiration (Fig. 10–3), because of the resistance to water movement through root tissues, and on a hot summer day water deficits develop even in plants growing in moist soil. These deficits, which are large enough to cause the often observed midday shrinkage of tree trunks, usually are eliminated by water absorption overnight. However,

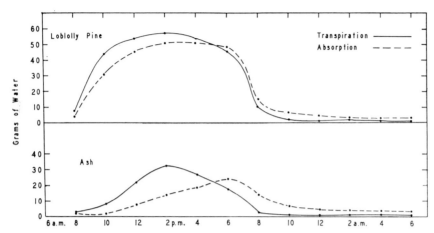

FIG. 10–3. The relationship between water absorption and water loss by transpiration of tree seedlings growing in pots of soil supplied with water by porous porcelain autoirrigators. From Kramer (1937).

as soil moisture is depleted, absorption becomes slower and the temporary daily deficits develop into a permanent deficit which completely stops growth, as shown in Fig. 10–4.

It should be clear that water deficits can be caused by either (1) excessive loss of water in transpiration; (2) slow absorption from dry, cold, or poorly aerated soil; or (3), perhaps most often, a combination of the two. Deficits caused by excessive transpiration alone are common, but usually shorter and less severe than those caused by inadequate absorption. However, periods of hot, windy weather can cause water deficits from excessive transpiration even in plants growing in moist soil. On the other hand, cool, showery, and humid weather sometimes reduces transpiration so much that plants growing in relatively dry soil are subjected to only small water deficits and show small reductions in growth.

The importance of transpiration in producing water deficits in plants sometimes is underestimated, although it is supported by numerous observations. The work of Loomis (1934) and Thut and Loomis (1944) on corn in Iowa indicated that water supply to the growing regions of plants is limited more often by excessive transpiration than by deficient soil moisture. Observations by Reed (1939) that southern pines make more height growth at night than during the day, and the frequently observed midday shrinkage of tree trunks both indicate that transpiration produces water deficits sufficient to reduce growth almost every sunny day. The importance of transpiration in producing water deficits also is shown in

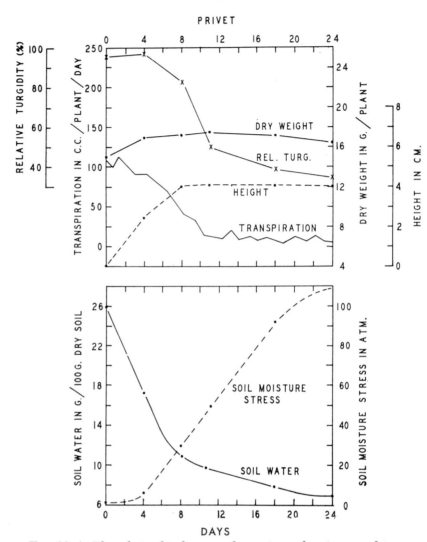

Fig. 10–4. The relationship between decreasing soil moisture and increasing soil moisture stress, and growth, transpiration, and relative turgidity of privet plants. From Slatyer (1957).

experiments of Schroeder and Wieland (1956), presented in Fig. 10–5. Avocado fruits usually shrink on sunny days, but this shrinkage was prevented on days when the trees were sprayed intermittently with water for an hour before noon.

It might be expected that where reduction in growth is observed for entire seasons this could be attributed to deficient soil moisture resulting from deficient rainfall, but there are exceptions to this

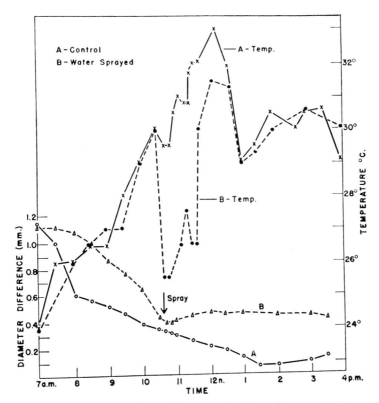

FIG. 10–5. The effect of sprinkling on the diurnal water deficit and the diameter growth of avocado fruits. Line A shows fruit diameter on an unsprayed tree, while line B indicates that spraying the tree for an hour prevented further shrinkage. From Schroeder and Wieland (1956).

generalization. For example, Coile (1936) found several instances where growth of southern pines and rainfall were not well correlated, and the temperature data suggest that this was because of variation in transpiration. Some examples for loblolly pine in southwestern Louisiana follow:

1927: Rainfall above average, temperature high, growth low
1928: Rainfall below average, temperature low, growth high
1931: Rainfall below average, temperature low, growth high
1932: Rainfall above average, temperature high, growth low

The chief effect of higher-than-average temperatures is to increase evaporation and transpiration and produce unusually severe water deficits in the trees, while lower-than-average temperatures reduce transpiration, compensating for less soil moisture. These and other similar data suggest that transpiration often has more effect than soil moisture on the internal water balance and hence on tree growth. The interrelationships between tree growth and various environmental factors such as temperature, soil moisture, and relative humidity have been described by Fritts (1958).

It also should be pointed out that excessive rainfall can reduce growth, because saturated soil decreases the absorption of both water and minerals. Trees on poorly drained sites may show less-than-average water content in wet years (Fraser and Dirks, 1959). Such trees might be expected to make less-than-average growth, also. These observations all emphasize the fact that tree growth is controlled directly by the internal water balance or degree of turgidity, which in turn is controlled by the relative rates of water absorption and water loss. Sometimes one and sometimes the other process dominates the water balance. As a result, tree growth is not always closely correlated with rainfall or with soil moisture. An understanding of these facts should help to explain the discrepancies between soil moisture and growth that sometimes trouble investigators in agronomy, horticulture, and irrigation research. This situation has been discussed in more detail by Hagan *et al.* (1959).

The importance of the water balance of plants ought to receive more consideration in connection with research on plant water relations than it usually is given. Measurements of soil-moisture content or soil-moisture tension are not adequate indicators of the moisture stress which exists in the plants under study. We need to make direct, quantitative measurements of plant water stress, either in terms of relative turgidity or preferably in terms of diffusion-pressure deficit (Slatyer, 1957, 1958). The latter is preferable because it expresses the water stress in plants in terms of its free energy deficit in units employed to express water stress in soil. The effect of decreasing soil moisture on the relative turgidity, diffusion-pressure deficit, and osmotic pressure of privet is shown in Fig. 10–4.

Summary

Water deficits affect tree growth by modifying the rates of various internal physiological processes and conditions which control growth. Growth is reduced indirectly by interference with various metabolic processes such as photosynthesis and nitrogen metabolism, and reduction in processes such as translocation and salt absorption. Growth is reduced directly because loss of turgor decreases cell enlargement. Water deficits not only reduce the amount of growth but also change the character of growth, as seen in the thicker leaves and earlier change from spring to summer wood in trees subjected to early summer droughts.

The internal water balance which controls growth is controlled in turn by the relative rates of water absorption and water loss. Sometimes one and sometimes the other process dominates the water balance. As a result tree growth is not always closely correlated with either rainfall or soil moisture, but sometimes with one and sometimes with the other.

The only reliable method of evaluating the water balance of a tree is to measure the internal water stress, preferably in terms of its diffusion-pressure deficit, although measurements of relative turgidity are useful. Such measurements ought to be made in connection with all research dealing with the effects of water on plant growth.

LITERATURE CITED

BIER, J. E. 1959. The relation of bark moisture to the development of canker diseases caused by native, facultative parasites. I. Cryptodiaporthe canker on willow. Can. Jour. Bot. 37: 229–238.

BROYER, T. C. 1950. On a theoretical interpretation of turgor pressure. Plant Physiol. 25: 135–139.

BURSTROM, H. 1956. Die Bedeutung des Wasserzustandes für das Wachstum. Handb. der Pflanzenphysiol. 3: 665–668.

CLELAND, R., and J. BONNER. 1956. The residual effect of auxin on the cell wall. Plant Physiol. 31(5): 350–354.

COILE, T. S. 1936. Effect of rainfall and temperature on the annual radial growth of pine in the southern United States. Ecol. Monog. 6: 533–562.

FRASER, D. A., and H. T. DIRKS. 1959. Internal water relations of yellow birch at Chalk River. Can. Jour. Bot. 37: 789–799.

FRITTS, H. C. 1958. An analysis of radial growth of beech in a central Ohio forest during 1954–1955. Ecol. 39: 705–720.

GATES, C. T. 1955. The response of the young tomato plant to a brief period of water shortage. I. The whole plant and its principal parts. Austral. Jour. Biol. Sci. 8: 196–214.

———. 1957. The response of the young tomato plant to a brief period of water shortage. III. Drifts in nitrogen and phosphorus. Austral. Jour. Biol. Sci. 10: 125–146.

GATES, C. T., and J. BONNER. 1959. IV. Effects of water stress on the ribonucleic acid metabolism of tomato leaves. Plant Physiol. 34: 49–55.

GOODE, J. E. 1956. Soil-moisture relationships in fruit plantations. Ann. Appl. Biol. 44: 525–530.

HAGAN, R. M., Y. VAADIA, and M. B. RUSSELL. 1959. Interpretation of plant responses to soil moisture regimes. Advances in Agron. 11: 77–98.

HEYN, A. N. J. 1940. The physiology of cell elongation. Bot. Rev. 6: 515–574.

KESSLER, B. 1959. Nucleic acids as factors in drought resistance of plants. Proc. 9th Internat. Bot. Cong. 2: 190.

KOZLOWSKI, T. T. 1958. Water relations and growth of trees. Jour. Forestry 56: 498–502.

KRAMER, P. J. 1937. The relation between rate of transpiration and rate of absorption of water in plants. Amer. Jour. Bot. 24: 10–15.

———. 1959. The role of water in the physiology of plants. Advances in Agron. 11: 51–70.

KRAMER, P. J., and T. T. KOZLOWSKI. 1960. Physiology of trees. McGraw-Hill Book Co., Inc., New York.

LEVITT, J. 1951. Frost, drought, and heat resistance. Ann. Rev. Plant Physiol. 2: 245–268.

———. 1956. The hardiness of plants. Academic Press, Inc., New York.

LOOMIS, W. E. 1934. Daily growth of maize. Amer. Jour. Bot. 21: 1–6.

MAGNESS, J. R., L. O. REGEIMBAL, and E. S. DEGMAN. 1933. Accumulation of carbohydrates in apple foliage, bark, and wood as influenced by moisture supply. Proc. Amer. Soc. Hort. Sci. 29: 246–252.

MOTHES, K. 1956. Der Einfluss des Wasserzustandes auf Fermentprozesse und Stoffumsatz. Encyclopedia Plant Physiol. 3: 656–664.

REED, J. F. 1939. Root and shoot growth of shortleaf and loblolly pines in relation to certain environmental conditions. Duke Univ. Forestry Bull. 4.

RICHARDS, L. A., and C. H. WADLEIGH. 1952. Soil water and plant growth. In: Soil Physical Conditions and Plant Growth. B. T. SHAW (ed.). Academic Press, Inc., New York. Pp. 73–251.

SANDS, K., and A. J. RUTTER. 1959. Studies in the growth of young plants of *Pinus sylvestris* L. II. The relation of growth to soil moisture tension. Ann. Bot. 23: 269–284.

SCHNEIDER, G. W., and N. F. CHILDERS. 1941. Influence of soil moisture on photosynthesis, respiration, and transpiration of apple leaves. Plant Physiol. 16: 565–583.

SCHROEDER, C. A., and P. A. WIELAND. 1956. Diurnal fluctuation in size in various parts of the avocado tree and fruit. Proc. Amer. Soc. Hort. Sci. 68: 253–258.

SLATYER, R. O. 1957. The influence of progressive increases in total soil moisture stress on transpiration, growth and internal water relationships of plants. Austral. Jour. Biol. Sci. 10: 320–336.

———. 1958. The measurement of diffusion pressure deficit in plants by a method of vapour equilibration. Austral. Jour. Biol. Sci. 11: 349–365.

THUT, H. F., and W. E. LOOMIS. 1944. Relation of light to growth of plants. Plant Physiol. 31: 117–130.

WADLEIGH, C. H., H. G. GAUCH, and O. C. MAGISTAD. 1946. Growth and rubber accumulation in guayule as conditioned by soil salinity and irrigation regime. U.S. Dept. Agr. Tech. Bull. 925.

11

Tree Growth in Relation to Soil Moisture

DONALD A. FRASER

Introduction

This is a sixth contribution to a series on ecological conditions as they affect tree growth at Chalk River, Ontario, Canada. The previous ones contained descriptions of the location, sites, and tree distribution in a hardwood stand under study (Fraser, 1954), as well as the influence of physical factors on radial increment (Fraser, 1956), the annual and seasonal march of soil moisture and soil temperature over a 7-year period (Fraser, 1957a, 1957b), and the progressive change in health of 241 yellow birch trees (*Betula lutea* Michx. f.) and their canopy over the period 1949–57 (Fraser, 1959). Since 1955, when an 8-acre plot was established in a conifer stand to ascertain factors influencing flowering in spruce (Fraser, 1958b), records similar to those taken in the hardwood stand have been collected. This paper discusses some relations between the seasonal water cycle and tree growth.

Sources of moisture to trees may be thought of in terms of precipitation that becomes primarily available through the roots when it permeates the soil (Briggs, 1897; Lebedoff, 1928; Kramer, 1944), and moisture directly available from the atmosphere in the form of fog or dew (Krečmer, 1951; Stone, 1957). Soil characteristics and topography influence the retention and lateral distribution of soil water, thus determining soil-moisture sites. Series of soil-moisture regimes were delimited by Bushnell (1942) and Hills (1945, 1953) in their evaluations of site, but little quantitative information on seasonal and annual variations of soil moisture was obtained.

Materials and Methods

The two 8-acre experimental plots at Chalk River (Fraser, 1954, 1958b), located on a loamy sand, were divided into soil-moisture

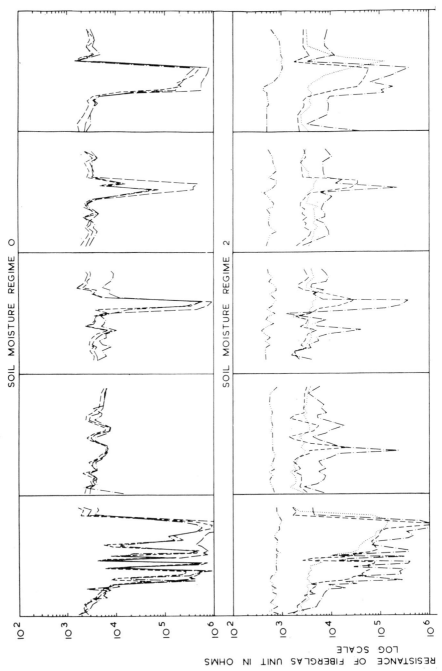

SOIL MOISTURE REGIME 0

SOIL MOISTURE REGIME 2

RESISTANCE OF FIBERGLAS UNIT IN OHMS
LOG SCALE

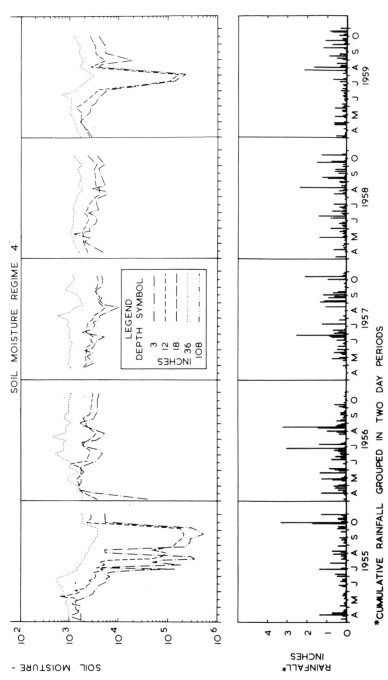

FIG. 11–1. March of soil moisture tension on moisture regimes 0, 2, and 4, as measured with fiberglas units during the 1955–59 period under the hardwood stand. Field capacity and wilting point are represented by about 800 and 250,000 ohms, respectively. Rainfall is indicated as histograms.

regimes as described by Hills (1945). According to this system the complete range of soil-moisture conditions from extremely dry to almost continuously saturated soil is represented by 11 indexes θ (theta), and 0 to 9 inclusive. Moisture regimes (MR) ranging from very dry (0) to very wet (6) are represented on the plots and were recognized through their soil-profile morphology. An electrometric method (Colman, 1948) was used to determine soil moisture on several sites; the calibration and location of stacks of Fiberglas units have already been described (Fraser, 1957a). Permanent wilting is indicated by a resistance of about 250,000 ohms, field capacity by about 800 ohms. These values were obtained from laboratory experiments on soil from the B horizon of the hardwood plot, and, since the structure of the soil is necessarily disturbed, the values represent only approximations of those in the field. The march of soil moisture indicated by the Fiberglas units on a very dry (MR 0), a moist (MR 2), and a wet (MR 4) site are shown in Fig. 11–1.

The temporal changes in the level of permanent water table (Fig. 11–2) were determined by direct measurements with a dipstick in pits. Since the presence of a pit may affect natural water-table levels, the data are stressed for their relative variations. A perched water table is seriously affected by a pit. Here it was not perched but extended down to bedrock. Thus the influence of a pit on a perched water table is not applicable in this study. The data were useful in following moisture trends on the very wet sites (MR 5 and 6) with a thick organic layer (up to 12 inches). The Fiberglas units were not particularly suitable in this organic horizon, since volume changes associated with drying and wetting cycles prevented intimate contact between the unit and the organic material.

The potential evapotranspiration for the period 1955–59 was calculated according to the method of Thornthwaite (1948). Together with the precipitation data for the same period, it provides an estimate of current water deficit or surplus. In Table 11–1, the difference between potential evapotranspiration and precipitation is listed for each month either as deficit or surplus water depending on which figure is larger. Water deficits were subtracted progressively from the soil-water storage on the three sites without seepage water, where each spring the soil was saturated owing to melting snow which provides a surplus of water. These soil-moisture regimes 0 (very dry), 1 (dry), and 2 (moist) were determined to have a maximum water-storage capacity of 3.50, 7.00, and 10.50

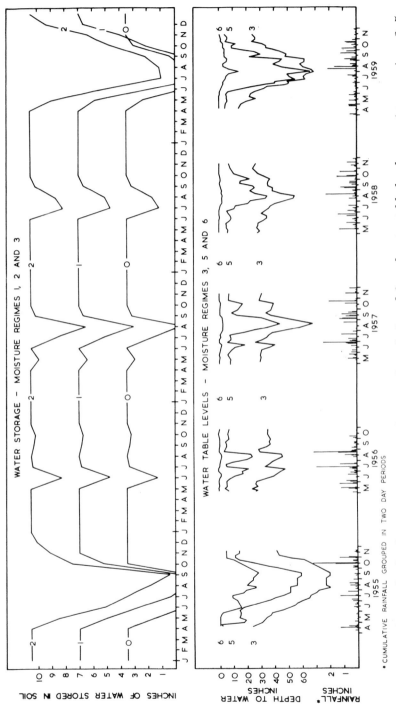

Fig. 11–2. March of soil water storage on moisture regimes 0, 1, and 2, and water table levels on moisture regimes 3, 5, and 6, under the hardwood stand. The values are only approximate.

TABLE 11-1

Moisture Data and Soil-Water Storage in Inches on Three Soil-Moisture Regimes, Chalk River, Ontario, Canada.*

	Oct.	Nov.	Dec.	Jan.	Feb.	Mar.	Apr.	May	June	July	Aug.	Sept.	Total
1954-55													
Potential evapo-transpiration	1.61	0	0	0	0	0	1.61	2.99	4.45	4.84	4.25	2.36	22.11
Precipitation	1.73	2.58	3.52	1.04	1.10	2.72	3.00	0.94	1.11	3.32	2.52	0.92	24.50
Deficit	0	0	0	0	0	0	0	2.05	3.34	1.52	1.73	1.44	10.08
Surplus	0.08	2.58	3.52	1.04	1.10	2.72	1.39	0	0	0	0	0	12.43
Run-off	1.59	1.68	1.37	1.12	0.78	0.73	4.18	2.46	1.00	0.56	0.35	0.21	16.03
Water-Storage Moisture Regime 2	10.50	10.50	10.50	10.50	10.50	10.50	10.50	8.45	5.11	3.59	1.86	0.42	—
Moisture Regime 1	7.00	7.00	7.00	7.00	7.00	7.00	7.00	4.95	1.61	0.09	-1.64	-1.68	—
Moisture Regime 0	3.50	3.50	3.50	3.50	3.50	3.50	3.50	1.45	-0.84	-0.84	-0.84	-0.84	—
1955-56													
Potential evapo-transpiration	1.57	0	0	0	0	0	0	2.05	4.45	4.37	3.74	1.97	18.15
Precipitation	8.61	1.65	0.92	1.91	1.76	1.29	3.01	4.81	2.21	6.45	7.33	1.78	41.73
Deficit	0	0	0	0	0	0	0	0	2.24	0	0	0.19	2.43
Surplus	7.04	1.65	0.92	1.91	1.76	1.29	3.01	2.76	0	2.08	3.59	0	26.01
Run-off	0.29	0.64	0.65	0.55	0.43	0.44	1.52	3.45	2.01	1.26	0.98	1.22	13.44
Water-Storage Moisture Regime 2	7.46	9.11	10.03	10.50	10.50	10.50	10.50	10.50	8.26	10.34	10.50	10.31	—
Moisture Regime 1	5.36	7.00	7.00	7.00	7.00	7.00	7.00	7.00	4.76	6.84	7.00	6.81	—
Moisture Regime 0	3.50	3.50	3.50	3.50	3.50	3.50	3.50	3.50	1.26	3.34	3.50	3.31	—

TABLE 11-1 (Continued)

1956-57

	Oct.	Nov.	Dec.	Jan.	Feb.	Mar.	Apr.	May	June	July	Aug.	Sept.	Total
Potential evapo-transpiration	1.14	0	0	0	0	0	1.18	2.76	4.45	4.84	3.35	2.17	19.89
Precipitation	1.05	1.85	1.49	0.94	1.24	1.13	1.89	2.15	5.50	3.03	1.15	5.98	27.40
Deficit	0.09	0	0	0	0	0	0	0.61	0	1.81	2.20	0	4.71
Surplus	0	1.85	1.49	0.94	1.24	1.13	0.71	0	1.05	0	0	3.68	12.09
Run-off	0.92	0.85	1.06	0.88	0.68	0.66	1.20	1.75	1.16	2.48	0.91	0.78	13.33
Water-Storage Moisture Regime 2	10.22	10.50	10.50	10.50	10.50	10.50	10.50	9.89	10.50	8.69	6.49	10.17	—
1	6.72	7.00	7.00	7.00	7.00	7.00	7.00	6.39	7.00	5.19	2.99	6.67	—
0	3.22	3.50	3.50	3.50	3.50	3.50	3.50	2.89	3.50	1.69	-0.51	3.17	—

1957-58

	Oct.	Nov.	Dec.	Jan.	Feb.	Mar.	Apr.	May	June	July	Aug.	Sept.	Total
Potential evapo-transpiration	1.10	0	0	0	0	0	0.94	2.28	3.31	4.53	3.86	2.36	18.38
Precipitation	3.47	2.50	1.31	2.56	1.64	1.17	1.42	2.48	3.55	2.17	4.38	3.85	30.50
Deficit	0	0	0	0	0	0	0	0	0	2.36	0	0	2.36
Surplus	2.37	2.50	1.31	2.56	1.64	1.17	0.48	0.20	0.24	0	0.52	1.49	14.48
Run-off	0.92	1.67	1.70	1.49	0.99	0.86	2.28	2.17	1.24	1.51	0.89	0.61	16.33
Water-Storage Moisture Regime 2	10.50	10.50	10.50	10.50	10.50	10.50	10.50	10.50	10.50	8.14	8.66	10.15	—
1	7.00	7.00	7.00	7.00	7.00	7.00	7.00	7.00	7.00	4.64	5.16	6.65	—
0	3.50	3.50	3.50	3.50	3.50	3.50	3.50	3.50	3.50	1.14	1.66	3.15	—

* The values are approximate and are given to two decimal points only, to conform with published meteorological records.

TABLE 11-1 (*Continued*)

		Oct.	Nov.	Dec.	Jan.	Feb.	Mar.	Apr.	May	June	July	Aug.	Sept.	Total
							1958-59							
Potential evapo-transpiration		0.47	0	0	0	0	0	1.06	3.39	5.16	5.98	5.28	3.07	24.41
Precipitation		3.81	2.24	2.37	2.53	1.58	1.39	2.67	2.12	0.96	1.92	5.12	4.10	30.81
Deficit		0	0	0	0	0	0	0	1.27	4.20	4.06	0	0	9.53
Surplus		3.34	2.24	2.37	2.53	1.58	1.39	1.61	0	0	0	0.14	1.03	16.23
Run-off		0.58	0.60	0.59	0.57	0.47	0.47	2.03	3.26	1.46	0.73	0.59	0.67	12.02
Water-Storage Moisture Regime	2	10.50	10.50	10.50	10.50	10.50	10.50	10.50	9.23	5.03	0.97	1.11	2.14	–
	1	7.00	7.00	7.00	7.00	7.00	7.00	7.00	5.73	1.53	-1.68	-1.54	-0.51	–
	0	3.50	3.50	3.50	3.50	3.50	3.50	3.50	2.23	-0.84	-0.84	-0.70	0.33	–

inches, respectively. The runoff in inches over the Petawawa drainage basin for each month, as estimated from the flow of the Petawawa River at its mouth, is also indicated. The changes in soil-water storage on these three sites are shown in Fig. 11–2. The water balance during the 5 years of study (Table 11–1) was tabulated for annual periods extending from October to the following September. In the treatment of runoff data, this is the actual procedure used by the Water Resources Branch of the Canada Department of Northern Affairs and National Resources. It includes all precipitation during the winter months. A carry-over into the next year of the precipitation occurring as snow in November and December could occur if the calendar year was used as a basis for tabulation. The data in Table 11–1 are given to two decimal points to conform with available meteorological tables; the values are only approximations, because of the intrinsic difficulty of making precise determinations in variable forest soils and the necessity of making certain general assumptions in their estimation. However they do indicate valid trends that are useful in interpreting the growth patterns of trees.

Radial growth of 16 tree species was measured at the 4-foot level with a dial gauge dendrometer (Figs. 11–3 and 11–4). The trees studied were in the 80- to 120-year age class. Decadent trees were not included. In yellow birch, which is of special interest because of the dieback condition prevalent in eastern Canada and the United States, 18 healthy trees were under study; in white spruce (*Picea glauca* [Moench] Voss) 20 healthy trees were studied. In these 2 species the numbers permitted segregation of the data according to soil-moisture regimes (Fig. 11–5). The other species represented and the number of healthy trees which were studied included:

Species		*Number*
White birch	(*Betula papyrifera* Marsh.)	6
Sugar Maple	(*Acer saccharum* Marsh.)	4
Basswood	(*Tilia americana* L.)	2
Trembling aspen	(*Populus tremuloides* Michx.)	8
Beech	(*Fagus grandifolia* Ehrh.)	3
Red oak	(*Quercus rubra* L.)	3
Ironwood	(*Ostrya virginiana* [Mill.] K. Koch)	2
Black spruce	(*Picea mariana* [Mill.] BSP.)	11
White pine	(*Pinus strobus* L.)	5
Red pine	(*Pinus resinosa* Ait.)	3
Balsam fir	(*Abies balsamea* [L.] Mill.)	4
Tamarack	(*Larix laricina* [Du Roi] K. Koch)	3
Hemlock	(*Tsuga canadensis* [L.] Carr.)	2
White-cedar	(*Thuja occidentalis* L.)	1

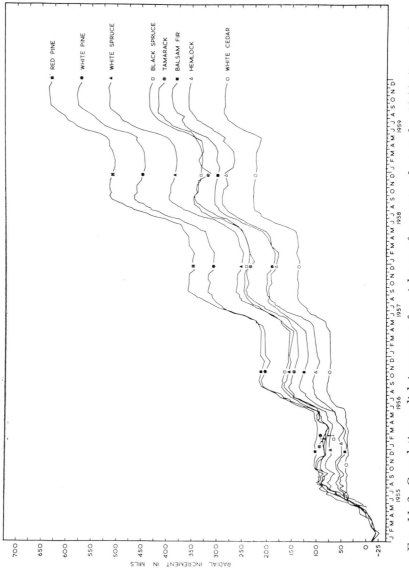

FIG. 11–3. Cumulative radial increment for eight conifer species during the 1955–59 period.

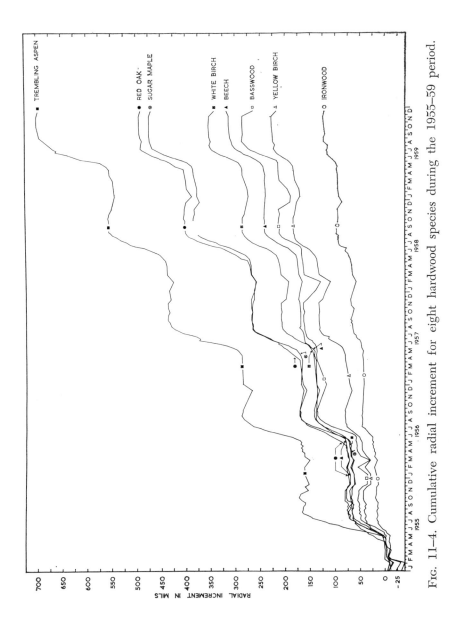

Fig. 11–4. Cumulative radial increment for eight hardwood species during the 1955–59 period.

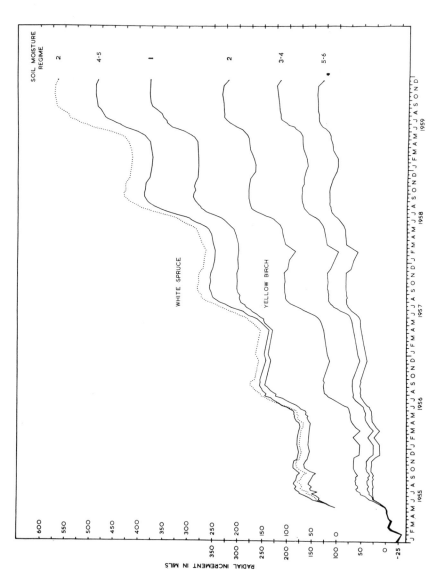

Fig. 11–5. Cumulative radial increment for white spruce on moisture regimes 1, 2, and 4–5, and yellow birch on moisture regimes 2, 3–4, and 5–6, during the 1955–59 period.

Observations and Results

WATER CYCLE. The seasonal and annual changes of rainfall, soil moisture, and potential evapotranspiration show considerable fluctuation. The soil approached field capacity throughout its depth on all sites following melting of the winter's snow in March and April. Thereafter soil moisture was dependent on the balance between summer rainfall and losses to ground water and evaporation, both direct and that owing to transpiration.

For the 5-year study, the May–September (summer) periods of 1955 and 1959 had 55 and 89 per cent of the average rainfall, respectively, as calculated for this part of the year. However, the immediate influence of soil-moisture deficit is apparent in June and early July, when most apical and radial growth occurs. Following

TABLE 11–2

RAINFALL IN INCHES AT PETAWAWA FOREST EXPERIMENT STATION. EACH ENTRY IN PARENTHESES IS THE PER CENT OF THE 5-YEAR AVERAGE.

	May	June	July	August	September	Total
1955	0.94(38)	1.11(42)	3.32(98)	2.52(61)	0.92(28)	8.81(55)
1956	4.81(192)	2.21(83)	6.45(191)	7.33(179)	1.78(53)	22.58(141)
1957	2.15(86)	5.50(206)	3.03(90)	1.15(28)	5.98(180)	17.81(112)
1958	2.48(99)	3.55(133)	2.17(64)	4.38(107)	3.85(116)	16.43(103)
1959	2.12(85)	0.96(36)	1.92(57)	5.12(125)	4.10(123)	14.22(89)
Average	2.50	2.67	3.38	4.10	3.33	15.97

these criteria the growing seasons of these 2 years were dry, having only 74 and 48 per cent, respectively, of the average rainfall. The soil-moisture and water-table levels during 1955 and 1959 confirm this thesis. Summer rainfall ranged from almost 9 inches in the very dry year 1955 to nearly two and one-half times that amount during the wet year 1956 (Table 11–2). Although the total amount of rainfall was more uniform (from 14 to almost 18 inches) in the other 3 years, the soil-moisture content varied considerably because of differences in the pattern of the rainfall. In the spring, a heavy rainfall is frequently lost as runoff, since the soil may be at, or close to, field capacity. An early thaw when the ground is still frozen will also result in runoff, the melt water becoming unavailable for future tree growth. Soil saturation may even depress tree growth in the spring, especially on the MR 4 and wetter.

RADIAL INCREMENT. Figure 11–3 shows the radial growth as measured with a dial gauge dendrometer during the period 1955 to 1959 for eight species of conifers and Fig. 11–4 shows it for eight species of hardwoods. In addition, growth curves for yellow birch and white spruce (Fig. 11–5) are shown for trees on three sites of the hardwood and softwood plots, respectively. The date of initiation and cessation of radial growth (when 5 per cent and 95 per cent of radial increment had occurred), length of growing season, and total growth increment are given in Table 11–3. The dendrometer records include radial changes due to new wood, phloem, and periderm, in addition to swelling caused by hydration. The value of these readings lies in their portrayal of the vigor of the tree and growth response to environmental factors.

White Spruce. Radial growth of white spruce was greatest on the moist site (MR 2) in all years except in the very dry summer of 1955, when trees located on the wet site (MR 4) had slightly more growth. The influence of the drought as it progressed from the high, shallow and dry soils to the lower, deeper and wetter ones is reflected in the 1955 growth curves.

In 1955, cambial activity in white spruce stopped by July 17, several weeks earlier than in the other 4 years of investigations. The summer of 1955 was one of the two dry summers during the study. However, in 1959, drought ceased with the onset of rain in early August, but in 1955 it persisted from early June into late September (Figs. 11–1 and 11–2). The effect of the 1959 June–July drought is more apparent in trees on the driest site, where the decrease in the growth rate occurred in the third week of June. The maximum growth occurred on all sites in 1958, when the growing season lasted 99 days. This was the year of the earliest initiation of growth, and wilting conditions prevailed for a short period on the driest site only.

Yellow Birch. This species was growing on deeper and moister sites than the white spruce. The driest site on the birch plot was comparable to the median site on the spruce plot. Thus, it is not surprising to find that yellow birch grew best during the 5 years on the MR 2 site (Table 11–3). The maximum growth occurred during 1957 and 1958, the years of intermediate rainfall, while the poorest growth was recorded in the very wet year 1956. The two dry years 1955 and 1959 produced a mediocre amount of growth, which suggests that a surplus of soil moisture in the wet year, rather than a deficit during the dry years, impeded growth on these sites. The additional growth during 1957 and 1958 is attributed to an

TABLE 11-3

TIME OF INITIATION AND CESSATION OF RADIAL INCREMENT, LENGTH OF GROWING SEASON, AND TOTAL RADIAL GROWTH OF 16 SPECIES OF TREES, 1955–59, CHALK RIVER, ONTARIO, CANADA.

Species	1955				1956				1957	
	Initiation	Cessation	Days	Radial Increment (Mils)	Initiation	Cessation	Days	Radial Increment (Mils)	Initiation	Cessation
White spruce on										
Site 1	May 13	July 18	67	67	June 2	Aug. 7	67	79	May 16	July 30
2	May 18	July 19	63	83	June 2	July 31	60	92	May 20	July 30
4-5	May 20	July 5	47	88	June 2	July 20	49	68	May 21	Aug. 6
1 to 5	May 16	July 17	63	82	June 2	Aug. 3	63	85	May 16	July 30
Yellow birch on										
Site 2	May 12	July 15	65	67	May 14	July 16	64	63	May 5	July 27
3-4	May 16	July 12	58	42	May 23	July 16	55	28	May 21	July 20
5-6	May 14	June 20	38	31	June 1	July 16	46	23	May 29	July 16
2 to 6	May 14	July 5	53	45	May 21	July 16	57	36	May 21	July 18
Red pine	May 5	Aug. 13	101	105	May 30	Aug. 26	89	117	May 23	Aug. 13
White pine	May 16	Aug. 5	82	100	June 2	Aug. 15	75	113	May 10	Aug. 4
Black spruce	May 25	Aug. 4	72	92	May 25	July 30	67	79	May 25	Aug. 5
Tamarack	May 19	July 16	59	102	June 18	July 20	33	55	May 30	Aug. 8
Balsam fir	May 1	June 16	47	59	May 10	July 20	72	78	May 7	July 21
Hemlock	May 1	July 14	75	62	May 26	July 12	48	47	May 16	July 20
White-cedar	May 4	June 10	38	41	May 21	June 12	23	39	May 17	Aug. 5
Trembling aspen	May 20	July 27	69	173	June 3	July 23	51	114	May 18	Aug. 10
Red oak	May 1	July 20	81	79	May 14	Aug. 10	89	92	Apr. 25	Aug. 8
Sugar maple	May 20	July 11	53	70	June 1	Aug. 6	67	101	May 14	July 28
White birch	May 12	July 17	67	73	May 21	July 30	70	71	May 15	July 23
Beech	May 12	July 20	70	82	June 8	Aug. 10	64	57	May 14	Aug. 15
Basswood	June 2	July 4	33	56	June 13	Aug. 4	53	81	June 2	July 5
Ironwood	June 10	July 4	25	20	May 28	July 18	53	27	June 12	Aug. 8

TABLE 11–3 (*Continued*)

	1957 (Cont.)		1958				1959			
	Days	Radial Increment (Mils)	Initiation	Cessation	Days	Radial Increment (Mils)	Initiation	Cessation	Days	Radial Increment (Mils)
White spruce on										
Site 1	76	57	May 1	Aug. 7	99	88	May 13	Aug. 30	110	87
2	72	106	May 14	Aug. 16	95	147	May 14	Aug. 22	101	142
4–5	78	101	May 14	Aug. 9	88	132	May 18	Aug. 20	95	98
1 to 5	76	97	May 10	Aug. 16	99	135	May 14	Aug. 20	99	121
Yellow birch on										
Site 2	84	80	April 17	July 17	92	72	May 10	June 29	51	53
3–4	61	52	April 15	July 20	97	52	May 20	July 15	57	51
5–6	49	29	April 17	July 8	83	34	May 20	June 29	41	27
2 to 6	59	52	April 17	July 18	93	51	May 16	July 2	48	43
Red pine	83	142	May 9	Sep. 5	120	157	May 13	Sep. 3	113	123
White pine	87	117	May 8	Aug. 21	106	147	May 22	Aug. 25	96	115
Black spruce	73	79	May 10	Aug. 10	93	99	May 16	Aug. 10	87	90
Tamarack	71	86	May 5	July 20	77	105	May 27	July 22	57	66
Balsam fir	76	67	May 5	July 30	87	104	May 6	Aug. 15	102	85
Hemlock	66	90	May 7	July 30	85	93	May 25	Aug. 19	87	67
White-cedar	81	60	May 7	July 25	80	90	June 1	July 20	50	59
Trembling aspen	85	149	May 7	Aug. 10	96	126	May 17	Aug. 19	95	145
Red oak	106	97	May 7	Aug. 5	91	136	May 5	July 15	72	90
Sugar maple	76	98	May 13	Aug. 5	85	118	May 15	July 22	69	90
White birch	70	65	April 18	July 30	104	79	May 15	July 9	56	69
Beech	94	34	May 20	Aug. 13	86	69	May 18	Aug. 20	95	76
Basswood	34	27	May 27	July 20	55	51	June 4	July 11	38	73
Ironwood	58	23	May 20	June 28	40	29	May 27	Aug. 15	81	26

early initiation of growth on most sites, because of favorable temperatures associated with abundant moisture.

Other Species. As may be seen in Table 11–3, initiation of radial increment occurred earliest in a ring-porous species (red oak, usually in late April or early May), and last in the diffuse-porous species (basswood, usually in June). During the 5-year period the date of initiation of radial growth varied considerably. For instance, the variation amounted to about 2 weeks in black spruce, where the time of initiation of radial increment ranged from May 10 in 1958 to May 25 in 1955, 1956, and 1957 (Table 11–3). On the other hand, in tamarack there was a 6-week interval; the time of initiation ranged from May 5 in 1958 to June 18 in 1956. Similar variations within species were apparent in the cessation of growth. This was particularly evident in 1955, when the summer drought curtailed radial increment during July or early August. Maximum growth occurred in most species in 1958. This year was marked by a long growing season and plentiful soil moisture.

The relation between radial and apical growth is indicated in Fig. 11–6 for a black spruce that was 40 feet high. Apical growth of the leader and the average apical growth of four branches in 17 whorls extending from the treetop to the bottom are shown as histograms. Cumulative radial growth at the 4-foot level during the summer is shown on the right side of the same figure. Apical growth approximated 7 inches in every year except 1957, when it was doubled. In 1957 radial and apical growth showed an inverse relation, for, whereas the former was greatly reduced, apical growth was greatest. In 1959, apical growth of this tree continued from the first week of June until early July (Fig. 11–7). Radial growth, on the other hand, usually continued into mid-August.

Discussion

The internal mechanism stimulating initiation of cambial activity of forest trees in temperate regions is considered to be a growth hormone from developing buds (Jost, 1891; Wareing, 1951; Fraser, 1952, 1958a). However, water is necessary for expansion and division of cells, and thus soil environment must be favorable for water absorption in the spring. Limiting conditions are imposed by soil moisture, especially during dry summers, and more frequently for those trees located on the drier sites.

The investigation at Chalk River indicates interrelations between radial growth, site, and climatic variations. In the dry sites (MR

BLACK SPRUCE

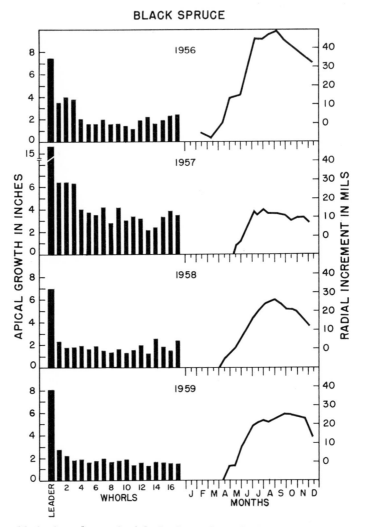

Fig. 11–6. Apical growth of the leader and 17 whorls (average of 4 branches per whorl) in a black spruce, and radial growth as measured with a dendrometer at the 4-ft. level of the same tree for the 1956–59 period.

0 and 1), the capacity for water storage in the loamy sand under study was dependent on the depth of soil; in the wetter ones on their orohydrography. In spring, all sites were saturated by the melting snows. Thereafter the evapotranspiration-rainfall balance of each summer controlled the soil-moisture reserves for that season (Fig. 11–2). Because of the proximity of the bedrock, MR 0 and MR 1 did not possess a permanent water table. In MR 2, the water

BLACK SPRUCE

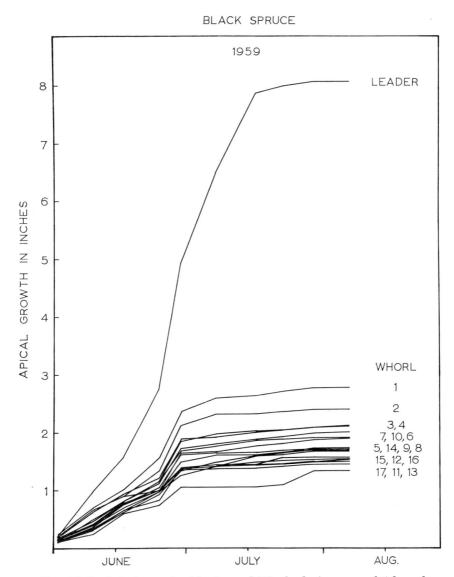

FIG. 11–7. Apical growth of leader and 17 whorls (average of 4 branches per whorl) of a black spruce during 1959.

table was usually below the 9-foot depth (Fig. 11–1) where water was probably available to sinker roots. On MR 3, the water table fluctuated from about 24 inches below the surface in the spring to a maximum depth of 80 inches in the very dry summer of 1955. In MR 5 and MR 6, the water table was closer to the surface (Fig.

11–2) than in any of the other sites. It was always on the surface in the spring and fell during the summer to various depths depending on seasonal weather. In the dry year 1955 it dropped to depths of about 60 and 30 inches on these two sites, respectively; during a year of average or high rainfall, the water table on MR 6 was always within a few inches of the surface.

Changes in soil moisture are remarkably similar in the upper horizons of the various sites. Under special circumstances there may even be a temporary reversal of moisture content in the dry and wet sites. This anomaly is apparent in the soil-moisture status on MR 0 and MR 2 during 1956, when almost 23 inches of rain fell (Fig. 11–1). The former is usually the drier of the two, but during this wet summer the bedrock located at the 1-foot depth prevented gravitational water from draining away immediately and made it wetter than the latter, where the deeper soil allowed the water to drain to a lower level. Theoretically, soil-water depletion during the summer of 1956 was the same on all sites (Fig. 11–2). As discussed in a previous paper (Fraser, 1957a), however, the application of potential evapotranspiration values to soil-water content does not allow for additional input of water into a site through a lateral seepage or, as in this instance, for the modifying influence of an impermeable layer in shallow soils.

The large depletion of soil moisture during the very dry summer of 1955 is evidenced through the soil's absorption of approximately 7 inches of surplus water in October of that year, for there was no increase in the November runoff (0.64 inch) following the exceptionally wet October (Table 11–1).

Wet summers are usually associated with lower temperatures and less sunshine (Fraser, 1958b). Thus it is difficult to separate the influence of moisture on tree growth from the concomitant effect of temperature and sunshine. Also, one year's weather may affect the next year's tree growth.

Soil moisture indirectly influences initiation of cambial activity through its effect on soil-profile development and soil aeration. Thus, on the wetter sites, which accumulate a thick organic layer, initiation of growth is delayed because this layer warms more slowly in the spring (Fraser, 1957b). The roots of trees on the very wet sites are distributed in the thick organic layer and rarely penetrate the saturated mineral soil. Thus, during the very dry summer of 1955, the roots were left dry when the water table fell and this was reflected in the abrupt cessation of radial growth in early July. The white spruce and yellow birch grew best on MR 2 which was intermediate in its moisture supply.

Summary

Annual variations in soil moisture, rainfall, and potential evapotranspiration are described for several sites on two 8-acre experimental plots at Chalk River, Ontario, Canada, for the 1955–59 period. Correlations are made between these data and radial growth at the 4-foot level of 16 species of forest trees. The applicability of evapotranspiration calculations to forest soil moisture is explored. Limitations of this procedure caused by shallow soils and seepage water are discussed.

At Chalk River, the soil was always close to field capacity in the spring, following the melt of winter snows. Initiation of radial increment in trees on the wet sites occurred as much as 2 weeks later than that in trees on the drier sites. In most species, radial growth was greatest in 1958, when early initiation contributed to a very long growing season. Radial growth of white spruce and yellow birch was best in trees on the moist (MR 2) site, except during the dry summer of 1955, when growth of white spruce was better on the wet (MR 4 and MR 5) sites.

Soil-moisture deficit in June and July has a more deleterious effect on tree growth than at any other season, since most of the radial and apical growth occurs then. When this interval is considered, the 1955 and 1959 summers were very dry with only 74 and 48 per cent, respectively, of the average rainfall for these two months. Growth in the stems of all trees studied ceased by early September, regardless of soil-moisture content.

LITERATURE CITED

BRIGGS, L. J. 1897. The mechanics of soil moisture. U.S. Dept. Agr., Bur. Soils, Bull. 10.

BUSHNELL, T. M. 1942. Some aspects of the soil catena concept. Soil Sci. Soc. Amer. Proc. 7: 466–476.

COLEMAN, E. A. 1948. Manual of instructions for use of the fiberglas soil moisture instrument. Berkeley Scientific Co., Richmond, Calif. 19 pp.

FRASER, D. A. 1952. Initiation of cambial activity in some forest trees in Ontario. Ecol. 33: 259–273.

——. 1954. Ecological studies of forest trees at Chalk River, Ontario, Canada. I. Tree species in relation to soil moisture sites. Ecol. 35: 406–414.

——. 1956. Ecological studies of forest trees at Chalk River, Ontario, Canada. II. Ecological conditions and radial increment. Ecol. 37: 777–789.

——. 1957a. Ecological studies of forest trees at Chalk River, Ontario, Canada. III. Annual and seasonal march of soil moisture under a hardwood stand. Canada Dept. of Northern Affairs and National Resources, Forestry Branch, For. Res. Div., Tech. Note No. 55.

——. 1957b. Ecological studies of forest trees at Chalk River, Ontario, Canada. IV. Annual and seasonal march of soil temperature on several sites under a hardwood stand. Canada Dept. North. Aff. Nat. Resources, Forestry Branch, Forest Res. Div., Tech. Note 56.

———. 1958a. Growth mechanisms in hardwoods. Pulp and Paper Mag. Canada 59: 202–209.

———. 1958b. The relation of environmental factors to flowering in spruce. In: The Physiology of Forest Trees. K. V. THIMANN (ed.). The Ronald Press Co., New York. Pp. 629–642.

———. 1959. Ecological studies of forest trees at Chalk River, Ontario, Canada. V. Nine years of observations on the condition of 241 yellow birch. Canada Dept. of North. Aff. Nat. Resources, Forestry Branch, Forest Res. Div., Tech. Note 69.

HILLS, G. A. 1945. A decimal system for the classification and mapping of Ontario Soils. Sci. Agr. 25: 253–272.

———. 1953. The identification and description of forest sites. Ontario Dept. Lands and Forests, Res. Div., Site Res. Manual 4. 71 pp.

JOST, L. 1891. Über Dickenwachstum und Jahresring Bildung. Bot. Ztg. 49: 484–495.

KRAMER, P. J. 1944. Soil moisture in relation to plant growth. Bot. Rev. 10: 525–559.

KREČMER, V. 1951. Rosa jako činitel, meteorologický, pudní, fysiologický, ecologický a rosa v lesnictví. (Dew as a meteorological, pedological, physiological and ecological factor, and dew in forestry.) Lesnická Práce 30: 340–375.

LEBEDOFF, A. F. 1928. The movement of ground and soil waters. Proc. 1st Internatl. Cong. Soil Sci. 1: 459–494.

STONE, E. C. 1957. Dew as an ecological factor. I. A review of the literature. Ecol. 38: 407–413.

THORNTHWAITE, C. W. 1948. An approach towards a rational classification of climate. Geog. Rev. 38: 55–94.

WAREING, P. F. 1951. Growth studies in woody species. IV. The initiation of cambial activity in ring-porous species. Physiol. Plant. 4: 546–562.

12

The Role of Carbon Dioxide in Soil

G. K. Voigt

In the opening sentence of his monumental monograph, Rabino-witch (1945) underscored the importance of photosynthesis by labeling it the most important biochemical process on earth. If one process can be set above all others in an area as complex as biology, photosynthesis would probably be chosen for this position. Aside from a half-dozen specialized forms of bacteria, green plants are the only known life forms able to combine stable inorganic materials into complex organic molecules. This reaction also con-stitutes the chief pathway for the transformation of solar energy upon which the hosts of consumer organisms inhabiting the earth are dependent. The over-all point of view, however, urges consid-eration of the other side of the coin—respiration. In respiration the products of photosynthesis undergo a complicated series of alter-nating syntheses and degradations and are ultimately liberated as carbon dioxide and water. All along this labyrinth of reactions, energy is released to the organisms effecting these changes.

In spite of its prominence in biology, photosynthesis would have ceased long ago were it not for the fact that respiration mobilizes a quantity of carbon approximately equal to that fixed each year by photosynthesis. If this discussion is restricted to land surfaces most of this release occurs in the soil. The carbon dioxide liberated by respiration diffuses back into the atmosphere to be used again, eventually in the process of photosynthesis. Decomposition assures a somewhat higher concentration of carbon dioxide in the atmos-phere immediately above the soil surface, particularly in the interior of sufficiently dense forest stands, which enjoy a greater freedom from wind movement and turbulence than lesser forms of vegetation. The increased carbon dioxide concentration probably compensates to some degree for the reduction in light intensity within forest stands (Fuller, 1948). Thus, much of the carbon dioxide released through the processes of soil respiration is probably utilized by the forest vegetation, particularly that of lesser stature, and is eventually returned to the soil. It is likely that the pattern of carbon dioxide absorption by taller shrubs and trees is altered to some degree by factors such as air turbulence (Huber, 1958). This pathway, beginning with the fixation of carbon in photosynthesis, involving deposition of organic debris on or in the soil, and culminating in the release of carbon dioxide by respiration, constitutes the carbon microcycle. It should be emphasized that this microcycle, whether it is considered in an individual forest stand or over the area of the entire land surface of the earth, is only a small portion of the total or macrocycle of carbon.

Some idea of the relationship between the micro- and macrocycles of carbon may be obtained by considering the values given by Goldschmidt (1954). The amount of carbon dioxide involved in the annual turnover of photosynthesis and respiration is about 10 per cent of the total amount in the atmosphere. The hydrosphere, especially the oceans, contains over 70 times as much carbon dioxide as the atmosphere. Even if these two reservoirs of carbon dioxide are considered together, they constitute less than 1 per cent of the total store of carbon dioxide of the earth. From the standpoint of forest biology, however, the microcycle is of most interest, and it is the purpose of this paper to consider one aspect of this cycle—the effect of respiratory carbon dioxide on plant-soil relationships. Although much of the discussion applies equally well to soil aeration and the behavior of other soil gases, the emphasis in this paper is placed on the behavior of carbon dioxide. It should be emphasized that this segregation is done only for convenience, since it is impossible to explain the complex interactions involved in biology in terms of a single factor. This is particularly true of carbon dioxide, because of the reciprocal relationship between this gas and oxygen and also because of the reciprocal relationships between the soil atmosphere in general and soil moisture.

Carbon Dioxide Concentration in Soils

The composition of the soil atmosphere differs from that of the outer atmosphere in several respects. The soil air is usually saturated with moisture except, perhaps, in the first few centimeters of the surface horizon. In addition, the ratio between oxygen and carbon dioxide in the soil air is much smaller than the same ratio in the outer atmosphere. The concentration of carbon dioxide in the outer atmosphere is usually given as 0.03 per cent by volume; in the soil the concentration of this gas varies from 0.03 to 4 or 5 per cent (Parker, 1923; Appleman, 1927; Furr and Aldrich, 1943) and values as high as 13 per cent have been observed (Boynton and Reuther, 1939). Leonard (1945) states that carbon dioxide concentrations as high as 60 per cent may be attained in the soil immediately adjacent to root surfaces. In a given volume of forest soil, these variations in the composition of soil air are due to the absorption of oxygen and release of carbon dioxide by soil respiration.

Soil respiration has been defined by Lundegårdh (1927) as the total of all soil processes in which carbon dioxide is produced. The release is accomplished chiefly through the metabolic activities of biologic agents inhabiting most natural soils. Because the characteristics of their environment influence the rate at which these metabolic activities proceed, it is to be expected that different soils show different rates of carbon dioxide evolution. Forest soils generally evolve more carbon dioxide than cultivated soils (Romell, 1922; Lundegårdh, 1927; Zonn and Alešina, 1953). The rate of carbon dioxide evolution in forest soils varies considerably, with most of the values falling between 0.2 and 0.7 gram of carbon dioxide per square meter per hour (Romell, 1922; Lundegårdh, 1927; Handley, 1954), but rates over 7 grams have been reported (Wallis and Wilde, 1957). The amount of carbon dioxide evolved by a soil may serve as an index of productivity (Waksman and Starkey, 1924). Smirnov (1955) found a direct relationship between the rate of carbon dioxide evolution and the annual increment of growth in stands of pine, birch, spruce, and hardwoods.

Observations of carbon dioxide production in soils made under laboratory conditions generally indicate higher values than those obtained from field measurements, particularly in short-term experiments. Such studies have some merit, however, since trends in the decomposition pattern may be observed even though the rates may be somewhat exaggerated. For example, Ivarson and Sowden (1959) noted marked differences between the amounts of carbon dioxide produced by a podzol soil and a brown forest soil in 168 days and the amount of carbon dioxide produced in the decomposition of the litter from these same soils. Such variations in activity probably reflect species composition on the two soils studied. In an individual species, the age and condition of the litter have considerable influence on the pattern of carbon dioxide production. Figure 12–1 shows the decomposition course of red pine litter as indicated by carbon dioxide evolution under laboratory conditions. The differences are probably related to the levels of easily decomposable organic substances such as sugars and less resistant nitrogen compounds contained in the two samples. Similar species differences have been observed under woodland conditions by Bocock and Gilbert (1957).

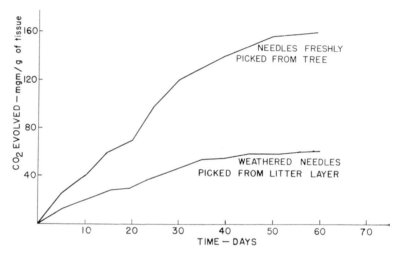

FIG. 12–1. Production of carbon dioxide during the decomposition of fresh and weathered red pine needles under laboratory conditions. The ground tissue was inoculated with a soil suspension and incubated at room temperature.

Although the surface horizons in soil are biologically more active in producing carbon dioxide, the highest concentrations of this gas are generally found in the atmosphere of lower horizons. Boynton and Reuther (1939) found a gradual increase with depth in the carbon dioxide content of orchard soils. Such variations are probably due to restricted diffusion caused by decreased pore space, especially at higher moisture contents (Boynton, 1938; Boynton and Compton, 1944). Boynton and his co-workers also noted the existence of seasonal variation in the composition of the soil atmosphere. Maximum concentrations of carbon dioxide were observed in midsummer, when biological activity in the soil was high. Seasonal changes in soil structure may also bear on this relationship. Joffe and Elson (1955) obtained their lowest values for soil aggregation in midsummer. This would tend to restrict gas diffusion.

Factors Governing Carbon Dioxide Concentration

The concentration of carbon dioxide in the soil atmosphere is essentially dependent upon two factors: the rate of production of carbon dioxide and its rate of diffusion through the soil volume. In the presence of a suitable energy source, the rate of production is a function of the quality and quantity of the organisms inhabiting the soil. Of these the micro-organisms contribute most to carbon dioxide production in their role as propagators of enzymatic chemical reactions (Goldschmidt 1954). All organic carbon added to the soil is not necessarily oxidized to the ultimate state even under aerobic conditions, because varying amounts of this carbon are transformed to cellular material (Lees and Porteous, 1950). Estimation of the relative contribution of bacteria and fungi to soil respiration is a formidable problem because of the difficulties of observing these organisms under truly natural soil conditions. It has been noted that fungi were more efficient than bacteria in oxidizing carbon supplied to test soils (Neller, 1918). Potter and Snyder (1918) observed that inoculation of sterilized soils with typical soil fungi produced as much carbon dioxide as did inoculation with the entire soil flora.

It is recognized that the roots of higher plants produce considerable amounts of carbon dioxide in normal metabolic activity. Van Bavel (1952a) theorized that if the periphery of the root system of a plant is taken as approximately hemispherical the most extreme values of partial pressure for soil gases are closely centered around the apex of the hemisphere corresponding to the portion nearest the stem. Verification for this idea may be obtained from observations on root concentration in different tree species (Laitakari, 1927; Lutz, 1927; Jacobs, 1955). Most of the roots occur close to the stem perhaps because of additions of moisture and nutrients contributed by rain water being added to the soil as stemflow (Voigt, 1960a, 1960b). Much of the apparent carbon dioxide production by plant roots, however, is actually due to the rhizospheric population of micro-organisms inhabiting the soil immediately adjacent to the roots of higher plants (Harley and Waid, 1955; Rovira, 1956; Starkey, 1958). This may be especially true for trees which participate in symbiotic relationships with some species of soil fungi. It has been demonstrated that mycorrhizal short roots respire more actively than non-mycorrhizal roots (Routien and Dawson, 1943; Kramer and Wilbur, 1949). Lundegårdh (1927) estimates that root respiration of higher plants forms approximately 30 per cent of the total soil respiration.

In addition to the carbon dioxide produced by respiring plants of all types, the composition of soil air is altered by the metabolic activities of soil animals. Although the production of carbon dioxide by soil fauna has received little attention, some idea of the contribution of these organisms may be inferred from the measurements of oxygen uptake made by Bornebusch (1930) and by assuming that a respiratory quotient of one is valid. His observations show that the biomass values for a particular soil indicate little about the activity of the animal population and in some cases they may be misleading because the respiration rate is lower for a large animal than for a smaller one. Bornebusch found that earthworms constituted 75 per cent of the biomass and were responsible for slightly over half of the total respiration in a beech mull soil. In a beech mor soil, earthworms made up 7 per cent of the total weight of animals and accounted for slightly over 3 per cent of the respiration, whereas some of the smaller animals accounted for 6 per cent of the biomass and 27 per cent of the respiration. Bornebusch estimated that soil fauna may be responsible for 25 per cent or more of the total organic-matter decomposition and hence carbon dioxide production in the soil.

The other important factor regulating the carbon dioxide concentration in the soil atmosphere is the rate at which soil gases move through the pore space to the outer atmosphere. It is generally agreed that this movement is due primarily to the process of diffusion in which each component gas responds to its individual concentration gradient or partial pressure more or less independently of the other gases in the mixture (Buckingham, 1904; Romell, 1922; Van Bavel, 1951, 1952b). The rate of mechanical diffusion may be altered directly and indirectly by thermal gradients and under special circumstances may be augmented by mass movements in response to barometric changes. The latter, however, apparently have little significance in the over-all process of soil aeration (Baver, 1956, pp. 209–210). For example, Fukuda (1955) found that the effect of barometric pressure differences due to wind movement is limited to a depth of 0.5 mm. even in coarse sandy soils.

The rate at which diffusion occurs is essentially a function of the amount of free pore space contained in a given volume of soil which, in turn, is governed by the structure of the soil and its moisture content. Soil structure is regulated by the texture of the soil particles and by the characteristics of the soil organic matter and its associated life forms. The solid mineral and organic framework surrounds the voids that constitute the pore space of the soil body. The diameter of these pores may range in size from less than a micron to old root channels measuring several centimeters. The availability of free pore space for diffusion of soil gases is dictated by precipitation, drainage, and evapotranspiration. When a soil is dry nearly all of its pores are occupied by the soil atmosphere. Under field conditions, however, a certain proportion of the pore space is filled with water. As a result, the space available for gas movement is reduced correspondingly. The tension forces regulating the water-holding capacity of the soil are determined to a large degree by the size and arrangement of the pores. At field capacity, those pores with diameters sufficiently small to exert a tension equal to, or greater than,

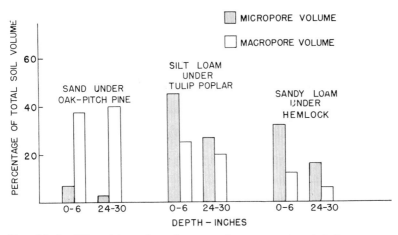

FIG. 12–2. Disposition of total pore volume in soils of different texture under different forest cover types.

the force of gravity are occupied by water. The pores with larger diameters have relinquished their water to gravitational attraction and are occupied by soil gases. The former are called capillary or micropores and the larger air-filled spaces are called non-capillary or macropores. The proportions of the void space occupied by water and air at field capacity in different forest soils is shown in Fig. 12–2. The observed variations are due to the interactions of many biological, chemical, and physical agents associated with different parent materials and forest cover types. It should also be emphasized that the apparent uniformity of pore size in some soils, due to the activity of specific fauna or plant roots, is misleading; the majority of the pore pattern exhibits complete dispersion. Because of this situation aerobic and anaerobic conditions may exist almost side by side. The natural soil structure and consequently its pore size distribution may be altered by compaction due to humans (Lutz, 1945), grazing livestock (Read, 1956) or logging operations (Steinbrenner and Gessel, 1955).

Because of the reciprocal relationship between soil water and soil gases, the moisture content of the soil attains paramount importance in the process of gas movement. When the vegetation has reduced the moisture content in a well-drained soil to the wilting point, conditions for gas exchange are optimum for that particular soil. Carbon dioxide diffuses freely in those pores large enough in diameter to be free of water and long enough to offer an unrestricted pathway to the atmosphere above the soil surface. Any increase in the moisture content of the soil causes a corresponding decrease in the rate of diffusion (Taylor, 1949; Domby and Kohnke, 1956). Thus the rate of diffusion is extremely low in soils in which drainage is impeded by impervious layers or topography. As a consequence, carbon dioxide concentrations attain maximum values under such conditions (Romell, 1922; Furr and Aldrich, 1943). In extreme situations where anaerobic conditions dominate, most of the carbon will be released as methane and other toxic compounds rather than in the oxidized state.

Carbon Dioxide in Plant-Soil Relationships

The effects of poor soil aeration on the activities of root systems of plants are well known. The relative contribution of deficiency of oxygen or excess of carbon dioxide to the injury and eventual death of the root system is obscure, however, because the two conditions are usually superimposed. Boynton and Reuther (1939) suggested that carbon dioxide concentrations in the soil atmosphere of less than 25 per cent are too low to influence root activity appreciably. Here again, the interaction of carbon dioxide and oxygen becomes evident, however. Hammond et al. (1955) observed a reduction in root growth of field crops at a carbon dioxide concentration of 5 per cent when the oxygen level was below one per cent. When the oxygen level was increased to 20 per cent, a carbon dioxide concentration of 20 per cent was required to reduce root growth. Leonard and Pinckard (1946) stated that carbon dioxide concentrations up to 15 per cent had no effect on the growth of cotton roots as long as the oxygen concentration was between 10 and 20 per cent. At ordinary oxygen levels, a concentration of 60 per cent carbon dioxide was required to prevent root growth. Cannon and Free (1925) found that willow roots grew in soils containing a carbon dioxide concentration of 45 per cent as long as the atmosphere contained 20 per cent oxygen. Boynton *et al.* (1938) postulated that different stages of root development may require different degrees of aeration. This idea may help to explain some of the apparently conflicting observations reported in the literature. From these observations it is evident that, although plant roots are susceptible to injury from high concentrations of carbon dioxide, the concentrations necessary to produce toxic effects preclude most well-drained upland forest soils.

When diffusion is retarded by a high moisture content in poorly drained soils or when the root concentration is abnormally high, as in densely seeded nursery beds, growth-retarding levels of carbon dioxide may be attained. It is possible that high concentrations of

TABLE 12–1

GERMINATION (IN PER CENT) OF TREE SEEDS IN FLATS OF CRUSHED QUARTZ OF DIFFERENT PARTICLE SIZES. THE CRUSHED QUARTZ WAS GRADED BY SIEVING, AND THE PORE VOLUMES OF THE DIFFERENT GRADES WERE DETERMINED. THE FLATS WERE KEPT AT APPROXIMATELY FIELD CAPACITY THROUGHOUT THE STUDY.

Macropore Volume (Per Cent)	Monterey Pine	Black Spruce	Paper Birch
30	66	78	87
18	60	69	78
8	27	10	29

this gas may be a factor in producing the border or edge effect observed in some nursery seedbeds, in which the seedlings around the perimeter of the bed grow more rapidly than those in the interior. This phenomenon is usually attributed to competition for moisture and/or nutrients, but, since it sometimes occurs in greenhouse cultures under relatively uniform conditions of soil moisture and fertility, consideration of additional factors appears necessary. Preliminary study has shown that this border effect can be eliminated by aeration and that the soil in aerated cultures contains considerably less carbon dioxide than non-aerated soils.

Seed germination may be affected by carbon dioxide concentration of the soil atmosphere although this apparently varies with species (Kidd and West, 1917; Heydecker, 1955) and Thornton (1944) concluded that in general, extremely high levels of carbon dioxide were required to inhibit germination. Table 12–1 shows the

relationship between macropore space in crushed quartz of different particle size and germination of seeds of different tree species.
The lower germination values in the seedbeds having the least
macropore space suggest toxic levels of carbon dioxide as a controlling factor, but it is highly probable that a deficiency of oxygen
was also involved.

Specific functions of plant roots likely to be affected by carbon
dioxide toxicity include transpiration and uptake of nutrient ions.
Work with field crops has indicated that high carbon dioxide concentrations may reduce both of these processes by as much as 50
per cent (Chang and Loomis, 1945; Fawzy *et al.*, 1954; Hammond
et al., 1955). There is little information on the behavior of forest
trees under the influence of controlled carbon dioxide concentrations but observations of the effects of flooding lead to the suggestion that carbon dioxide is certainly involved. Parker (1950) reported a substantial reduction in transpiration in tree seedlings
growing in flooded soils. This indicates a mechanism at least parallel
to that found in other plants. Kramer (1940, 1951) stated that one
factor involved in the rapid reduction in transpiration may be decreased permeability of the protoplasm and protoplasmic membranes, but he emphasized that injury from flooding is complex in
origin and several factors are involved. This qualification is underscored by variations in different species. Generally, growth is reduced by flooding (Hunt, 1951; Leyton and Rousseau, 1958), but
in some species, e.g., willow, root growth has been observed to continue for a week or more in the complete absence of oxygen (Leyton and Rousseau, 1958). Huikari (1954) found that seedlings of
birch, pine and spruce were able to grow in cultures sealed with
paraffin to insure anaerobic conditions. McDermott (1954) observed that the growth rate of alder was accelerated by short intervals of soil saturation and that saturation sustained for more than a
month did not inhibit growth. Tree roots may also adapt themselves to a changing environment. Le Barron (1945) described a
140-year-old black spruce tree that had developed at least five separate strata of roots in response to increasing depth of peat. The
replacement of old roots by development of new roots on the stem
above the original root collar was attributed to the better aeration
near the peat surface.

At least in principle, waterlogged soils probably affect the process
of ion uptake in the same way as transpiration, i.e., through the
effect of excess carbon dioxide and other factors on the physiologic
characteristics of the root protoplasm. A reaction of far greater sig-

nificance to tree growth involves the participation of respiratory carbon dioxide in nutrient uptake by roots in well-drained soils characterized by relatively low levels of carbon dioxide. It is currently understood that tree roots in most forest soils accumulate their nutrients from essentially three sources: the soil solution, colloidal surfaces, and molecular and lattice structures. These forms exist as a continuum of equilibria. The process of nutrient accumulation by tree-root systems may be visualized as a form of competition for ions between living and non-living colloidal surfaces. The living organisms, including microbes as well as roots of higher plants, adsorb ions on certain areas of their outer surfaces. These adsorbed ions are exchanged for other ions originating as metabolic by-products and are absorbed. The metabolic ions may originate simply from the solution of carbon dioxide in water and subsequent formation of H^+ and HCO_3^- or from more complex reactions that occur within the organisms. The metabolic ions are then subject to replacement by ions arising from the soil solution or by direct exchange with ions from non-living colloidal surfaces in sufficiently close proximity so the oscillation volumes of the ions in question overlap (Jenny, 1951).

The importance of this ionic exchange cannot be overemphasized, for not only is it the basis of ion accumulation in trees and other plants, but it also constitutes the foundation of chemical weathering in rocks and soils (Nikiforoff, 1949; Keller and Frederickson, 1952). In the arena of competition for ions, the living colloidal surfaces enjoy a distinct advantage over the non-living surfaces. As long as metabolism continues, the root surface is continually being recharged with hydrogen ions. Because hydrogen occupies the highest position in the lyotropic series, it is able to replace lower-order ions in equal concentration from the surfaces of non-living colloids. There are several important consequences of this trend. In addition to the nutritional benefits to forest vegetation, the intensity of the weathering process is increased appreciably over that which prevails in the presence of carbonic acid alone (Reiche, 1950). Carbonic acid is a weak acid; it dissociates only to a slight extent (K_1 value is 3×10^{-7} at 25° C.) and the pH value of a saturated solution of carbon dioxide at room temperature is about 4.3. The hydrogen-ion activity of plant root surfaces or clay minerals is considerably higher; values as low as pH 2.0 have been recorded for roots (Williams and Coleman, 1950) and pH 2.6–2.7 for bentonite and humus saturated with hydrogen (Graham, 1954). It should be emphasized that these maximum values are never attained under normal conditions because of the presence of other ions in the soil solution. However, the values do emphasize the potential weathering capacity of such colloids.

It has long been recognized that the constant pressure of hydrogen-ion production by soil respiration is a dominant factor in promoting an acid environment in soils occupied by higher plants and associated organisms (Noyes and Yoder, 1918; Truog, 1918). This is especially true in forest soils because the distribution of forest vegetation is generally correlated with climatic regions having sufficient precipitation to produce active leaching. Theoretically, this saturation of soil colloids with hydrogen and removal of basic cations by leaching form the basis of forest soil deterioration which has received considerable attention in Europe. In actuality, however, in most forest soils the process is counterbalanced to varying degrees by the cyclical nature of nutrient uptake and subsequent nutrient return prevalent in forest vegetation. Leaching losses are reduced by the filtering effect of the root network that permeates the upper layers of the profile. While it is recognized that many factors are involved in soil formation it would appear that broadscale soil degradation through acidification alone is of greater significance geologically than biologically. Wilde (1958, p. 439) emphasized that "soil sickness" is invariably associated with a history of previous agricultural use or with parent materials low in nutrients and high in silica. This viewpoint is corroborated by the observation that even though many areas of this country have been occupied by forest vegetation more or less continuously for thousands of years, there is little evidence of soil deterioration in the absence of man's interference.

Summary

Soil aeration is nearly always included among the primary factors influencing tree growth; poor aeration is usually equated to poor growth. This relationship has been validated by empirical observations as well as controlled experiments with flooded soils. Unfortunately, the majority of these studies has not been sufficiently extended to allow evaluation of the relative contribution of high levels of carbon dioxide or deficiencies of oxygen to the decline in soil productivity. With present limited knowledge, it appears that the primary cause of decreased root activity of most species in poorly drained or flooded soils is a lack of oxygen rather than toxic levels of carbon dioxide. The latter is merely a reflection of conditions leading to the former. It should be emphasized that this conclusion is based upon gross measurements of the composition of the soil atmosphere that do not allow examination of the really critical region of the soil immediately adjacent to the surface of the plant root. In this respect, measurements of the soil atmosphere suffer the same shortcomings as soil moisture determinations. It may well be that when suitable procedures make possible close scrutiny of the root region, new significance will be assigned to carbon dioxide in regulating root activities. Further development and application of the platinum microelectrode suggested by Lemon and Erickson (1955) should elucidate the behavior of oxygen in the root environment; similar microtechniques are needed for collecting carbon dioxide. Such refinements in collaboration with tracer techniques should also make possible more precise evaluation of the claims that plants obtain part of their carbon from the carbon dioxide of the soil (Livingston and Beal, 1934; Wilde, 1958, p. 95).

It is in well-drained soils, therefore, that carbon dioxide plays what is perhaps its most significant role with greatest efficiency. Here the carbon dioxide of respiration and possibly other metabolic by-products insure a nearly constant supply of hydrogen ions to occupy the exchange sites on the root surfaces. The hydrogen ions are subsequently exchanged for nutrient cations that enter the transaction from either the soil solution or directly from a closely adjacent colloidal surface. Such an arrangement enables the plant root to enjoy a favorable balance of power in the competition for ions prevailing among colloidal surfaces present in the soil system. This process also gives the plant root a certain amount of buffering capacity that may serve to protect the metabolic processes against relatively extreme pH changes as the plant roots move through the soil. It is likely that the nutrient exchange reactions on tree-root surfaces operate in an acid environment even in calcareous soils. Theoretically, the pressure of hydrogen-ion production insures a predominance of hydrogen ions in the ionic population surrounding non-living colloids as well, owing to exchange reactions. Although forest soils eventually attain varying degrees of acidity, complete dominance of soil colloids by hydrogen is usually prevented by the cyclic addition of nutrient ions to the system through litter deposition and decomposition.

LITERATURE CITED

APPLEMAN, C. O. 1927. Percentage of carbon dioxide in soil air. Soil Sci. 24: 241–245.

BAVER, L. D. 1956. Soil Phys. 3d ed. John Wiley & Sons, Inc., New York.

BOCOCK, K. L., and O. J. W. GILBERT. 1957. The disappearance of leaf litter under different woodland conditions. Plant and Soil 9: 179–185.

BORNEBUSCH, C. H. 1930. The fauna of forest soil. Det Forstl. Forsøgsv. i Danmark 11: 1–158.

BOYNTON, D. 1938. Concerning the pore space in two orchard soils of different productivity. Proc. Amer. Soc. Hort. Sci. 35: 315–319.

BOYNTON, D., and O. C. COMPTON. 1944. Normal seasonal changes of oxygen and carbon dioxide percentages in gas from the larger pores of three orchard subsoils. Soil Sci. 57: 107–117.

BOYNTON, D., J. DE VILLIERS, and W. REUTHER. 1938. Are there different critical concentrations for the different phases of root activity? Sci. 88: 569–570.

BOYNTON, D., and W. REUTHER. 1939. Seasonal variation of oxygen and carbon dioxide in three different orchard soils during 1938, and its possible significance. Proc. Amer. Soc. Hort. Sci. 36: 1–6.

BUCKINGHAM, E. 1904. Contributions to our knowledge of the aeration of soils. U.S. Dept. Agr. Bur. Soils Bull. 25.

CANNON, W. A., and E. E. FREE. 1925. Physiological features of roots with special reference to the relationship of roots to aeration of the soil. Carnegie Inst. Wash. Pub. 368.

CHANG, H. T., and W. E. LOOMIS. 1945. Effect of carbon dioxide on absorption of water and nutrients by roots. Plant Physiol. 20: 221–232.

DOMBY, C. W., and H. KOHNKE. 1956. The influence of soil crusts on gaseous diffusion. Soil Sci. Soc. Amer. Proc. 20: 1–5.

FAWZY, H., R. OVERSTREET, and L. JACOBSON. 1954. The influence of hydrogen ion concentration on cation absorption by barley roots. Plant Physiol. 29: 234–237.

FUKUDA, H. 1955. Air and vapor movement in soil due to wind gustiness. Soil Sci. 79: 249–256.

FULLER, H. J. 1948. Carbon dioxide concentration of the atmosphere above Illinois forest and grassland. Amer. Midland Nat. 39: 247–249.

FURR, J. R., and W. W. ALDRICH. 1943. Oxygen and carbon-dioxide changes in the soil atmosphere of an irrigated date garden on calcareous very fine sandy loam soil. Proc. Amer. Soc. Hort. Sci. 42: 46–52.

GOLDSCHMIDT, V. M. 1954. Geochemistry. A. MUIR (ed.). Clarendon Press, Oxford, England.

GRAHAM, E. R. 1954. Weathering according to the cationic bonding energies of colloids. Proc. 2d Natl. Conf. on Clays and Clay Minerals. Nat. Res. Council Pub. 327: 492–498.

HAMMOND, L. C., W. H. ALLAWAY, and W. E. LOOMIS. 1955. Effects of oxygen and carbon dioxide levels upon absorption of potassium by plants. Plant Physiol. 30: 155–161.

HANDLEY, W. R. C. 1954. Mull and mor formation in relation to forest soils. Forest Comm. Bull. 23. London.

HARLEY, J. L., and J. S. WAID. 1955. The effect of light upon the roots of beech and its surface population. Plant and Soil 7: 96–112.

HEYDECKER, WALTER. 1955. Production of controlled atmospheres in the soil. In: Soil Zoology. D. K. McE. KEVAN (ed.). Academic Press, Inc., New York. Pp. 445–448.

HUBER, B. 1958. Recording gaseous exchange under field conditions. In: The Physiology of Forest Trees. K. V. THIMANN (ed.). The Ronald Press Co., New York. Pp. 187–195.

HUIKARI, O. 1954. Experiments on the effect of anaerobic media upon birch, pine and spruce seedlings. Comm. Inst. Forest Fenn. 42.5: 3–13.

HUNT, F. M. 1951. Effects of flooded soil on growth of pine seedlings. Plant Physiol. 26: 363–368.

IVARSON, K. C., and F. J. SOWDEN. 1959. Decomposition of forest litters. I. Production of ammonia and nitrate nitrogen: Changes in microbial population and rate of decomposition. Plant and Soil 11: 237–248.

JACOBS, M. R. 1955. Growth habits of the eucalypts. Forestry and Timber Bur., Dept. of the Interior, Canberra, Australia.

JENNY, H. 1951. Contact phenomena between adsorbents and their significance in plant nutrition. In: Mineral Nutrition of Plants. E. TRUOG (ed.). University of Wisconsin Press, Madison, Wis.

JOFFE, J. S., and J. ELSON. 1955. Conductivity of soil-water extract as an index of soil structure. Plant and Soil 6: 84–91.

KELLER, W. D., and R. F. FREDERICKSON. 1952. Role of plants and colloidal acids in the mechanism of weathering. Amer. Jour. Sci. 250: 594–608.

KIDD, F., and C. WEST. 1917. The controlling influence of carbon dioxide IV. On the production of a secondary dormancy in seeds of Brassica alba following treatment with carbon dioxide and the relation of this phenomenon to the question of stimuli in growth processes. Ann. Bot. 31: 457–488.

KRAMER, P. J. 1940. Causes of decreased absorption of water by plants in poorly aerated media. Amer. Jour. Bot. 27: 216–220.

———. 1951. Causes of injury to plants resulting from flooding of the soil. Plant Physiol. 26: 722–736.

KRAMER, P. J., and K. M. WILBUR. 1949. Absorption of radioactive phosphorus by mycorrhizal roots of pine. Sci. 110(2844): 8–9.

LAITAKARI, E. 1927. The root system of the pine (Pinus sylvestris). Acta Forest Fenn. 33: 1–306. English summary. 306–380.

LE BARRON, R. K. 1945. Adjustment of black spruce root systems to increasing depth of peat. Ecol. 26: 309–311.

LEES, H., and J. W. PORTEOUS. 1950. The release of carbon dioxide from soils percolated with various organic materials. Plant and Soil 2: 231–241.

LEMON, E. R., and E. A. ERICKSON. 1955. Principle of the platinum microelectrode as a method of characterizing soil aeration. Soil Sci. 79: 383–392.

LEONARD, O. A. 1945. Cotton root development in relation to natural aeration of some Mississippi Blackbelt and Delta soils. Jour. Amer. Soc. Agron. 37: 55–71.

LEONARD, O. A., and J. A. PINCKARD. 1946. Effect of various oxygen and carbon dioxide concentrations on cotton root development. Plant Physiol. 21: 18–36.

LEYTON, L., and L. Z. ROUSSEAU. 1958. Root growth of tree seedlings in relation to aeration. In: The Physiology of Forest Trees. K. V. THIMANN (ed.). The Ronald Press Co., New York. Pp. 467–475.

LIVINGSTON, B. E., and RUTH BEAL. 1934. The soil as a direct source of carbon dioxide. Plant Physiol. 9: 237–259.

LUNDEGÅRDH, H. 1927. Carbon dioxide evolution of soil and crop growth. Soil Sci. 23: 417–453.

LUTZ, H. J. 1927. Successional tendencies in the woodlands and their bearing on silvicultural practice. M.F. thesis. Yale School of Forestry, New Haven, Conn.

———. 1945. Soil conditions of picnic grounds in public forest parks. Jour. Forestry 43: 121–127.

McDERMOTT, R. E. 1954. Effects of saturated soil on seedling growth of some bottomland hardwood species. Ecol. 35: 36–41.

NELLER, J. R. 1918. Studies on the correlation between the production of carbon dioxide and the accumulation of ammonia by soil organisms. Soil Sci. 5: 225–241.

NIKIFOROFF, C. C. 1949. Weathering and soil evolution. Soil Sci. 67: 219–230.

NOYES, H. A., and LESTER YODER. 1918. Carbonic acid gas in relation to soil acidity changes. Soil Sci. 5: 151–161.

PARKER, F. W. 1923. Carbon dioxide production of plant roots as a factor in the feeding power of plants. Soil Sci. 17: 229–247.

PARKER, J. 1950. The effects of flooding on the transpiration and survival of some southeastern forest tree species. Plant Physiol. 25: 453–460.

POTTER, R. S., and R. S. SNYDER. 1918. The production of carbon dioxide by molds inoculated into sterile soil. Soil Sci. 5: 359–377.

RABINOWITCH, E. I. 1945. Photosynthesis. Vol. I. Interscience Publishers, Inc., New York.

READ, R. A. 1956. Effect of livestock concentration on surface-soil porosity within shelterbelts. U.S. Forest Serv. Rocky Mountain Forest Range Expt. Sta. Res. Notes 22. 4 pp.

REICHE, P. 1950. A survey of weathering processes and products. Rev. ed. University of New Mexico Publications in Geology. 3. The University of New Mexico Press, Albuquerque. 95 pp.

ROMELL, L. 1922. Luftväxlingen i marken som ekologisk faktor. Middel. Statens Skogsforsoksanst. 19: 125–359. Also: The aeration of the soil as an ecological factor. Translated by A. T. BLIDBERG. U.S. Forest Serv. Translation. 55.

ROUTIEN, J. B., and R. F. DAWSON. 1943. Some interrelationships of growth, salt absorption, respiration and mycorrhizal development in Pinus echinata Mill. Amer. Jour. Bot. 30: 440–451.

ROVIRA, A. D. 1956. Plant root excretions in relation to the rhizospheric effect. III. The effect of root exudate on the numbers and activity of micro-organisms in soil. Plant and Soil 7: 209–217.

SMIRNOV, V. N. 1955. K voprosu o vzaimosvjazi meždu produkcieĭ počvennoĭ uglekisloty i proizvoditeljnostjju lesnyh počv. (The interrelation of CO_2 production by the soil and the productivity of forest soils.) Pochvovedenie (Pédologie) 6: 21–23. Povolžskiĭ Lesotehniceskiĭ Institut im. M. Gorjkogo, Ioskar-Ola. A.P.B. In: Forestry Abs. 17: 1132. 1956.

STARKEY, R. L. 1958. Interrelations between microorganisms and plant roots in the rhizosphere. Bact. Rev. 22: 154–172.

STEINBRENNER, E. C., and S. P. GESSEL. 1955. The effect of tractor logging on physical properties of some forest soils in southwestern Washington. Soil Sci. Soc. Amer. Proc. 19: 372–376.

TAYLOR, S. A. 1949. Oxygen diffusion in porous media as a measure of soil aeration. Soil Sci. Soc. Amer. Proc. 14: 55–61.

THORNTON, N. C. 1944. Carbon dioxide storage. XII. Germination of seeds in the presence of carbon dioxide. Contrib. Boyce Thompson Inst. 13: 355–360.

TRUOG, E. 1918. Soil acidity. I. Its relation to the growth of plants. Soil Sci. 5: 169–195.

VAN BAVEL, C. H. M. 1951. A soil aeration theory based on diffusion. Soil Sci. 72: 33–46.

———. 1952a. A theory on the soil atmosphere in and around a hemisphere in which soil gases are used or released. Soil Sci. Soc. Amer. Proc. 16: 150–153.

———. 1952b. Gaseous diffusion and porosity in porous media. Soil Sci. 73: 91–104.

VOIGT, G. K. 1960a. Distribution of rainfall under forest stands. Forest Sci. 6: 2–10.

———. 1960b. Alteration of the composition of rainwater by trees. Amer. Midland Nat. 63: 321–326.

WAKSMAN, S. A., and R. L. STARKEY. 1924. Microbiological analysis of soil as an index of soil fertility. VII. Carbon dioxide evolution. Soil Sci. 17: 141–161.

WALLIS, G. W., and S. A. WILDE. 1957. Rapid method for the determination of carbon dioxide evolved from forest soils. Ecol. 38: 359–361.

WILDE, S. A. 1958. Forest soils: Their properties and relation to silviculture. The Ronald Press Co., New York. 537 pp.

WILLIAMS, D. E., and N. T. COLEMAN. 1950. Cation exchange properties of plant root surfaces. Plant and Soil 2: 243–256.

ZONN, S. V., and A. K. ALEŠINA. 1953. Ogazoobmene meždu počvoĭ i atmosferoĭ pod pologom lesnyh nasaždeniĭ. (Gas exchange between soil and atmosphere under forest stands.) Dok. Akad. Nauk S.S.S.R. 92(5): 1035–1038. A. P. B. In: Forestry Abs. 15: 2197. 1954.

13

Progress and Problems in Mineral Nutrition of Forest Trees

STANLEY P. GESSEL

Recent reviews such as that of Leyton (1958) and conferences such as that held at Duke University (1959) indicate a renewed interest in forest-tree nutrition. As these reviews and conferences have brought the subject up to date, this paper will deal more specifically with progress subsequent to the Duke Conference. The object is to summarize progress by subject-matter groups and highlight certain specific problems.

Mineral Requirements of Forest Trees

Despite the seemingly elementary nature of mineral-requirement investigations, considerable activity has taken place. These studies reflect that the simple recognition of needs of forest trees for elements is the first step in the accumulation of information on forest tree nutrition. Considerable ingenuity is currently being displayed in mineral-requirement investigations, and valuable additions to our knowledge of forest-tree growth requirements are being made. Investigations are proceeding with both macro and micro nutrients, and forest trees are being shown to have the same elemental needs as other plants, but at different levels. Elemental nutrient-deficiency symptoms are being recognized and catalogued as well as corresponding foliar nutrient contents under controlled conditions. Representative of these investigations is that of Swan (1960) working at the Pulp and Paper Research Institute of Canada. This institute has started a program of improved production on forest land and, as the basis for field work, is investigating the nutrient needs of pulp species under controlled growing conditions.

Ingestad (1959) in Sweden has experimented with mineral nutrition of birch and Norway spruce. Nutrient levels have included a range sufficient to enable establishment of levels which are considered to be optimum for growth of the species. Ingestad also associates foliage levels for a number of elements with this optimum growth and compares different species. Purnell (1959) gives similar information on Monterey pine in Australia and deficiency symptoms for each element.

Mineral nutrition of trees is also studied by the use of soil pot tests employing trees as test plants. Such work has considerable diagnostic value for forest soil fertility standards even though results may not be directly applicable to field conditions. Recent work in Oregon * suggests that controlled environment conditions as provided by a growth chamber improve the sensitivity and reliability of soil pot tests using Douglas-fir, as compared to greenhouse growth.

Exploratory work on the elements essential for tree growth and comparative levels of the elements in nutrient solutions for maximum growth is now well developed, but a certain amount of this work must continue, particularly to relate to the needs of major forest tree species. Eventually a catalogue of the needs of the major forest tree species will be available as reference data for consideration of nutritional problems. Such data will provide a better basis for judgment as to whether a given species requires a high or low fertility status soil in order to make the best growth. However it will undoubtedly be found that the ecological nutrient requirement may be somewhat different than the pure culture requirement.

To date controlled nutrient studies have been concerned with the seedling stage of trees and into the early years of the life cycle. The use of this period to predict needs of mature trees may be erroneous, especially since the rates of physiological processes may change over the tree life cycle. At the same time most of the above experiments have been evaluated by weights of plants or plant parts. This method may not give a correct evaluation of the nutritional status of a tree best able to grow and compete in a natural environment. Consideration should also be given to expression of plant composition on other than a percentage basis.

Other mineral nutrition problems needing work relate to the relationship between mineral nutrition and photosynthetic efficiency. Tomi and Wolfe (1956) have shown an inverse correlation between degree of nitrogen deficiency and leaf chlorophyll content for citrus.

* Personal communication from D. Lavender, Oregon Forest Board Research Laboratory.

The role of food reserves, both organic and inorganic, in the growth process of forest trees should be investigated. In this connection the nutrient status of a forest tree seedling which will insure best survival and growth after transplanting is still uncertain. Most evidence indicates that an optimum nutrient status for best growth after outplanting is similar to an optimum for greenhouse growth and that adequate reserve storage is needed for initial growth. A further elaboration of mineral nutrition and water requirement of forest trees is also needed.

Diagnosis of Nutrient Needs

The expanding interest in forest tree nutrition has stimulated considerable work in the diagnosis of nutrient needs. Resultant work has followed two major lines: (a) soil analysis and (b) foliar analysis. The decision as to whether soil or foliage analysis is the best diagnostic technique cannot be made at the present time. Both procedures find use in forest research and practice now and will in the future as well.

SOIL ANALYSIS. Considerable work is in progress in various parts of the world relating soil properties to forest land productivity, and use, e.g., Wittich (1960), Lutz (1958). These investigations stress the role of the soil in both yield of forests and certain management problems. Only in unusual situations has a functional relationship between nutrient content of soil and forest tree growth been indicated from soil-site studies, but this is more a mechanism of the type and purpose of the study rather than the lack of relationships. One serious problem is that soil nutrient determination can not be easily and rapidly made in the field, while some physical determinations can. For the most part, significant results in nutrient studies have been obtained on soils which do have a mineral deficiency. For instance, a study by Baur (1956) in Australia showed a definite relationship between total soil phosphate and growth of planted slash pine. Soil phosphorus content was carefully mapped for the entire area and used as the basis for phosphate application at planting time. The goal was to bring soil phosphate up to 70 ppm, as this value was considered essential for good growth.

This writer has found a valid relationship between total soil nitrogen and growth of forest trees. It is known that for most soils in the Pacific Northwest less than 0.1% nitrogen is a critical level and nitrogen deficiency is a factor in growth of Douglas-fir. However nitrogen response at soil nitrogen levels much above this value has been observed. Such results eliminate soil nitrogen analysis as a diagnostic technique until the nitrogen cycle and nitrogen balance in forest soils are studied further.

Stoate has worked with soil analysis and tree growth on Vancouver Island in British Columbia as well as Australia. Most of his British Columbia data are unpublished to date but some (Stoate, 1957) indicate success in using total soil phosphate as a diagnostic tool, as he had previously found in Australia (1950). He has found good relationships between total soil phosphate and forest site for some areas but has not been able to relate response to phosphate application.

Phosphate availability to forest trees is still a perplexing problem in forest soil analysis. It is a common soil pot test experience to be able to grow Douglas-fir on most Pacific Northwest forest soils, but not agricultural plants or even some hardwood species. For instance, one study shows a response by Eucalyptus to phosphorus but lack of response by Douglas-fir. Certainly the differential ability of forest trees to extract elements from soils is of major importance in this area and must be more completely investigated before the soil analysis can be used. It is interesting to note that some time ago Tidball (1956) discovered that heat treatment of a forest soil, as in a forest fire, resulted in more available phosphorus as measured by most of the chemical extractions, but actually less uptake by Douglas-fir growing on these soils.

In a large measure the relationship of soil chemical properties to forest tree growth is still clouded with many uncertainties and currently does not have a concise set of standards. This is due to lack of information on forest tree requirements, forest tree-forest soil interrelationships, and confusion of methodology in forest soil analysis. A rather large-scale study is now in progress in the northwestern United States to relate forest soil analysis to forest land productivity and may produce useful information. However, at the current writing, no definitive work has appeared in this field and it will probably be some time before anything conclusive is available.

FOLIAR ANALYSIS. Foliar analysis has recently been improved as a diagnostic tool. The major recent contribution has brought out additional standardization of procedures, particularly in collection and preparation of material. In the case of forest trees, collection of the proper sample is frequently a difficult task. All results, however, point to the fact that proper standardization of age of foliage, season, position in the crown, and relative position of the tree within the stand are important variables. Depending upon the element, variations in these procedures can cause extreme variation in results (Will, 1957).

The writer's experience with Douglas-fir in the Pacific Northwest indicates best results by using current year's foliage, collected between September and December from the upper one third of the crown of dominant or co-dominant trees. Even with such standardization considerable variation in the content of some elements may exist within a given stand of individual trees on an area as small as one-tenth acre. The role of tree parentage as a variable needs to be further investigated.

The publication of foliar analysis results from many parts of the world showing critical and normal expected levels of elements under different growing conditions is making foliar analysis a better technique. These levels can also be related to color and other general

TABLE 13–1

DEFICIENT AND OPTIMUM LEVELS OF VARIOUS ELEMENTS IN NORWAY SPRUCE FOLIAGE. (FROM INGESTAD, 1959.)

Level	Element (Per Cent dry weight)						
	N	P	K	Ca	Mg	S	Fe
Deficient.........	1.0	0.05-0.11	0.03	0.02	0.02 to 0.07	0.11	0.003
Optimum	2.0	0.2	0.90	0.08 to 0.19	0.11	0.2	0.006

foliage characteristics. The recent publication by Bruning (1959) is a valuable addition to this diagnostic field. Unpublished results in the Pacific Northwest showed that color as determined from a Munsell Color Chart was in direct relation to the total nitrogen content of Douglas-fir foliage and this in turn to the general health and vigor of the trees.

Ingestad (1959) has completed foliar analysis work on Norway spruce, and birch (1957). For both species, levels of elements in the foliage for optimum as well as reduced growing conditions are given. The tolerance of each species to changes in the foliage nutrient levels are also detailed. A summary of his results is given in Table 13–1.

As more information develops, it will be possible to use foliar analysis for diagnostic purposes for all growing conditions and species. It is already apparent that differences between species are large for some elements and very small for others. Nitrogen needs seem to vary greatly among species while potassium composition is more constant over a rather wide range of growing conditions.

Foliar analysis may also be useful in other forest tree problems. For instance, the drain of nutrient supply, particularly nitrogen, occasioned by a heavy seed crop in Douglas-fir has been frequently

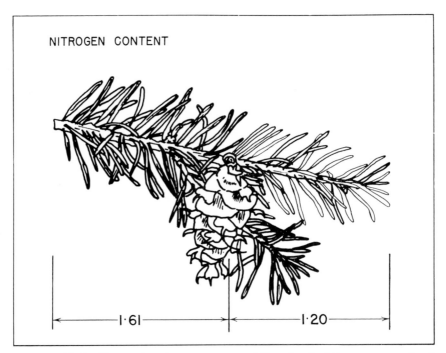

NITROGEN CONTENT

$\leftarrow$———1·61————$\rightarrow$$\leftarrow$———1·20———$\rightarrow$

FIG. 13–1. Change in nitrogen content of Douglas-fir foliage as a result of seed production.

observed. Foliage produced beyond the point of cone attachment to the branch is very chlorotic and reduced in nitrogen content, showing the ability of seed crop to have first call on nutrients within the tree (Fig. 13–1). Therefore the nutrient needs of the forest tree for specific functions must also be taken into account in foliar diagnosis.

Elemental Cycles and Total Mineral Requirements

Beginning with work of Rennie (1955), Leyton (1958), and others a great deal of emphasis has recently been put on the total nutrient needs of forest plants. For many years it had been presumed that the elemental needs of forest trees were very small and that forest cover was truly a conserving medium for soils. With increasing emphasis on maximum production from forest land and almost complete harvest of the forest crop, the elemental drain is now considered, at least by some writers.

TABLE 13–2

PER CENT DISTRIBUTION OF NUTRIENTS IN DIFFERENT PARTS OF A CROP.
(FROM WRIGHT AND WILL, 1958.)

| Plot | Parts | Per Cent of Total | | | | |
		N	P	K	Ca	Mg
Plot A	Needles	39	43	39	26	22
Corsican pine	Branches	27	27	31	39	36
18 years	Bark	22	22	17	22	27
	Wood	12	8	13	13	15
Plot B	Needles......	32	38	32	19	19
Corsican pine	Branches.....	23	23	25	41	35
28 years	Bark.........	23	27	23	22	26
	Wood	22	12	20	18	20
Plot C	Needles	28	32	27	17	18
Corsican pine	Branches	19	20	22	32	25
48 years	Bark.........	25	29	23	20	26
	Wood........	28	19	28	31	31
Plot D	Needles......	39	38	32	22	25
Scots pine	Branches.....	26	30	31	34	30
18 years	Bark	20	20	18	24	19
	Wood	15	12	19	20	26
Plot E	Needles	30	29	20	17	12
Scots pine	Branches.....	27	31	29	29	25
28 years	Bark	17	20	18	23	18
	Wood	26	20	33	31	45
Plot F	Needles......	25	24	19	11	11
Scots pine	Branches	26	29	29	18	23
64 years	Bark	18	25	19	41	18
	Wood	31	22	33	30	48

In support of this viewpoint investigations in progress and completed, show that the percentage composition of elements is high in the leaves, bark, and stem wood with lesser amounts in the bole wood. Table 13–2, from the work of Wright and Will (1958) for Corsican and Scots pine illustrates this point. However, the greater volume of bole wood makes for a considerable total quantity of elements when removed from the area. Table 13–3, also from Wright and Will (1958), shows the distribution for the same species as

TABLE 13–3

TOTAL DRY WEIGHT AND NUTRIENT CONTENT OF A CROP. (FROM WRIGHT AND WILL, 1958.)

Plot	Parts	Dry Matter	Lbs. per Acre			
			N	P	K	Ca
Plot A	Needles	2,800	28.0	4.6	17.0	17.0
Corsican pine	Branches ...	5,700	19.5	2.9	14.0	25.0
18 years	Bark	4,400	16.0	2.3	7.5	14.0
	Wood.......	10,100	8.5	0.9	5.5	9.0
	All parts ...	23,000	72.0	10.7	44.0	65.0
Plot B	Needles....	4,300	29.0	4.6	23.0	21.0
Corsican pine	Branches...	9,700	21.0	2.8	17.5	45.0
28 years	Bark	11,500	21.0	3.3	16.5	24.0
	Wood	35,500	20.0	1.5	14.0	20.0
	All parts ...	61,000	91.0	12.2	71.0	110.0
Plot C	Needles....	5,000	46.0	6.3	32.0	24.0
Corsican pine	Branches...	10,000	31.5	4.0	26.0	45.0
48 years	Bark	19,000	41.5	5.8	27.5	28.0
	Wood	66,000	46.0	3.8	33.5	43.0
	All parts ...	100,000	165.0	19.9	119.0	140.0
Plot D	Needles....	5,500	53.0	5.6	33.0	14.0
Scots pine	Branches	11,700	35.0	4.4	32.0	21.0
18 years	Bark	6,500	27.0	3.0	18.5	15.0
	Wood	25,300	20.0	1.8	19.5	12.0
	All parts ...	49,000	135.0	14.8	103.0	62.0
Plot E	Needles....	4,200	60.0	6.4	23.0	13.0
Scots pine	Branches ..	12,500	54.0	6.9	33.5	22.0
28 years	Bark	7,500	34.0	4.5	20.5	18.0
	Wood	59,800	52.0	4.5	38.0	24.0
	All parts ...	84,000	200.0	22.3	115.0	77.0
Plot F	Needles....	4,200	45.5	4.9	17.0	20.0
Scots pine	Branches...	14,900	47.5	5.9	26.0	32.0
64 years	Bark	12,700	33.0	5.1	17.0	74.0
	Wood	74,200	57.0	4.4	29.0	54.0
	All parts ...	106,000	183.0	20.3	89.0	180.0

Table 13–2 on a total pounds-per-acre basis, as well as changes with age from 18 to 48 years for Corsican pine and to 64 years for Scots pine. Remezov (1956) has provided data for a number of different forest types showing the age of greatest consumption for several elements (Table 13–4).

The importance of a consideration of the total elemental cycle has been recently emphasized by Ovington (1959, 1960). The usually low beginning fertility status of most forest soil and the fact that large quantities of elements can be immobilized in the tree and

TABLE 13–4

CONSUMPTION OF ELEMENTS OF NUTRITION BY DIFFERENT TYPES OF FORESTS.
(FROM REMEZOV, 1956.)

| Type of Forest | Age | kg/ha Annually | | | |
		N	Ca	K	P
Pinetum	14	36.7	22.3	17.3	4.2
vacciniosum	30	47.0	43.0	19.4	5.9
	45	56.8	36.1	19.8	5.1
	70	25.4	21.6	8.9	2.5
	95	13.0	13.5	4.6	1.3
Piceetum	24	16.2	14.7	7.6	2.6
myrtilloso	38	61.8	52.0	37.8	12.8
oxalidosum	50	39.9	33.6	18.8	6.4
	72	33.0	31.4	14.8	4.3
	93	27.6	25.5	9.0	3.8
Tilietum	13	59	77	30	6
aegopodioso-	25	85	111	50	9
caricosum	·40	73	96	42	8
	74	87	115	46	11
Queroetum	12	50	96	30	15
aegopodiosum	25	154	223	68	18
	48	75	134	41	18
	93	49	84	20	12
	130	68	122	26	11
Tremuletum	10	68	118	40	12
aegopodioso-	25	107	161	80	12
caricosum	30	120	181	86	13
	50	85	123	75	8
Betuletum	10	199	109	125	24
mixto-herbosum	25	160	88	122	22
	37	67	63	45	12
	62	42	45	32	11

litter for a long time lend support to the need for such data. The effect of different management practices on the cycle is being evaluated.

Total elemental cycle investigations are also important in understanding problems related to the efficiency of elements applied to a forest stand. It is particularly desirable to know how much of the element enters into the organic cycle immediately, or how much is lost through soil leaching. Also important is how much of the element taken up may be recycled and continue to function to supply nutrient needs, or how much is deposited in more permanent portions of the tree and removed from the cycle in the harvest. For instance, potassium may go through a rapid cycle and the same ions be used more than once in a growing season, as compared to a slower cycle for phosphorus.

Litter accumulation and humus layers are being studied for amounts and chemical composition as part of this work. The most active studies in this field seem to be taking place in New Zealand (Will, 1957, 1959) at the present time. Methods to accelerate the breakdown of deep raw humus layers and thus get elements contained therein back into a useful cycle have been under intensive study in Germany (Wittich, 1952). This is also the subject of considerable thought in the Pacific Northwest where thick humus layers on alpine soils pose definite forest soil problems.

The general importance of the forest debris layer is brought out by recent data of Ovington and Madgwick (1959), who found that after 33 years there were about equal quantities of dead and living material in a Scots pine plantation. The following distribution of elements was found:

Element	Portion in Forest Ecosystem (Per Cent)	
	Litter and Dead Plants	Boles of Trees
K	42	22
Ca	59	21
Mg	39	29
P	66	10
N	82	5

The complete dry weight of organic matter and elements for the same stand is given in Table 13–5. For all elements except magnesium the weight in the litter exceeds that in the living tree.

Other Problems

The nature of the response to a particular element and the growth processes involved in the tree are basic questions yet to be answered. For instance, a great deal of evidence indicates a universal nitrogen deficiency of soils and forest plants in northwestern America. However, the reasons why supposedly good forest soils should be deficient in nitrogen are not known. There is apparently a nitrogen reserve effect, as seedlings grown in the nursery for 2 years with a nitrogen spray at the end of the second year still show height growth stimulation of 20 per cent four years after out-planting. As another example both height and diameter growth of trees are increased by nitrogen addition but the position of greatest volume change within the tree is not known.

TABLE 13-5

DISTRIBUTION (IN KILOGRAMS PER HECTARE) OF ORGANIC MATTER AND NUTRI-ENTS IN 33-YEAR-OLD PLANTATION OF *Pinus sylvestris*. (FROM OVINGTON AND MADGWICK, 1959.)

Item	O. D. Weight	Na	K	Ca	Mg	P	N
Leaves	7,300	3	43	36	6	9	89
Living branches	14,000	2	39	30	7	7	52
Dead branches	9,700	1	4	13	2	2	27
Boles	118,800	—	84	115	24	12	97
Roots	32,700	1	43	27	11	7	48
Rootlets	3,400	1	11	6	2	4	33
Total for living trees	185,900	8	224	227	52	41	346
Ground flora	10	1	1	1	1	1	1
Dead trees (exclusive of root system)	9,600	1	1	6	1	1	9
Fresh litter (L)	2,900	1	3	11	1	2	28
More decomposed litter (F–H).	107,700	33	162	311	30	76	1,594
Total	306,100	43	390	555	83	119	1,977

The importance of a continuous and certain seed crop from forest trees is beginning to receive needed attention. Many seed produc-tion areas are being set up and an integral part of treatment of such areas is maintenance of proper tree nutrition. In recent years, a number of studies have shown the role of tree nutrition in seed production (Steinbrenner, *et al.*, 1960; Mergen and Voigt, 1960). Results have been mainly in improved quantity of seed from a given area and are similar to those reported for oranges by Tomi and Wolfe (1956). The possibility of causing stands to produce seed at an earlier age, and making seed yield less variable have also been demonstrated. These experimental treatments are being put to immediate use by practicing foresters, without benefit of com-plete information.

The question of improved forest tree nutrition and subsequent changes in growth rate invariably lead to consideration of quality of the forest product. Quality studies are somewhat beyond the realm of tree nutrition, but nevertheless do confront the forest-tree nutritionist. Changes in length of fibers, cell wall thickness, and general density are all involved. Some recent work by Rendle (1958) suggests that density increases with distance from pith and therefore it would be more economical to increase growth rates of larger trees. Quality of product can also refer to other uses of trees such as Christmas trees, in which case foliage color, and density are important factors and can be controlled through tree nutrition.

Forest-Tree Nutrition Work in the Pacific Northwest

Basic studies on elemental needs of forest trees has been in progress for ten years. Results for western red cedar (Walker *et al.*, 1955) have been published and work has been completed on several other species but has not, as yet, been published. Some attention has also been given to the best composition of nutrient solutions for growth of conifers. Various cultural techniques have been used in greenhouse work from nutrient solution to sand cultures and pot tests.

So far, nutrition survey work has led to more intensive development of specific problems. The role of soil phosphorus has proved to be puzzling and is currently being examined further by determining various kinds of soil phosphorus to relate to uptake. Many soils demonstrating unique phosphorus problems are unusually high in iron and aluminum, and are filled with iron concretions. Undoubtedly iron phosphates are formed which are available to Douglas-fir but not to some other plants. Mycorrhizae have been conveniently used to explain this absorption of phosphorus by forest trees by Stone (1949). Techniques now under investigation will allow pure culture growth of mycorrhizal fungi and forest trees, and more detailed study of phosphorus problems (Trappe, 1957).

Nitrogen nutrition studies of forest trees include the following:

1. Diagnostic techniques using both soil and plants
2. Fixation of nitrogen in forest soils, particularly associated tree species such as red alder
3. The role of nitrogen in flowering and seed production
4. The effect of nitrogen status on quality of the forest crop
5. The cycle of nitrogen in a forest community

The diagnostic procedure study is important not only as a basis for recommending application of elements to forest lands but also to an understanding of elemental content of forest soils and distribution of elements within the plant. At the present time, a large-scale cooperative project for analysis of soils from experimental plots or areas of known forest production is underway. The analytical procedures have been standardized and results can be related to soil treatments or to production records.

Foliar analysis is being continued with crown class of trees, position of sample in the crown, age of needles, and season of the year as variables. In addition, data on the distribution of nitrogen within the tree, comparing wood, bark, needles, cones, seed have been collected. The nitrogen content of a standardized foliage sample has been related to color for diagnostic purposes. A nitrogen content of less than 1.1 per cent for Douglas-fir is considered to be critical.

Studies carried out in conjunction with the Pacific Northwest Forest and Range Experiment Station have added further information to our understanding of the role of red alder in the nitrogen supply of forest soils. In one extensive study (unpublished), soil nitrogen under a mixed 30-year-old alder–Douglas-fir stand was higher than under pure Douglas-fir of the same age on the same soil. Nitrogen content of the Douglas-fir foliage in the mixed stand is doubled over that of pure Douglas-fir and the trees are more vigorous. The role of understory vegetation associations in nitrogen nutrition and the nutrient requirements of some of the understory species are also being considered.

The tension lysimeter perfected by Cole (1960) is being used to study movement of water and essential elements in both treated and untreated forest stands. At the same time, an attempt is being made to determine the distribution of nitrogen within the forest community several years after application. Results should give some indication of efficiency of use of nitrogen by the forest as well as the regions of accumulation of nitrogen. Data from the study should help assess the importance of reserve storage for the beginning of growth following dormant periods. A recent review by Oland (1959) on apple trees indicates that this reserve is most important in the initiation of growth and that deficiency effects differ with the type of climate during the dormant period.

Large-scale field studies of the past few years have provided ample evidence of the growth response from addition of nitrogen to forest trees throughout the Pacific Northwest. Response is not only in total wood production but also for specialized forest crops such as seed. Studies are now in progress to evaluate the quality of the wood produced in relation to growth rate and treatment. For this purpose, wood laid down over a period of ten years is now available. A preliminary study has already been completed on one phase of this work (Erickson and Lambert, 1958). More intensive work will include detailed physical and chemical analysis of wood from treated and untreated trees.

Response to nitrogen by Douglas-fir has posed additional interesting problems such as whether the growing season is extended by fertilizer treatment or growth processes accelerated. The inter-relationship of mineral nutrition and water supply is investigated by soil moisture studies on treated plots as well as by irrigation treatments.

LITERATURE CITED

BAUR, G. N. 1959. A soil survey of a slash pine plantation, Barcoongere, N. S. W. Austral. Forestry 23(2): 78–87.
BEADLE, W. C. W., and Y. T. TCHAN. 1955. Nitrogen economy in semi-arid plant communities. I. The environment and general considerations. Proc. Linn. Soc. N. S. Wales Vol. LXXX (1) No. 377: 62–70.
BRUNING, D. 1959. Forstdüngung; Ergebnisse alterer und jüngerer Versuche. (Radebeul) Neumann Leipzig. 210 pp.
COLE, D. W., S. P. GESSEL, and E. E. HELD. 1960. Tension lysimeter studies in glacial till and coral atoll soils. Proc. Soil Sci. Soc. 25: 321–325.
ERICKSON, H. D., and G. M. G. LAMBERT. 1958. Effects of fertilization and thinning on chemical composition growth and specific gravity of young Douglas fir. Forest Sci. 4(4): 307–315.
GAGNOM, D., A. LAFOND, and L. P. AMIOT. 1958. Mineral nutrient content of some forest plant leaves and of the humus layer as related to site quality. Can. Jour. Bot. 36(2): 209–220.
HEIBERG, S. O., L. LEYTON, and H. LOEWENSTEIN. 1959. Influence of K Fertilizer level on red pine planted at various spacings on a K-deficient site. Forest Sci. 5(2): 142–153.
INGESTAD, T. 1958–59. Studies on manganese deficiency in a forest stand. Medd. Fran. Statens Skogsforskningsinstitat. 48(4). 20 pp.
———. 1959. Studies on the nutrition of forest tree seedlings. II. Mineral nutrition of spruce. Physiol. Plant. (12): 568–593.
INTERNATIONAL POTASH INSTITUTE. 1959. The nutrition of citrus crops. 67 pp.
ISHIZAKA, Y., and A. TANAKA. 1955. A proposed method to determine adequate amount of fertilizer to be applied to crops. Soil and Plant Food 1(1): 5–6.
LEYTON, L. 1958. The mineral requirements of forest plants. Handb. der Pflanzenphysiol. Berlin. 4: 1026–1037.
LUTZ, H. J. 1958. Geology and soil in relation to forest vegetation. 1st North Amer. Forest Soils Conf. 75–85.
MERGEN, F., and G. K. VOIGT. 1960. Effect of fertilizer application on two generations of slash pine. Proc. Soil Sci. Soc. In press.
MILLER, R. B., and F. B. HURST. 1957. The quantity and nutrient content of hard beech litter. N. Zeal. For. Res. Note 8. 14 pp.
Mineral nutrition of trees: A symposium. 1959. Duke Univ. Forestry Bull. 15. 184 pp.
NICHOLES, D. J. D. 1957. The function of trace metals in the nitrogen metabolism of plants. Ann. Bot. 21(84): 587–598.
OLAND, K. 1959. Nitrogenous reserves of apple trees. Physiol. Plant. 12: 594–618.
OVINGTON, J. D. 1956. The composition of tree leaves. Forestry 29(1): 22–28.
———. 1960. The nutrient cycle and its modification through silvicultural practice. 5th World Forestry Cong., Seattle, Wash. In press.
OVINGTON, J. D., and A. A. I. MADGWICK. 1959. Distribution of organic matter and plant nutrients in a plantation of Scots pine. Forest Sci. 5(4): 344–355.
PURNELL, E. M. 1958. Nutritional studies of Pinus radiata (Don.). I. Symptoms due to deficiency of some major elements. Austral. Forestry 22(2): 82–87.
REMEZOV, N. P. 1956. The role of the biological circulation of the elements in soil formation under forests. 6th Internatl. Cong. Soil Sci. 43: 269.
———. 1958. Relation between biological accumulation and eluvial process under forest cover. Soviet Soil Sci. 6: 589–599.

RENDLE, B. J., and E. W. J. PHILLIPS. 1958. The effect of rate of growth (ring width) on density of softwoods. Forestry 31(2): 113–120.

RENNIE, P. J. 1955. The uptake of nutrients by mature forest growth. Plant and Soil 7(1): 49–95.

———. 1959. Some long term effects of the tree growth on soil productivity. Proc. 9th Internatl. Bot. Cong. Vol. II. Sect. 2A.

RUTTER, A. J. 1955. The relation between dry weight increase and linear measures of growth in young conifers. Forestry 28(2): 123–135.

———. 1957. Studies in the growth of young plants of *Pinus sylvestris*. I. The annual cycle of assimilation and growth. Ann. Bot. 21(83): 399–426.

STEINBRENNER, E. C., J. W. DUFFIELD, and R. K. CAMPBELL. 1960. Increased cone production of young Douglas fir following nitrogen and phosphorus fertilization. Jour. Forestry 58(2): 105–110.

STOATE, T. N. 1950. Nutrition of the pine. Austral. Forestry and Timber Bur. Bull. 30. 61 pp.

———. 1957. Types of tree producing soils. Proc. West. Forestry Conserv. Assoc. 48:25–26.

STONE, E. L. 1949. Some effects of mycorrhizae on the phosphorus nutrition of Monterey pine seedlings. Soil Sci. Soc. Proc. 14: 340–345.

SWAN, H. S. D. 1960. The mineral nutrition of Canadian pulpwood species. I. The influence of nitrogen, phosphorus, potassium and magnesium deficiencies on the growth and development of white spruce, black spruce, Jack pine, and western hemlock seedlings grown in a controlled environment. Woodlands Res. Index 116. 66 pp.

TAMM, C. O. 1951. Removal of plant nutrients from tree crowns by rain. Physiol. plant. 4: 184–188.

———. 1951. Seasonal variation in composition of birch leaves. Physiol. plant. 4: 461–469.

TIDBALL, R. R. 1957. The effect of dry heat on available phosphorus in forest soils. Unpublished Master's thesis, University of Washington College of Forestry.

TOMI, E. L., and H. S. WOLFE. 1956. A study of some responses of Florida citrus trees to nitrogen application and irrigation. Proc. Amer. Soc. Hort. Sci. 65: 113–120.

TRAPPE, J. M. 1957. Some probable mycorrhizal associations in the Pacific Northwest. Northwest Sci. 31(4): 183–185.

VAN ECK, W. A., and E. P. WHITESIDE. 1958. Soil classification as a tool in predicting forest growth. 1st North Amer. Forest Soils Conf. 218–226.

VYVYAN, M. C. 1957. An analysis of growth and form in young apple trees. I. Relative growth and net assimilation in 1 and 2 yr. old. Ann. Bot. 4(83): 479–497.

WALKER, R. B., S. P. GESSEL, and P. G. HADDOCK. 1955. Greenhouse studies in mineral requirements of conifers: Western red cedar. Forest Sci. 1(1): 51–60.

WILL, G. M. 1957. Variations in the mineral content of Radiata pine needles with age and position in tree crown. New Zeal. Forest Res. Note 11, Rpt. New Zeal. Jour. Sci. and Technol. 38(7): 13–25.

———. 1959. Nutrient return in litter and rainfall under some exotic conifer stands in New Zeal. New Zeal. Forest. Res. Note 18. Rpt. New Zeal. Jour. of Agr. 2(4): 719–734.

WITTICH, W. 1952. Der heutige Stand unseres Wissens vom Humus und neue wege zur Losung des Rohhumusproblems im Walde. Schriftenreihe der Forst. Fakult., Gottingen Univ. 4. 106 pp.

———. 1960. Classification, mapping and interpretation of soils for forestry purposes. 5th World Forestry Cong. In press.

WRIGHT, T. M. 1957. Abnormalities in nutrient uptake by Corsican pine on sand dunes. Jour. Soil Sci. 8(1): 150–157.

WRIGHT, T. M., and G. M. WILL. 1958. The nutrient content of Scots and Corsican pines growing on sand dunes. Forestry 31(1): 13–25.

14

Root Grafting and Non-competitive Relationships Between Trees

F. H. Bormann

The principal relationship between plants is thought to be one of competition for required components of the environment. Thus individuals growing close together are thought to alter each other's environment by utilizing available supplies of water, nutrients, and light; stresses induced by overutilization result in a general reduction of growth and often in the death of some of the competing organisms. This theory is admirably supported by facts gathered not only through centuries of empirical experience in growing plants, but also through more recent experiments designed specifically to test the effects of competition.

Although the competition theory was probably developed through experience gained with herbaceous agricultural plants, it has been widely accepted by forest botanists and used to explain relationships between forest trees. Thus, under certain conditions, the success of some trees and the failure of others is generally ascribed to differences in the competitive ability of the individuals. This idea is the touchstone from which most botanists proceed in their analysis of forest tree behavior. It also underlies the universally accepted idea in forestry that under given environmental conditions each tree has, in theory, an ideal growing space. The regular spacing of trees in a forest tree plantation or in artificially thinned forests is a reflection of this theory.

It now appears that the interpretation of the tree as a strictly individual entity is, in many instances, open to serious question. Evidence amassed, particularly in the last decade, indicates that root grafts or fusions between roots of two or more trees are common. The existence of continuity of conducting tissues between trees opens the possibility that biological activities in one may be directly influenced by another through biophysical and biochemical forces exerted through natural root grafts. These forces exerted directly by one tree on another may play an important role, along with competition, in shaping the nature of the forest community.

Three categories of root grafts occur in nature. Although the most common type involves self grafts or grafts between roots of an individual tree, these are germane to the present discussion only when they enter into complexes of grafts between trees. Interspecific grafts between roots of trees of different species, although of considerable biological interest, are relatively rare so far as is now known. Intraspecific grafts between roots of trees of the same species are common and it is with these that most of the following paragraphs will deal.

For a long time, natural root grafts have been known as a botanical curiosity and reports of their occurrence have appeared sporadically throughout the literature of botany and forestry. These came primarily from direct sightings of grafts or from observations that certain seemingly dead stumps continued to live and grow in diameter. It was discovered that these living stumps were invariably connected to living trees through root grafts—a conclusion confirmed by injection of radioisotopes into stumps and their later detection in adjacent trees (Fig. 14–1). Additional reports are found in the literature of plant pathology where root grafts were found to be responsible for the transmission of disease organisms from tree to tree.

Prior to 1950, although dozens of articles contained reports of root grafts, there was little recognition of their widespread occurrence or their potential significance in forest ecology. Since that time, by means of tracer techniques and excavation, the occurrence and function of root grafts have received increasing study from botanists around the world, particularly in the United States, Finland, and the Soviet Union.

For the past 4 years, the writer has studied root grafting in white pine forests growing on a wide range of sites in New Hampshire, Maine, and Vermont, and the results of this continuing study indicate that grafting is a much more common phenomenon than previously suspected.

In 1957, 84 experimental plots were established in five white pine stands selected to represent different age classes and various soil conditions (Bormann and Graham, 1959). Each plot was composed of a central donor tree, whose top was removed and whose stump was injected with either a radioisotope or dye, and the adjacent potential receptor trees. These were examined periodically for the presence of the injected substance. Of the 81 trees and 3 living stumps injected, 41 were found to be grafted to a total of 54 receptor

Fɪɢ. 14–1. A living stump showing graft connections with the living tree on the left.

trees (Table 14–1). These data indicated that root grafting involving 30 to 67 per cent of the injected trees occurred on all sites—regardless of age of stand, soil, or drainage conditions.

Exposure of the root systems on several plots revealed networks of grafts between trees and indicated that often several trees were united rather than two or three, as shown by our detection methods. A union of several trees whose grafted roots were exposed on the surface of a bog is probably characteristic of similar unions found in upland situations—especially in old natural stands (Fig. 14–2). In the bog union, the roots of six large trees are fused into one anastomosing root network.

These results of the injection study were substantiated by other studies on the prevalence of living stumps in natural stands and on

TABLE 14–1

NATURAL ROOT GRAFTS IN WHITE PINE STANDS, DETECTED THROUGH USE OF
RADIOISOTOPES AND DYES. ALL STANDS LOCATED IN NORTHERN NEW ENGLAND.
(FROM BORMANN AND GRAHAM, 1959.)

Stand Number	Average Age of Stand (Years)	Density (Stems per 100 m²)	Average d.b.h.(cm.)	Number of Donor Stumps	Number of Donor Stumps Grafted	Number of Receptor Trees
1	15	117	7	20	10	11
2	19	69	8	20	6	7
3	27	30	16	20	10	14
4	39	16	20	9	4	5
5	55	4	31	12	8	14
5	Stumps	4	31	3	3	3
			Total	84	41	54

the per cent of damage incurred by translocation of poison from
treated to non-treated trees in white pine stands thinned with silvi-
cides (Fig. 14–3) (Bormann and Graham, 1959). A more recent
report indicates that entire quarter acre blocks of 35-year-old, naturally occurring stands were wiped out following thinning with
ammate (S. W. Pulitzer, personal communication). Further evidence on the intensity of grafting comes from Professor K. A.
Armson who found the roots of all the trees in a 90-year-old white
pine stand on thin sandy soil to be fused into a single network
(personal communication).

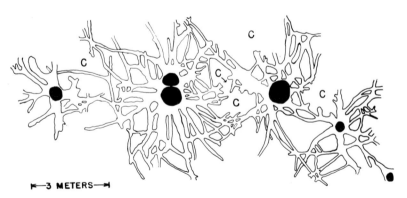

⊢—3 METERS—⊣

FIG. 14–2. Diagram of a root network exposed on the surface of a deep,
partially drained peat soil. Black circles represent stumps and C's indicate areas
where some roots have been removed by chopping. Both self-grafts and intraspecific grafts are found in the complex. From Bormann and Graham (1959).

The evidence to date indicates that grafting occurs in stands of all ages, and in stands growing in coarse sand, loams, stony soils, soils free of stones, well-drained soils, poorly drained soils, and extremely wet peat soils. It is concluded that given proper spacing conditions, grafting will occur among white pine trees growing under the whole range of conditions tolerated by the species population.

FIG. 14–3. The tree on the right was killed by ammate translocated through natural root grafts from the tree on the left. From Bormann and Graham (1959).

Evidence from other investigations suggests that our results may be applicable to a wide range of forest tree species. Notable work by Yli-Vakkuri (1953) in Finland indicates that up to 28 per cent of the trees in older Scots pine forests are grafted. In the U.S.S.R., Junovidov (1952) has estimated 26, 30, and 45 per cent, respectively, of the trees in young forests of Siberian pine, larch, and fir are grafted. Among 35-year-old trees in a plantation of Crimean pine, Beskaravainya (1956) found 50 per cent of the trees to be grafted. Studying a German spruce stand, Wichmann (1925) found 462 living stumps and 3,334 living trees. Since the root system of each stump was grafted to at least one living tree, and many of the trees were undoubtedly grafted to each other, this stand must have been a maze of root grafts. The extreme of root grafting has been reported by Kuntz and Riker (1956) for dense stands of northern pin oak growing in Wisconsin. Using radioisotope tracers they found practically all trees to be united with their neighbors.

In summation, Graham and Bormann (unpublished) have compiled a bibliography of 171 references containing reports of intraspecific root grafting in 105 species of forest trees. Based on the degree of grafting mentioned in each report and the number of times grafting has been reported for each species, they have concluded that grafting is a common phenomenon in 63 of these species including such important trees as white, red, and Scots pine, European and American beech, Douglas-fir, eastern hemlock, red oak, and American elm. Thus, there seems little doubt that intraspecific root grafting is a widespread phenomenon of considerable potential importance.

The role of intraspecific grafts in the physiology and ecology of grafted trees is slowly unfolding. The movement of water, minerals, food, dyes, and poisons, up to distances of 43 feet between trees, indicates that grafts function in the transport of substances (Bormann, 1959). In a study of the rate of water intake by freshly cut stumps, Graham (1960) found a correlation between the rate of intake and weather conditions conducive to high water losses through the leaves of trees grafted to the stumps. Apparently stresses on the water-conducting system, developed as a result of water loss from the intact trees, were felt throughout the grafted root system and were, in part, responsible for regulating the rate of intake by the stumps.

Another indication of how one tree may influence another is provided by the observation that radioisotopes moving in the root system of one tree are frequently shunted through grafts to the root system of another tree (Yli-Vakkuri 1953, Bormann and Graham, unpublished data). The observation that radioisotopes move predominantly from tall, vigorous oaks to small oaks, has prompted the suggestion that the former may aid in the survival of the latter (Kuntz and Riker, 1956).

To better understand the development of unions of grafted trees within a stand, Bormann and Graham (1959) studied grafting in white pine stands of various ages. Based on these data the following hypothesis is proposed:

Early in the life of a stand, some trees become grafted together in unions, while other trees remain as individuals. As the stand matures and the trees become larger, root systems increase in size, and a union may coalesce with an adjacent union or individual. Throughout this period, the tendency to add new members to the union is counteracted by the death of some of the members. However, death of a tree proceeds from the top down and often the root system remains alive and functional within the graft complex for years after the top has decayed and toppled over. In the older

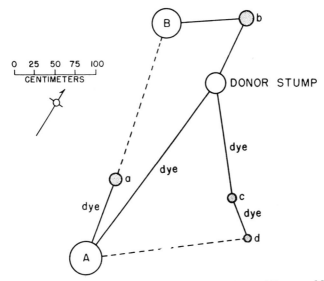

Fig. 14–4. Diagram of a union of trees detected in a 55-year-old stand by means of dye injection. Living trees are represented as open circles, while living stumps are shown as shaded circles. Solid lines mark grafts disclosed by dye transfer and/or excavation. From Bormann and Graham (1959).

stands, the union is often represented by one to several robust trees surrounded by one to several living stumps (Fig. 14–4). As a particular union matures the more vigorous trees come to dominate the group, while less vigorous companions succumb, leaving only their roots to function in the union. The exact function of a "captured" root system is not known, but it seems likely that it is at first utilized by the dominant tree in the absorption of water and minerals. Later, living stumps may prolong their survival at the expense of the dominant tree and in a sense parasitize it. This is one of the fundamental areas for future research.

The discovery of the mechanisms by which a few trees are able to dominate a union is a major objective. Perhaps because of some initial advantage of size, vigor, or heredity these trees are able to establish gradients that cause water and minerals absorbed by the root complex to move primarily to them at the expense of their less vigorous companions. Another mechanism by which dominant trees may influence smaller trees grafted to them was suggested by the results of recent field work (Bormann, unpublished data).

The initiation, in the spring, of cambial growth within the twigs, branches, and trunk of a tree is thought to be triggered by an auxin moving down the stem from the site of its production in the expanding buds (Wareing, 1951). A study of the stumps of trees detopped in early March and known to be free of grafts with intact trees indicated that, although many stay alive for the first growing season after cutting, none exhibit diameter growth. The cambial zone was always found adjacent to last summer's wood. Microscopic examination of the cambial regions of these stumps indicated that the cells were alive and healthy. Stored food (starch grains) was present in some as was cyclosis. In general, these sections conformed to Abbe and Crafts' (1939) description of the cambial region prior to cambial activation. The failure of the cambium to resume activity was apparently due to the lack of the triggering factor. Conversely, stumps grafted to living trees resumed normal cambial activity probably following the transfer of the triggering factor through grafts from the intact tree. Apparently one tree has been able to initiate activities in the stump of the other. This raises the speculation that large trees whose buds break first would be able to initiate cambial activities in smaller trees grafted to them before their own buds break. The implications of this are not wholly clear, but premature initiation may introduce a serious element of disharmony into the normal processes of development and mobilization of stored foods. Perhaps this is one of the ways that larger trees gradually bring about the demise of the tops of smaller trees while their roots are retained as part of the root complex.

What is the ecological importance of root grafting? Often abandoned or disturbed land is occupied by dense stands composed of a single species; for example, white pine and red spruce in New England; red, white, and jack pine in the Lake States; and loblolly, shortleaf, and longleaf pine in the Southeast. These stands of single species, and others like them throughout the world, are supposed to exhibit competition par excellence since the trees are crowded and each tree has almost identical requirements. Attrition over a period of a few years is great, and often up to 98 per cent of the trees may be eliminated in five to ten decades. The usual explanation for this ecological paring process is severe competition.

Experience with white pine, however, indicates that the importance of competition as a factor in stand development may be severely overrated. It seems likely that competition plays the important role during the first five or ten years of the existence of a stand. Thereafter, unions begin to form and the stand must be visualized as being composed of unions of grafted trees interspersed with non-grafted individuals. The number of trees in any stand occurring in unions or as individuals is primarily a function of the age of the stand and the space between trees. In the extreme, it is conceivable that an entire stand may be united in a single anastomosing root network. Competition may eliminate the less-fit individuals or unions, but, within the unions, which often contain the majority of trees in the stand, forces operating through root grafts will determine which trees will remain as dominant entities.

Whether or not these results apply to other species is a matter for future research, but it seems likely that some of the numerous species where root grafting is common will react in a similar way. In other species, it is probable that root grafting may have different effects; for example, in oak stands root grafts may aid in the survival of smaller trees while in white pine they may hasten the demise of smaller trees.

At any rate, these findings, that many forest trees do not always occur as individual entities, and that biological forces other than competition may play a major role in shaping a developing stand, open a wholly new aspect of basic research in interplant relationships. They also bring into question practices in applied forestry based either on the concept of the forest tree as an individual or on the concept of competition as the dominant biotic force in stand development.

LITERATURE CITED

ABBE, L. B., and A. S. CRAFTS. 1939. Phloem of white pine and other coniferous species. Bot. Gaz. 100: 695–722.

BESKARAVAINYA, M. M. 1956. The formation of groups in pine plantings of the Kamyshinsk Forest Improvement Support Point. In Russian. Agrobiologyia 1: 143–146. (Biol. Abs. 32(11): 38517. 1958.)

BORMANN, F. H. 1959. Intraspecific root grafts and transport. Proc. 9th Internatl. Bot. Cong. 2: 40–41.

BORMANN, F. H., and B. F. GRAHAM, JR. 1959. The occurrence of natural root grafting in eastern white pine, Pinus strobus L., and its ecological implications. Ecol. 40: 677–691.

GRAHAM, B. F., JR. 1960. Natural root grafting and the intake of dye by freshly cut stumps of eastern white pine, Pinus strobus L. Ecol. 41: 56–64.

JUNOVIDOV, A. P. 1952. Intraspecific relationships in the forest. In Russian. Lesn. Hoz. 5(8): 11–13. (F.A. 16: 3887. 1955.)

KUNTZ, J. E., and A. J. RIKER. 1956. The use of radioisotopes to ascertain the role of root grafting in the translocation of water, nutrients, and disease inducing organisms among forest trees. Proc. Internatl. Conf. Peaceful Uses Atomic Energy. 12: 1440148. (Geneva, Switzerland.)

WAREING, P. F. 1951. Growth studies in woody species. IV. The initiation of cambial activity in ring porous species. Physiol. Plant. 4: 546–562.

WICHMANN, H. E. 1925. Wurzelverwachsungen und Stockuberwallung bei Abietineen. 261. Ges. Forstw. 51: 250–258.

YLI-VAKKURI, P. 1953. Tutkimuksia puiden välisistä elimellisistä juuryihteyksistä männiköissä. German summary. Acta. Forest. Fenn. 60: 1–117.

15

Physiological Aspects of Mycorrhizae of Forest Trees

Elias Melin

As is well known, most forest trees live in close association with certain soil fungi that cause characteristic fungus-root structures called mycorrhizae. The ectotrophic (and ectendotrophic) mycorrhizae, especially those of pine, spruce, beech, oak, and birch have been studied in great detail. Facts accumulated during the last few decades confirm the view that these mycorrhizae are nutrient-absorbing structures beneficial to or even essential for trees in most habitats. During recent years the interest in ectotrophic mycorrhizae has increased appreciably all over the world. On the other hand, surprisingly little attention has been paid to the endotrophic tree mycorrhizae and therefore not much is known about their physiology. This paper deals exclusively with ectotrophic and ectendotrophic mycorrhizae, whose study has engaged the writer for many years. Because of the short time available, this discussion will be confined mainly to the conditions for mycorrhizal formation.

The first question arising in this connection is: Why are tree mycorrhizae formed in nature? A few years ago it was not unusual to hear a teleological answer: mycorrhizae are formed because they are necessary for the development of seedlings and trees. Such an explanation of mycorrhizal development is, of course, scientifically unacceptable. The first phase in the development of mycorrhizae seems logically to be that sufficiently virulent hyphae of a mycorrhiza-producing fungus enter the rootlets, since these contain metabolites essential for development of the fungus. The second phase consists of an interaction between substances released by the invading hyphae and the root cells. This interaction produces the mycorrhizae. For an understanding of the nature of these structures

247

it is therefore important to know the fungal species which give rise to them in nature.

Kelley (1950) has claimed that there are no mycorrhizal fungi but only a mycorrhizal state. According to him, almost any fungus can apparently be a mycorrhiza producer and he therefore attaches little importance to the identity of the fungus. However, he has produced no evidence supporting his view. The first biological analyses of tree mycorrhizae were performed by the writer about 40 years ago (Melin, 1921, 1923, 1925). From mycorrhizae of pine and spruce a number of fungi were isolated which, with seedlings in pure cultures, produced mycorrhizae with the same appearance as those from which they had been isolated. Most of the mycorrhizal mycelia had clamp-connections characteristic of *Basidiomycetes*, although only a few isolates could be identified. Other pure culture experiments showed, however, that a great number of forest soil mushrooms belonging to the higher fungi (*Hymenomycetes* and *Gasteromycetes*) produce ectotrophic and ectendotrophic mycorrhizae with trees. This finding has been confirmed by later studies in Sweden and elsewhere. It is a remarkable feature that many different fungal species are able to form mycorrhizae with the same tree species. In Scots pine (*Pinus silvestris*), which has been studied most thoroughly in this respect, more than 40 species, some of them only slightly related, have so far been proved to be mycorrhizal fungi. The actual number may no doubt be many times larger.

It has been shown by the writer and other workers that different tree mycorrhizal fungi and even different strains of the same fungal species can differ physiologically in a good many respects (Melin, 1953, 1960; Moser, 1959). It is therefore of greatest interest to discover the common reason for their associations with roots. Already 75 years ago Frank suggested that the fungal associates obtain carbohydrates from their higher partner. Björkman (1942, 1944, 1949), who studied conditions for the formation of tree mycorrhizae, provided powerful support for this hypothesis. In his experiments with pine seedlings he found a correlation between the amounts of soluble carbohydrates in the roots and mycorrhizal frequency. He concluded that conditions for development of mycorrhizae are optimal when the roots contain a surplus of sugar, whereas a deficiency of soluble carbohydrates in the roots strongly suppresses the formation of mycorrhizae. Therefore, factors influencing the amounts of soluble carbohydrates in the roots, particularly light and available amounts of nitrogen and phosphorus in the soil, indirectly influence mycorrhizal frequency.

By means of the isotope technique Uppsala workers have recently been able to prove that tree mycorrhizal Basidiomycetes obtain carbonaceous substances from the roots (Melin and Nilsson, 1957). The test material consisted of pine seedlings aseptically grown in Erlenmeyer flasks and inoculated with known mycorrhizal fungi. When mycorrhizae had formed, the intact seedlings were exposed for ½ to 1 hour to an atmosphere containing C^{14}-labeled CO_2. The seedlings were then left intact for 5 hours, to make sure that the tagged photosynthate had reached the roots. The radiocarbon contents of uninfected root tips and those of hyphal sheaths of the mycorrhizae were then compared. It was evident from these experiments that great amounts of carbonaceous compounds originating from photosynthesis had been transferred to the associated mycorrhizal mycelia.

It may be concluded that a similar flow of organic material from the mycotrophic host plant to its fungal associate occurs in nature, even though it may vary quantitatively as well as qualitatively with various external and internal conditions. This flow no doubt contains substances indispensable for the mycorrhizal fungi. It seems likely that some of these substances are responsible for the first phase in mycorrhizal development.

A large part of the organic material obtained from the roots may serve as a source of energy for the fungus, in accordance with the hypothesis of Björkman. Our physiological investigations have shown that tree mycorrhizal fungi use simple carbohydrates, particularly glucose, maltose, and sucrose, as carbon and energy sources. They generally lack the ability to produce cellulase or have only a slight capacity to form adaptive enzymes for cellulose decomposition. However, there are exceptions to this rule. In a few cases, it has been found that cellulose-decomposing species such as *Tricholoma fumosum* and *Boletus subtomentosus* also are able to form mycorrhizae with pine under pure culture conditions (Lindeberg, 1948; Norkrans, 1950; Modess, 1941). So far as can be judged from present knowledge, the "sugar"-requiring types, however, dominate, and these may constitute the prototype for the fungal partners of ectotrophic tree mycorrhizae.

It seems unlikely that the sugar-requiring tree mycorrhizal fungi are able to satisfy their carbon requirements from the humus of forest soils, which contains only small amounts of sugars and other soluble carbohydrates. Some experiments with various species support this assumption. Autoclaved raw humus from coniferous woods in Sweden was used as a culture medium. When this humus contained no inhibitory substances the fungi grew fairly well when sugar had been added. In the control series without sugar, on the other hand, only a very slight growth occurred. It may therefore be true that, in nature, tree roots may constitute the main carbon source for sugar-requiring mycorrhizal fungi.

Regarding cellulose-decomposing fungi it seems unlikely that these produce the same physiological type of mycorrhiza as do sugar-requiring species. They may get their carbonaceous food material from the soil as well as from the roots, and have therefore been assumed to be facultative mycorrhizal fungi in nature. When living in mycorrhizal association with trees, they probably do not produce cellulase as long as soluble carbohydrates are available in the roots. However, when the roots no longer offer any excess of sugars or other soluble carbohydrates, cellulase is formed, which makes it possible for the hyphae to enter the cortical cells (Norkrans, 1950). According to Norkrans, this may furnish an explanation for ectendotrophic tree mycorrhizae.

MacDougal and Dufrenoy (1944, 1946) found that isolated segments of mycorrhizal pine roots could survive for many seasons like chlorophyll-less plants. These roots produced new mycorrhizae of normal appearance. These remarkable findings indicate that carbon compounds available to the fungal associate occurred in sufficient amounts in the soil concerned and these particular mycorrhizae had been formed by fungi that could utilize complex compounds of the soil as carbon and energy sources.

It remains to be seen whether cellulose-decomposing mycorrhizal fungi affect tree growth in other ways than sugar-requiring ones.

Besides carbohydrates, the flow of organic material from the roots also contains several other compounds essential for the normal development of tree mycorrhizal fungi. Exudates of attached roots of aseptically grown pine seedlings as well as exudates of excised pine roots contain vitamins, e.g., thiamin, and several amino acids, particularly glutamic acid and aspartic acid (Eriksson, 1960; Melin, 1960). Like many saprophytic soil Basidiomycetes, most tree mycorrhizal fungi were found to be deficient in one or more B-vitamins as well as in one or more amino acids or their corresponding keto acids (Norkrans, 1950, 1953; Melin, 1953, 1954, 1960). However, different fungal associates of the same tree species and even different strains of the same fungus have different demands in these respects. This indicates that, in nature, the main sources of these metabolites for tree mycorrhizal fungi may not be the roots but the soil. Deficiencies of tree mycorrhizal fungi in B-vitamins or amino acids (or their corresponding keto acids) may therefore be excluded as factors leading to their mycorrhizal relations to trees (Melin, 1954).

Finally, the roots also produce growth-promoting metabolites other than B-vitamins and amino acids, which are essential to the growth of tree mycorrhizal fungi. These unknown metabolites have been called "Factor M." The response of mycorrhizal Basidiomycetes to this factor was studied in "maximum" media containing, besides sugar and salts, ten B-vitamins and a mixture of nineteen amino acids (Melin, 1954; Melin and Das, 1954). Figure 15–1 il-

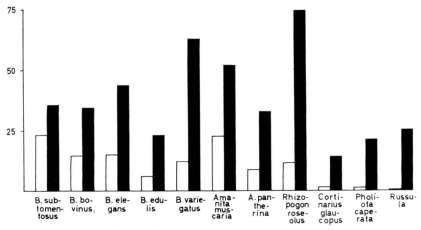

Fig. 15–1. Mycelial yield (dry weight in mg.) of various tree mycorrhizal *Basidiomycetes* in maximum nutrient solution with (black columns) and without (white columns) excised pine roots.

lustrates the results of a series of experiments with different species cultivated in such a nutrient solution in the presence of excised pine (*Pinus silvestris*) roots. As is shown, fungal growth was greatly promoted, although different species responded differently. The weakest response was found in some *Boletus* species and in *Amanita muscaria*, the strongest in slow-growing species such as *Russula xerampelina* and *Pholiota caperata*.

In other experiments, live tomato roots were found to affect the growth of tree mycorrhizal fungi in a similar way to pine roots. Since excised tomato roots grow much more rapidly in pure culture than pine roots, they have been used to a large extent for further studies of the M-factor. Figure 15–2 shows the growth curve of *Boletus variegatus* in maximum nutrient solution, supplemented with live tomato roots as activator. The growth rate of the mycelia

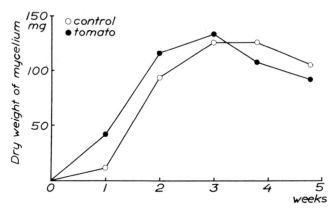

FIG. 15–2. Growth curves of *Boletus variegatus* D. in maximum nutrient solution with (solid symbols) and without (hollow symbols) excised tomato roots. From Melin and Das (1954).

was increased by the M-factor, particularly in the first stage of development, but the maximum mycelial yield reached about the same value as in the control. The growth curve of *Russula xerampelina* demonstrates quite a different behavior (Fig. 15–3). In the control the hyphal growth was very poor and soon ceased completely, with a maximum yield of less than 0.1 milligram, whereas the M-factor caused an average yield of 90 milligrams mycelial dry

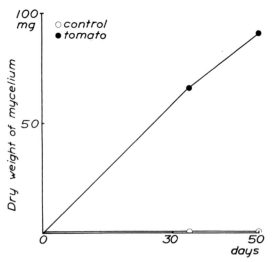

FIG. 15–3. Growth curves of *Russula xerampelina* in maximum nutrient solution with (solid symbols) and without (hollow symbols) excised tomato roots. From Melin and Das (1954).

weight in 50 days. It is evident that this fungus was capable of utilizing the nutrient solution only in the presence of the M-factor. This seems to indicate that it was unable to synthesize this factor. *B. variegatus*, on the other hand, was apparently only partially deficient in the M-factor.

In recent experiments some further *Russula* species tested (e.g., *R. aeruginea* Lindbl. ap Fr. and *R. fragilis* Pers ex Fr.) and *Lactarius helvus* (Fr.) Fr. had similar curves of growth response as *R. xerampelina*, whereas among others *L. rufus* (Scop. ex Fr.) Fr. and *L. mitissimus* (Fr.) Fr. had growth response curves similar to that of *B. variegatus*.

The influence of the M-factor on the growth rate of tree mycorrhizal fungi was also studied on agar plates by using the auxanographic method introduced by Beyerinck. In these experiments rapidly growing strains of *B. variegatus* were mainly used as test material. Measured volumes of a homogeneous suspension of very minute hyphal pieces were thoroughly mixed with melted nutrient agar (42–44° C) which had been supplemented with B-vitamins and amino acids, as mentioned above. Excised roots placed either directly in the nutrient agar or in celluloid sacs in the agar medium rapidly increased the development of the hyphal inocula around the root, which could be observed already after a few days. Figure 15–4 shows the effect of a pine root on the growth of the hyphal inocula after seven days of incubation. It is obvious that the M-factor, at least in part, had exuded from the root to the rhizosphere. The effect of root-exudates produced in redistilled water was also assayed by the cylinder plate method, as illustrated by Fig. 15–5.

The M-factor also conspicuously affected the germination of basidiospores of mycorrhizal Basidiomycetes. As is well known, these spores often have great difficulties in germinating on ordinary media in pure culture (Fries, 1943). In some cases, e.g., in the genus *Russula*, it seemed almost impossible to induce germination. It is therefore of great interest that excised roots, when added to a maximum nutrient medium, were able to induce germination of basidiospores in mycorrhizal Basidiomycetes, resulting in the development of fungal colonies. In some cases, e.g., *Boletus luteus* L. ex Fr. and *B. piperatus* Bull. ex Fr., the spores germinated in the nutrient solution also in the absence of roots (incubation period about 4 weeks). However, germination was greatly accelerated when roots were added, as is shown in Fig. 15–6. In this case the spores of *B. luteus* had germinated and formed mycelial colonies only around the root in 14 days. In other cases, e.g., *Amanita muscaria* (L. ex Fr.) and *Paxillus involutus* (Batsch ex Fr.) Fr., the spores germi-

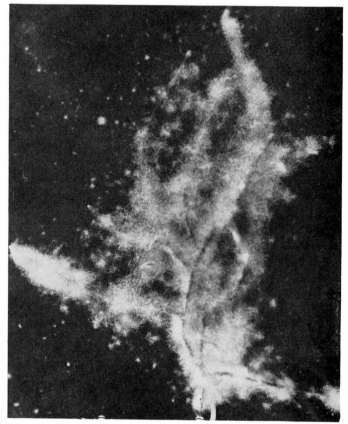

Fig. 15–4. *Boletus variegatus* E. Mycelial growth produced by a fungal suspension in an agar plate with maximum nutrient medium supplemented with excised pine root (4 months old). Incubation period 7 days. ×2.

nated only when the maximum nutrient medium had been supplemented with roots. A few species belonging to the genera *Cortinarius, Lactarius,* and *Russula* also showed good spore germination in synthetic nutrient solution in the presence of roots. *Russula adusta* (Pers. ex Fr.) and *Russula rosacea* Fr. germinated only when the solution had been supplemented with pine roots, whereas other species such as *R. fragilis* Pers. ex Fr., *R. integra* L. ex Fr., *Lactarius helvus* (Fr.) Fr. and *Cortinarius semisanguineus* (Fr.) Gill. also germinated in the presence of tomato roots as activator. It may be assumed that this spore germination factor is factor M.

However, it must be mentioned in this connection that experiments to study the spore germination capacity of several other *Russula* species were completely unsuccessful. This is difficult to

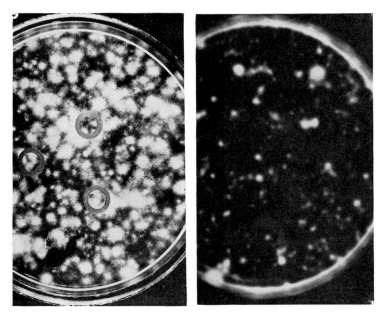

FIG. 15–5. *Boletus variegatus* F. Mycelial growth produced by a fungal suspension in agar plates with maximum nutrient medium, *right:* without supplement (control), *left:* supplemented with exudate of excised pine root. The glass cylinders contained exudate (about 25 units per plate) produced in redistilled water in 5 days at 4° C. Incubation period 8 days. ×0.8.

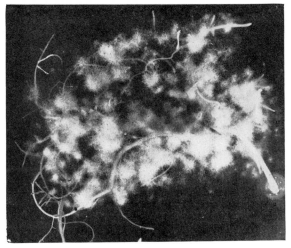

FIG. 15–6. *Boletus luteus.* Mycelial colonies produced by a suspension of basidiospores in an agar plate with maximum nutrient medium supplemented with excised pine root. Incubation period 14 days. ×1.7.

explain, but it seems that the nutrient solution used was not suitable in all cases.

Further experiments have confirmed that the M-factor is composed of at least two components, one of which is soluble and the other insoluble in water. The latter is also available to the fungal hyphae, presumably owing to their enzymatic activity.

The production of the M-factor in the roots seems to be influenced at least to a certain degree, by external supplies of certain

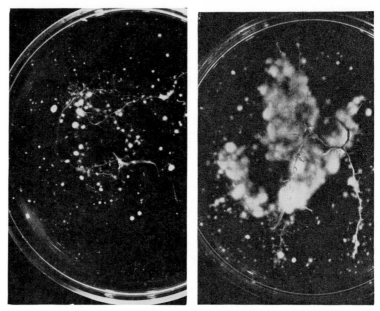

FIG. 15–7. *Boletus variegatus* C. Mycelial growth produced by a fungal suspension in agar plates with maximum nutrient medium supplemented with roots of pine seedlings grown aseptically for 10 months at different levels of N and P. Seedlings grown *left:* at very low, *right:* at moderate levels of N and P (N_0P_0 and N_3P_2, respectively, according to Björkman, 1942, p. 133). Incubation period 8 days. $\times 0.8$.

nutrients. Its growth-promoting action was compared in roots of pine seedlings grown aseptically in a nutrient medium with varied amounts of nitrogen and phosphorus, according to Björkman (1942). In agar plates with maximum nutrient medium roots of seedlings which had received no extra additions of these elements (N_0P_0, Björkman) caused very slight or no increase in the growth rate of *B. variegatus*, whereas roots of seedlings with relatively low, moderate or high amounts available had a strong growth-promoting effect (Fig. 15–7). In these experiments, roots of seedlings which had received different supplies of either or both of these elements showed no certain differences in their M-factor effects. Although these results seem to show a trend, no definite conclusions can be drawn until more quantitative experiments have been performed.

The M-factor has not as yet been definitely identified. However, it may be closely bound up with the metabolism of the root cells. It does not seem to be included among known B-vitamins, purine and pyrimidine bases or the amino acids in casein-hydrolysate. It is of interest that it is inactivated in the presence of adenine or its derivatives (Melin, 1959).

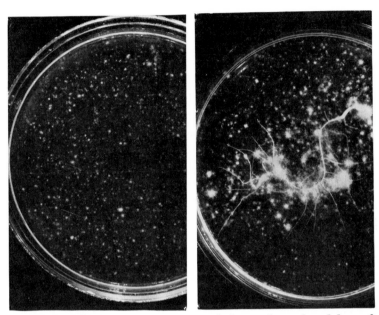

FIG. 15–8. *Boletus variegatus* F. Mycelial growth produced by a fungal suspension in agar plates with maximum nutrient medium, *left:* without supplement, *right:* supplemented with an excised tomato root grown for 18 days according to White (1943). Incubation period 7 days. ×0.8.

In studying the interactions of roots and mycorrhizal mycelia it should not be forgotten that the roots also produce metabolites inhibiting the growth of mycorrhizal fungi. Such fungistatic substances have been found to occur in live tomato roots as well as in live pine roots, where they seem to be produced in definite loci in the cells (Melin, 1960). In both cases they exude to a certain degree from the roots, although they seem to have a comparatively low rate of permeability through the plasma membranes of the root cells. Figure 15–8 illustrates the effect of an excised tomato root on the growth of *B. variegatus* in a maximum nutrient agar medium. The fine rootlets did not stimulate the hyphal growth, and there is reason to believe that, in this case, the action of the M-factor of the exudate had been reduced by fungistatic root metabolites. In other experiments tomato seedlings grown in Erlenmeyer flasks in terralite with appropriate nutrients were inoculated with *B. variegatus*. It was found that the *Boletus* hyphae did not enter the rootlets, presumably owing to the action of fungistatic root-metabolites.

Extracts of crushed or dried tomato roots showed a strong fungistatic activity, as illustrated by Fig. 15–9.

The fine rootlets of excised pine roots, contrary to those of tomato, had a strong growth-promoting effect on *B. variegatus* (Fig. 15–4). However, live pine roots also produce growth-inhibiting metabolites, which could be observed in exudates at higher levels of exuded material (Melin, 1960).

There is experimental evidence indicating that the fungistatic root-metabolites concerned are physiologically and chemically different in pine and tomato. In tomato they prevent the entrance of tree mycorrhizal hyphae into the roots; in pine they may confine the mycorrhizal fungus to its definite parts of the infected rootlets.

The results obtained support the view that the formation of ectotrophic mycorrhizae in pine and other trees is largely controlled by growth-promoting as well as growth-inhibiting root-metabolites. If the environmental conditions are suitable, the M-factor induces a strong development of the mycorrhizal mycelia around the roots. Besides an excess of soluble carbohydrates in the roots, the M-factor may also be an important cause of the entry of the fungal hyphae into the rootlets. In the writer's opinion the mycorrhizal fungus behaves primarily as a parasite, although, contrary to many real parasites, it does not, as a rule, seem to produce substances toxic to the host. After infection of the rootlets by appropriate mycelia capable of producing auxin in sufficient amounts (Slankis, 1951, 1958), a mycorrhizal equilibrium seems to be established by defensive action of the host with the aid of growth-inhibiting root metabolites. Whether fungistatic substances are formed also as a result of infection by mycorrhizal fungi, as in the case of orchid bulbs (Gaumann and Kern, 1959), remains to be ascertained. The interactions between host and fungus leading to a tree mycorrhizal alliance are certainly of a complex nature and deserve continued study. As yet only a start has been made in our attempts to understand these relationships.

Finally, it may be emphasized that, as shown by several workers, different tree mycorrhizal associations are not physiologically identical, even in the same tree species. Young (1940) and Moser (1956) demonstrated that different mycorrhizal Basidiometes af-

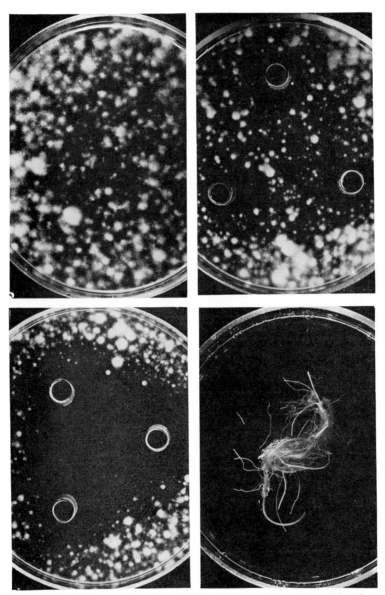

Fig. 15–9. *Boletus variegatus* C. Mycelial growth produced by the same volumes of a fungal suspension in maximum nutrient agar medium, *upper left:* without supplement (control), *upper right:* supplemented with extract (about 18 units per plate) of tomato roots that had been thoroughly crushed aseptically before extraction, *lower left:* with extract (about 22.5 units per plate) of freeze-dried tomato roots, *lower right:* with a freeze-dried tomato root. Excised tomato roots 25 days old. Extracts produced in redistilled water in 5 days at 4° C. Incubation period 8 days. ×0.8.

fected the growth of pine and larch seedlings differently. Krangaus (1955), comparing the effects of two strains of *Boletus luteus* on growth of pine seedlings, found that one of these strains was more effective than the other. These and other similar observations indicate that it will be an important task in the field of practical forestry to study the effects of different mycorrhizal fungi (and their strains) on tree growth under different soil conditions.

Discussion

Edward Hacskaylo

It is indeed an honor to have the opportunity to discuss the paper of our most eminent authority on mycorrhizae. The paper itself has given us a good insight into the varied and fundamental studies of mycorrhizae that have been pioneered by Professor Melin over the past 40 years. It is always a pleasure to read the results of research from Professor Melin's laboratory because the experiments are always well designed and clearly illustrate the point that he is trying to investigate.

We are finding that increasing attention is being given to studies on mycorrhizae in many countries throughout the world. The studies do not rely so much on observational data as they did in years past, but carefully controlled experiments are more the rule than the exception. It would seem from Professor Melin's paper that a good many of the questions regarding mycorrhizae and their functions have been answered. This is indeed true. However, as one might suspect, there are many problems that remain to be solved. As was pointed out by Professor Melin, we cannot assume that tree mycorrhizae are formed because the tree needs them. We have to approach the research from the standpoint of observing what is occurring and then through experimentation learn why it does occur.

The complexity of mycorrhizae is great because we are dealing not only with one organism but with two from very wide ends of the scale of the plant kingdom. We know species of fungi that form mycorrhizae on pine for example, and we know some of the general characteristics of the morphology and the physiology of the fungi. Some of the important things still to be better understood, however, are the physiological differences between the individual fungus species, especially in combination with the root system. There has been some progress made in this area, but in reality we know very little regarding whether one fungus is more capable of translocating nutrients from the soil into the root than is another, or whether some of these fungi might have a tendency to be pathogenic. That is not to say that I believe the mycorrhizal fungi are in general pathogenic. However, since we are dealing with parasitism there is always the possibility that the interactions between host and parasite could be detrimental to one of the members. This is of interest not only to the theoretical researcher but of course is of great interest to the practical investigator.

The classical experiments that have been carried out in Professor Melin's laboratory have done much to clarify the exchanges between the fungal associates and higher partners. For example, Björkman's (1942) work on the relationship between soluble carbohydrates in the roots and the frequency of mycorrhizae has widespread significance in relation to the results of investigators who have observed the effects of availability of nutrients to abundance of mycorrhizae. There certainly must be a relationship between the amount of nitrogen and phosphorus within the plant and the disposition of the photosynthate. We can be quite sure that readily available quantities of these elements would promote assimilation of the carbohydrates within the shoot and result in a reduced amount of carbohydrate being translocated to the roots. I am inclined to believe that the carbohydrate content of the root must be related to the secretion of some materials into the rhizosphere that promote the development of the fungus on and within the root. It does not seem, from Professor Melin's evidence, that the M-factor is the total explanation of this phenomenon. It is at this point that I feel one of our biggest gaps exists in understanding the mechanism of mycorrhizal formation. We can enumerate the following as taking place in the root area: secretion of a growth regulator by the fungi involved causing a part of the change in the morphology in the short root; secretion of the M-factor by the root that stimulates the development of the fungus mycelium; secretion of enzymes by the fungus to permit penetration of the root and finally exchanges of materials by the intimately associated organisms. There are many compounds undoubtedly involved in the exchanges and we must learn more about their role in the metabolism of the organisms. We do not know, for example, the form in which phosphorus and other elements move from the mycelium to the root tissue. As is the case in the plant root system that has no mycorrhizae, we know very little of a definite nature regarding mechanisms of absorption. It has been suggested to me that perhaps the mycorrhizal system creates more free space and thereby permits greater movement of nutrients into the plant. Certainly I would not be willing to accept any such speculation as fact without experimental evidence to support it.

One of the very fascinating things that Professor Melin's research has uncovered concerns the M-factor whereby it is possible to stimulate growth in species of fungi that have been exceedingly difficult to handle previously in culture. After the M-factor is better understood, who can say what might be a possible application of such a growth stimulator in microorganisms? There is more to be known, also, regarding the fungistatic root compounds, especially in limiting the penetration of fungus hyphae to definite tissues in the root. The balance between the root and fungus is indeed remarkable and we are almost totally ignorant of factors that maintain this balance.

From today's discussion I am sure it is quite apparent to all of you that to work with the mycorrhizal relationship one must have a great deal of patience and be willing to progress slowly, devising new techniques for almost every experiment. Eventually, we shall develop reasonable and complete explanations of the physiological mechanisms in mycorrhizae just as in the studies on other living organisms. We look not only to Professor Melin's laboratory for leadership in this work but also to the many other laboratories throughout the world for cooperation in the effort to solve our problems.

LITERATURE CITED

Björkman, E. 1942. Über die Bedingungen der Mykorrhizabildung bei Kiefer und Fichte. Symb. Bot. Upsal. 6(2): 1–190.
———. 1944. The effect of strangulation on the formation of mycorrhiza in pine. Svensk. Bot. Tidskr. 38: 1–14.
———. 1949. The ecological significance of the ectotrophic mycorrhizal association in forest trees. Svensk Bot. Tidskr. 43: 223–262.
Eriksson, P. 1960. Unpublished data.
Fries, N. 1943. Untersuchungen über die Sporenkeimung und Mycelentwicklung bodenbewohnender Hymenomyceten. Symb. Bot. Upsal. 6(4): 1–81.
Gäumann, E., and H. Kern. 1959. Über chemische Abwehrreaktionen bei Orchideen. Phytopath. Ztschr. 36: 1–26.
Kelley, A. P. 1950. Mycotrophy in plants. New Ser. Plant Sci. Books 22: 1–223.
Krangaus, R. A. 1955. Experiment with pure cultures of fungi suspected of forming mycorrhizal infection in oak and pine. In Russian. Proc. Conf. on Mycotrophy in Plants, Moscow; 235–240.
Lindeberg, G. 1946. On the occurrence of polyphenol oxidases in soil-inhabiting Basidiomycetes. Physiol. Plant. 1: 196–205.
MacDougal, D. T., and J. Dufrenoy. 1944. Mycorrhizal symbiosis in Aplectrum, Corallorhiza and Pinus. Plant Physiol. 19: 440–465.
——— and ———. 1946. Criteria of nutritive relations of fungi and seed plants in mycorrhizae. Plant Physiol. 21: 1–10.
Melin, E. 1921. Über die Mykorrhizenpilze von Pinus silvestris L. and Picea Abies (L.) Karst. Svensk Bot. Tidskr. 15: 192–203.
———. 1923. Experimentelle Untersuchungen über die Konstitution und Okologie der Mykorrhizen von Pinus silvestris and Picea Abies. Mykol. Untersuch. u. Ber. (von R. Falck) 2: 73–331.
———. 1925. Untersuchungen über die Bedeutung der Baummykorrhiza. Eine okologisch-physiologische Studie. Gustav Fischer, Jena. Pp. 1–152.
———. 1953. Physiology of mycorrhizal relations in plants. Ann. Rev. Plant Physiol. 4: 325–346.
———. 1954. Growth factor requirements of mycorrhizal fungi of trees. Svensk Bot. Tidskr. 48: 86–94.
———. 1959. Studies on the physiology of tree mycorrhizal Basidiomycetes. I. Growth response to nucleic acid constituents. Svensk Bot. Tidskr. 53: 135–154.
———. 1960. Unpublished data.
Melin, E., and V. S. R. Das. 1954. Influence of root-metabolites on the growth of tree mycorrhizal fungi. Physiol. Plant. 7: 851–858.
Melin, E., and H. Nilsson. 1957. Transport of C^{14}-labelled photosynthate to the fungal associate of pine mycorrhizae. Svensk Bot. Tidskr. 51: 166–186.
Modess, O. 1941. Zur Kenntnis der Mykorrhizabildner von Kiefer und Fichte. Symb. Bot. Upsal. 5(1): 1–146.
Moser, M. 1956. Die Bedeutung der Mykorrhiza für Aufforstungen in Hochlagen. Forstw. Centbl. 75: 1–18.

————. 1959. Beitrage zur Kenntnis der Wuchsstoffbeziehungen im Bereich ecto-tropher Mycorrhizen I. Arch. Mikrobiol. 34: 251–269.

NORKRANS, B. 1950. Studies in growth and cellulolytic enzymes of *Tricholoma:* With special reference to mycorrhiza formation. Symb. Bot. Upsal. 11(1): 1–126.

————. 1953. The effect of glutamic acid, aspartic acid, and related compounds on the growth of certain *Tricholoma* species. Physiol. Plant. 6: 584–593.

SLANKIS, V. 1951. Über den Einfluss von β-Indolylessigsaure und anderen Wuchs-stoffen auf das Wachstrum von Kiefernwurzeln. Symb. Bot. Upsal. 11(3): 1–63.

————. 1958. The role of auxin and other exudates in mycorrhizal symbiosis of forest trees. In: The Physiology of Forest Trees. K. V. THIMANN (ed.). The Ronald Press Co., New York. Pp. 427–443.

WHITE, P. R. 1943. A handbook of plant tissue culture. Jaques Cattel Press, Lancaster, Pa.

YOUNG, H. E. 1940. Mycorrhizae and the growth of *Pinus* and *Araucaria*. The influence of different species of mycorrhiza-forming fungi on seedling growth. Jour. Austral. Inst. Agr. Sci. 6: 21–25.

16

Temperature and Tree Growth Near the Northern Timber Line

PEITSA MIKOLA

Introduction

Finland is suitably located for studies on the relationship between temperature and forest growth. The country lies between 60 and 70 degrees north latitude, extending from the southern border of the northern coniferous zone or taiga up to the Arctic tundra. There are no large differences in elevation and the geological structure is uniform. The temperature decreases gradually towards the north, and the effect of this phenomenon is clearly reflected in the growth of trees.

Annual and long-term variations in tree growth, due to climatic fluctuation, have received attention in several forest growth studies in the Scandinavian countries and especially in the Finnish National Forest Surveys. Such surveys have been performed in Finland three times, and in comparing the growth data of the different surveys, the climatic variations should be taken into consideration. Therefore, in the last two surveys, material has been collected from all parts of the country for the study of growth variations (Ilvessalo, 1942, 1956; Eklund, 1944; Mikola, 1950). On the basis of these growth studies and meteorological data it has been possible to investigate the relationship between tree growth and climatic factors, in particular temperature, in different parts of the country.

The following review is concentrated mostly in the Scots pine (*Pinus silvestris*) that alone accounts for 50 per cent of the Finnish timber resources. It also forms the northern limit of the coniferous forests against the tundra. The second important tree species is Norway spruce (*Picea abies*). As will be seen later, pine and spruce depend on climatic factors in slightly different ways, and interesting comparisons can be made in this respect.

Relation between temperature and tree growth, near the timber line in particular, has also received attention when the recent climatic development and its consequences have been studied.

The main results of the Finnish studies concerning growth fluctuations and the relationship between climatic factors and forest growth can be summarized as follows. They are also well confirmed by Swedish and Norwegian investigations (e.g., Erlandsson, 1936; Ording, 1941; Eklund, 1957).

Radial Growth

The decisive climatic factor affecting radial growth of trees under northern conditions is the temperature of the growing season (Hustich, 1948). Any possible influence of other factors is masked by the dominant effect of temperature. Thus the effect of deficient rainfall can be traced only in exceptionally dry summers on the driest sites, and the harmful effect of excessive moisture on wet peatlands in rainy summers (Mikola, 1950). Only a little further south, in Denmark for instance, the rainfall of the growing season has proved to be the most important climatic factor affecting tree growth (Holmsgaard, 1955).

The decisive influence of summer temperature increases from south to north and is most accentuated at the northern timber line. The annual variation of radial growth, expressed as the variation coefficient or mean sensitivity likewise increases towards the north. This is explained by the fact that the limiting growth factor, the summer temperature, is more unfavorable in the north, and finally at the timber line the temperature fluctuates from year to year on both sides of a critical limit, and therefore the annual variation of ring width reaches its maximum at the timber line.

When annual radial growth of Scots pine was compared with different thermal indices the best correlation was found between growth and July temperature. This correlation is quite evident even in southern Finland, but is still better in the northern part of the country. There are two reasons for the better correlation in the north. First, further south there are other climatic factors which exert some influence and modify the effect of temperature; in the north the temperature effect is more dominant. Secondly, the growing season is longer in the south and there the weather conditions of June and August may also affect growth, although less than the July weather, while near the northern timber line the short growing season coincides approximately with the month of July.

Both the beginning and the length of the growing season vary from year to year. Thus the decisive period need not always be July, but occurs earlier, in some years, later in others, and moreover, may vary in length. The dates of onset of radial growth may differ by as much as a whole month, as has been demonstrated by Romell (1925) in northern Sweden. Therefore, some other meteorological data might show still better correlation with radial growth than the mean July temperature. Thus in northern Sweden, for instance, Erlandsson (1936) found a very high correlation between the annual radial growth of pine and the number of days when the maximum temperature exceeds a certain limit, $+19°$ C in this case. Under conditions where temperature is the growth-limiting factor, the temperature aggregate or thermal sum during the growing season is probably decisive, and therefore the maximum temperatures may be more important than the mean temperature of a fixed period. However, because the monthly mean temperatures are most easily obtained from meteorological statistics, they have generally been used when the relationship between temperature and tree growth was studied.

The beginning of the growing season influences radial growth of Scots pine in an interesting way, which was detected when the constituents of the annual ring, the earlywood and the latewood, were compared with climatic factors. The earlier growth starts in the spring, the broader is the latewood ring and the higher is the percentage of latewood in the whole ring. In the annual rings of pine the width of the latewood varies relatively more than that of the earlywood. It is concluded that, in southern Finland at least, the length of the period of earlywood formation is almost constant from year to year. Since, however, radial growth ceases almost simultaneously every year round the middle of August, the amount of latewood is proportional to the length of the whole growing season. In pine the variation of the July temperature also has a more distinct effect on the width of the late- than the earlywood. The growth of the earlywood takes place partly at the expense of nutrient reserves and is therefore also dependent on the weather conditions of early spring and even of the preceding summer, although in complicated ways. The growth of latewood, on the other hand, is to a greater extent determined by prevailing temperature conditions.

Radial growth of Norway spruce also depends mainly on the temperature of the growing season. There are, however, some slight differences from the reaction of pine. Thus, the most decisive period for spruce growth is a little earlier than for pine. If ring width and monthly mean temperatures are compared, then the highest correlation for pine growth is obtained with the July temperature, while for spruce growth highest correlation usually is with June temperature. In the annual rings of spruce the latewood width varies very little from year to year, and the variation of the whole ring width is mainly due to different amounts of earlywood. There is even relatively good correlation between the width of the earlywood and the mean temperature of June.

The difference between Scots pine and Norway spruce in their relation to summer temperature is clearly visible if climatic conditions are studied in summers when one species has grown better and the other less well than in the preceding year. If spruce has grown better, for instance, and the pine less well, then the early summer has usually been warmer and the late summer cooler than in the preceding year, and vice versa.

Temperature of the growing season also has some influence on radial growth of the following years. This lag effect is most pronounced near the timber line, where the poorest growth often occurs in the year following a climatically unfavorable year. There may be several reasons for such a lag effect, e.g., the influence of temperature on the vitality and nutrient reserves of the tree. Temperature also has an influence on the green surface area of the tree, which in turn affects other growth phenomena. The green surface area depends on both the length and number of needles formed each year, the relations of which to temperature are discussed below.

Height Growth and Needle Length

The annual height growth of Scots pine is determined mainly by temperature of the preceding summer. Good correlation exists between the length of the terminal shoot and the July and August temperatures of the preceding year. This was shown by Hesselman (1904) in Sweden more than 50 years ago and is explained by the fact that the number of needles on a shoot is predetermined in the bud, which is formed in the preceding summer, and the length of the shoot depends mainly on the number of needles it bears.

The length of the needles, on the other hand, depends on climatic conditions prevailing during their growth, temperature being the most important factor.

Figure 16–1 shows variations in shoot growth, needle length at leading shoots of Scots pine and mean July temperature near timber line in northern Finland. The graphs are based on measurements of top shoots and their needles in ca. 30-year-old trees. In side branches the variation is of the same order, as well as in older trees.

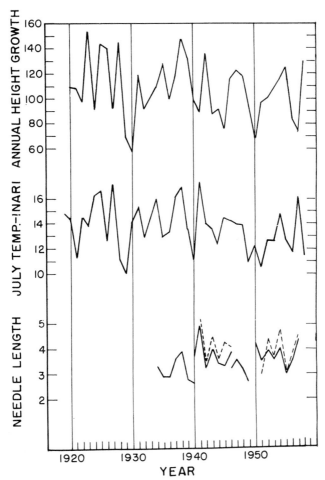

Fig. 16–1. Annual height-growth indices (100 = normal growth) and length of needles of terminal shoots (cm.) of Scots pine at the Finnish timber line, compared with the mean July temperatures of the same region.

Further south the variation is somewhat smaller, as it is in radial growth also.

Recent Trends in Temperature and Tree Growth at the Timber Line

The northern timber line is determined by temperature and coincides very closely everywhere around the North Pole with the isotherm of +10° C mean temperature of the warmest month. Temperature, however, is primarily the limiting factor for the reproduction of trees and hence for the very existence of forests. According to several authors, the ripening of Scots pine seed requires a mean temperature of +10.5° C during four summer months. Such warm summers are exceptional at the timber line, occurring, according to some authors, only once in 100 years (Renvall, 1912). For the vegetative growth of this species less warmth is needed, a mean temperature of ca. +8.5 ° C for four months reported as the minimum requirement (Helland, 1912). As was mentioned before, however, mean temperatures are probably not the best climatic indicators, although generally used. Thus, the summer temperatures fluctuate near and even on both sides of the critical values, and therefore both annual and long-term variations in tree growth are extremely pronounced at the timber line.

During the first decades of this century many Scandinavians were pessimistic regarding the future of the present timber line. In the 1920's and the 1930's, however, the climatic amelioration received increasing attention (Keränen, 1952; and others), although its remarkable effect on both growth and reproduction of the northernmost pine forests was not noticed until the end of the 1930's. Since that time, several papers have been published concerning the consequences of the climatic change at the timber line in Finnish Lapland (Hustich 1940, 1945, 1948; Mikola, 1952; and others).

In recent years, growth and reproduction of pine forests at the Finnish timber line have been investigated (Mikola, 1950, 1952). The trend after the 1930's has been especially studied, and some practical aspects have been considered, viz., the possibilities of silvicultural management of the timber line forests. Some of the main results of these recent studies are shown in Fig. 16–3 and 16–4.

Figure 16–2 shows the present location of the timber line of Scots pine in northern Scandinavia. On the map are marked the places where material for tree ring studies has been collected. Meteorological stations are few and most of them only recently established in this region. In Figure 16–1, where height growth and needle length are compared with temperature, meteorological data from Inari were used. They extend only as far back as 1908, and therefore when longer records are needed, data from Karesuando or Karasjoki, starting in 1880 and 1890 respectively, must be used.

Figure 16–3 shows the annual ring indices from six localities marked on the map, each graph representing mean values for about twenty trees. The great uniformity of growth variation in different localities can be noticed. All the analyses show a deep growth depression in the years 1902–11 and then a continuous increase until the 1930's. The more northern the locality, the deeper is the

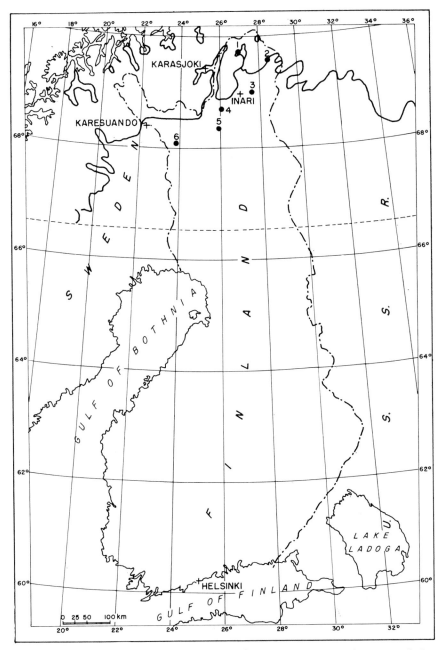

Fɪɢ. 16–2. The northern timber line of Scots pine in Scandinavia and the location of the sample stands (see Fig. 16–3).

depression and the steeper the increase. Thus in the two northern-most localities the ring index in the years 1902–11 was 60 to 80 per cent below the normal level and two decades later even 100 per cent above it.

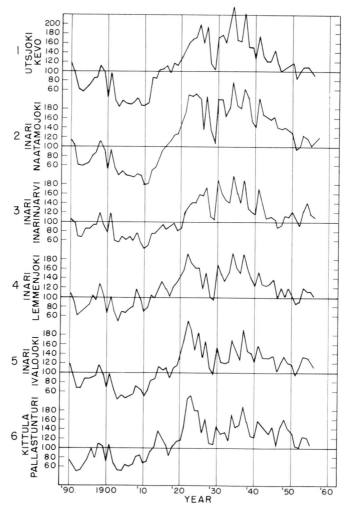

Fɪɢ. 16–3. Annual ring indices of Scots pine in 1890–1957 in six stands near the northern timber line.

Figure 16–4 shows the mean of all the six graphs of Figure 16–3, compared to the July temperature curve of Karesuando. The correlation between July temperature and radial growth is easily noticed, especially the effect of unfavorable years.

There may be several reasons for the deep growth depression in the period 1902–11. First, there were several cool summers. In Karesuando, for instance, in four summers the temperature was probably below the minimum limit for the existence of forests ($+10°$ C mean temperature of the warmest month or $+8.5°$ C mean of four months). The health of the trees evidently suffered and therefore the unfavorable summers exerted a prolonged lag

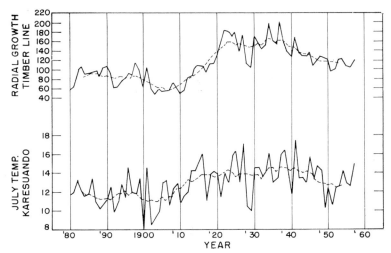

FIG. 16–4. Mean values of all six index series of Fig. 16–3, and the July temperatures in Karesuando. The smoothed curves (broken lines) show the general trend of temperature and tree growth, each point representing a mean of 9 years.

effect. Several contemporary papers also give written evidence of great frost damage in pine stands of the timber line in 1902 (Mikola, 1952; and literature cited).

As shown in the Figures, both thermal development and tree growth reached a peak in the late 1930's. Thereafter the temperature was on the decline and forest growth followed the same trend.

Such large growth variations explain the widely different ideas on the retreat or advance of the northern timber line, expressed at different periods. In 1910, pessimism prevailed while in the 1940's an advance of the timber line was predicted. Today these contradictory ideas can be revised in the light of climatic growth variations.

LITERATURE CITED

EKLUND, B. 1944. Ett försök att numeriskt fastställa klimatets inflytande på tallens och granens radietillväxt vid de båda finska riksskogstaxeringarna. Norrlands Skogsvårdsförbunds Tidskr.

————. 1957. The annual ring variations in spruce in the centre and northern Sweden in their relation to the climatic conditions. Meddel. från Statens Skogsforskningsinst. 47.

ERLANDSSON, S. 1936. Dendro-chronological studies. Data, 23 från Stockholms Högsk. Geokronologiska Inst.

HELLAND, A. 1912. Traegraendser og sommårvarmen. Tidskr. for Skogbruk. 20.

HESSELMAN, H. 1904. Om tallens höjdtillväxt och skottbildning somrarne 1900–1903. Meddel. från Statens Skogsförsöksanstalt. 1.

HOLMSGAARD, E. 1955. Tree-ring analyses of Danish forest trees. Det Forstl. Forsøgsv. i Danmark. 22.

HUSTICH, I. 1940. Tallstudier sommaren 1939 i Enare och Utsjoki. Acta Soc. pro Fauna et Flora Fenn. 62.

————. 1945. The radial growth of the pine at the forest limit and its dependence on the climate. Soc. Sci. Fenn. Commun. Biol. 9.

————. 1948. The Scotch pine in northernmost Finland and its dependence on the climate in the last decades. Acta Bot. Fenn. 42.

ILVESSALO, Y. 1942. The forest resources and the condition of forest of Finland: The second national forest survey. Commun. Inst. Forest. Fenn. 30.

————. 1956. The forests of Finland from 1921–24 to 1951–53: A survey based on three national forest inventories. Commun. Inst. Forest. Fenn. 47.

KERÄNEN, J. 1952. On temperature changes in Finland during the last hundred years. Fenn. 75: 5–16.

MIKOLA, P. 1950. On variations in tree growth and their significance to growth studies. Commun. Inst. Forest. Fenn. 38.

————. 1952. On the recent development of coniferous forests in the timber-line region of northern Finland. Commun. Inst. Forest. Fenn. 40.

ORDING, A. 1941. Annual ring analyses of spruce and pine. Meddel. fra Det Norske Skogforsøksv. 7.

RENVALL, A. 1912. Die periodischen Erscheinungen der Reproduktion der Kiefer an der polaren Waldgrenze. Acta Forest. Fenn. 1.

ROMELL, L. G. 1925. Växttidsundersökningar å tall och gran. Meddel. från Statens Skogsförsksanstalt. 22.

17

Temperature Effect on Optimum Tree Growth

HENRY HELLMERS

Introduction

In another paper of this volume, Mikola has reported his findings obtained from field studies on the limiting and variable effect of temperature on tree growth near the northern tree line. The present paper is concerned with another aspect of temperature, namely, the temperature conditions that result in maximum tree growth.

Observations and studies to determine temperature effects on plant growth have been made for hundreds of years. However, temperature has always been a difficult factor to evaluate because it has an indirect effect on growth through its influence upon practically every other factor that affects growth directly (Billings, 1952; Kramer and Kozlowski, 1960; Went, 1943, 1953, 1957). The papers cited above include excellent reviews of the present state of knowledge pertaining to temperature effects on growth. Daily and seasonal thermoperiodicity, heat sums, and lethal effects are discussed. Detailed reviews available on special phases include one on resistance to extreme temperatures by Levitt (1951) and one on temperature control of dormancy in woody plants by Samish (1954). Temperature effects upon seed germination have been studied in more detail than for any other single phase of the life cycle of trees (Baldwin, 1942; Crocker and Barton, 1953; Toole et al., 1956; U. S. Forest Service, 1948). The work on germination suggests the large amount of work yet to be done in determining temperature effects on other phases of tree growth. Determination of the temperature requirements of different species for maximum tree growth is one of the problem areas.

The writer has endeavored to assemble and analyze the available information on heat requirements for optimum growth of trees. Obviously, information on optimum temperatures can be obtained only from plants grown under controlled temperature conditions. Field studies of forest vegetation have contributed little to knowledge of this subject because, in the field, as temperature approaches the optimum other factors gradually become limiting and there is no sharp change in the growth pattern. There are also many difficulties under laboratory conditions. Growth responses may differ with the time of day that heat is applied, the length of time that heat is applied, the part of the plant to which heat is applied, and the age of the tree. Genetic variability within a species is a major problem when working with conifers (Mirov, 1957; Callaham, 1960) and may make the results difficult if not almost impossible to interpret for some of the more variable species.

Temperature and Optimum Tree Growth

Growth occurs over a wide range of temperatures, but somewhere within this range there are temperature conditions which promote optimal growth. However, growth per se is a multi-reaction process and the optimum temperature condition need not, and probably does not, coincide with the optimum for all or any of the component processes that together produce growth. Differences in temperature conditions for optimum growth, like morphological and biochemical differences, help to define a species and the variation within a species (Mirov, 1956).

The results that follow show how heat affects growth of different species of trees. The data are from experiments wherein the various workers used controlled-temperature chambers or greenhouses in which the air temperature is the reported temperature. Seedlings or 1-year-old stock were used. All environmental factors were kept as constant as possible and presumably close to the optimum, with temperature being the only experimental variable.

TREE GROWTH AND DAY-NIGHT TEMPERATURE DIFFERENTIAL. Growth of loblolly pine (*Pinus taeda* L.) and northern red oak (probably *Quercus rubra* L.) was studied under a series of day and night temperature combinations by Kramer (1957a; 1957b). Results were measured in terms of shoot growth of 1-year-old seedlings over a period of 8 months. He found that most shoot growth in both species was made under the condition with the largest day-night temperature differential: a day temperature 12° C. to 13° C. higher than the night temperature. Growth decreased as day and night temperatures approached equality, regardless of the absolute temperature level.

To obtain plants for an experiment on flowering, Bonner and Hellmers grew loblolly pine seedlings for 64 weeks.* These seedlings were grown under a greater range of temperature conditions than Kramer (1957a) used. The plants, like Kramer's, grew tallest under the conditions with a maximum day-night temperature differential. In the study reported here, this differential was 16° C. (Table 17–1). While these two studies showed that a day-night

TABLE 17–1

Height Growth of Loblolly Pine Seedlings Grown 64 Weeks from Cotyledon Stage Under Different Day and Night Temperature Combinations.

Day Temperature	Night Temperature		
	7° C.	17° C.	26° C.
	Height in Centimeters		
30° C.	-	52 (6.4)	29 (6.6)
23° C.	60 (4.2)*	50 (5.6)	35 (7.0)
17° C.	43 (3.0)	38 (4.1)	-

*Numbers in parentheses are the average numbers of flushes of growth produced.

temperature differential was favorable, they did not necessarily indicate the optimal differential for maximum growth of loblolly pine. Further work is needed to determine that optimum.

In a 64-week experiment, which consisted of 25 trees under each condition, the greatest mortality occurred under the highest day and night temperature combination, under which 14 trees died. Losses under the other conditions were minor, consisting of 2 trees under one condition, 1 tree under another condition, and no losses under the four other conditions. The trees were grown under natural light extended with artificial light to make a 16-hour photoperiod.

Recurrent flushing of growth was closely related to temperature. In general, increased temperature, either day or night, caused an increase in the number of flushes (Table 17–1). Thus under field conditions in the natural range of loblolly pine, temperature would appear to have two obvious effects. In addition to the reduction in the growth rate with increasing night temperatures, as pointed out

* These results are from previously unpublished studies which were conducted in the temperature controlled conditions of the Earhart Plant Research Laboratory at the California Institute of Technology under a cooperative agreement between the Pacific Southwest Forest and Range Experiment Station and the Institute.

by Kramer (1957a), there was an increased tendency to form terminal buds. Vegis (1956) suggested that high temperatures cause the formation of the resting condition in tree buds. However, in this study, temperatures which were too high for good growth and which actually caused death did not keep the buds of loblolly pine dormant, once they had formed.

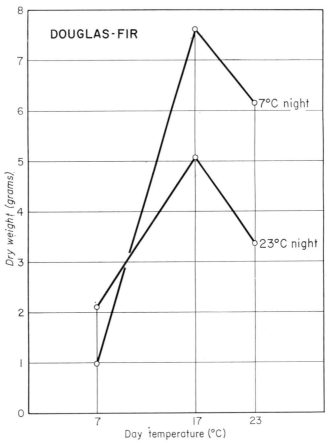

Fig. 17–1. Average top growth per plant of Douglas-fir seedlings grown under six different day-night temperature conditions.

Douglas-fir (*Pseudotsuga menziesii* (Mirb.) Franco) is another species which makes maximum growth with a day-night temperature differential (Hellmers and Sundahl, 1959) (Fig. 17–1). For this species a day 10° C. warmer than the night gave maximum production in dry weight. A 16° C. differential between day and night temperature was less favorable. It is interesting, however, that a 6° C. differential, with the night (23° C.) being warmer than the day (17° C.), resulted in larger plants than either a 7° C. or 23° C. constant temperature.

TREE GROWTH AND DAY TEMPERATURE. The top growth of redwood (*Sequoia sempervirens* (D. Don) Endl.) in the range of temperature studied responded significantly to day temperature

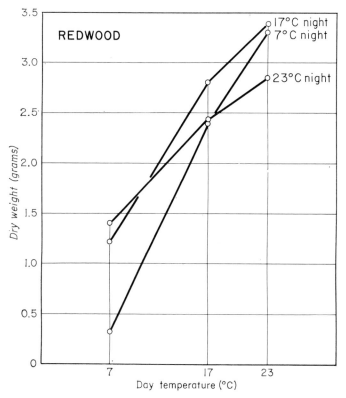

FIG. 17–2. Average top growth per plant of redwood seedlings grown under nine different day-night temperature conditions.

(Hellmers and Sundahl, 1959) (Fig. 17–2). Growth, dry weight, for 6 months at 7° C., 17° C., and 23° C. nights increased with increasing day temperatures. Only when the day temperature was held at 7° C. did the night temperature significantly affect growth. Day-night temperature differential appeared to have little if any effect on the top growth of redwood.

TREE GROWTH AND NIGHT TEMPERATURE. Digger pine (*Pinus sabiniana* Dougl.), which is native to the foothills around the Central Valley of California, was grown under the same temperature and light conditions by Bonner and Hellmers as were the loblolly pines.* The plants, 15 per treatment, were put under the test conditions when the seedlings were in the cotyledon stage. The study ran for 8 months. The results showed that night temperature was more effective than day temperature in promoting height growth. A night temperature of 17° C. was significantly more effective than either a 7° C. or a 26° C. night temperature (Table 17–2). Plants

TABLE 17–2

HEIGHT GROWTH OF DIGGER PINE SEEDLINGS GROWN 35 WEEKS FROM COTYLEDON STAGE UNDER DIFFERENT DAY AND NIGHT TEMPERATURE COMBINATIONS.

Day Temperature	Night Temperature		
	7° C.	17° C.	26° C.
	Height in Centimeters		
30° C.	–	22	13
23° C.	18	27	14
17° C.	11	28	–

under a constant 17° C. temperature day and night actually grew best but not significantly more than plants under a 17° C. night with warmer days.

TREE GROWTH AND TOTAL DAILY TEMPERATURE—"HEAT SUM." Trees of several species can be characterized as being affected by total daily heat, irrespective of time of application. The literature contains several good discussions of the various methods of calculating heat sums and of using them to delimit climatic zones or to determine stages of development in growth of specific crop plants (Clarke, 1954; Daubenmire, 1959; Livingston and Livingston, 1913; Livingston, 1916; Weaver and Clements, 1938; Went, 1957).

For the purpose of this paper, the heat sum is defined as the total daily degree-hours. It is calculated as follows: The temperature is the numerical value of the temperature above 0° C. times the length of time in hours that the plants were at that temperature during a 24-hour day. For example, plants at 7° C. for 24 hours received 168 degree-hours while plants at 23° C. for 16 hours and 10° C. for 8 hours received 368 + 80 for a total of 448 degree-hours.

Data from a recent study with Jeffrey pine (*Pinus jeffreyi* Grev. and Balf.) show a different temperature-growth relationship than was found in either loblolly pine, redwood, or digger pine (Hellmers, 1961).

The experiment was designed with fifteen temperature regimes to allow a comparison of growth under a series of day and night

* See footnote on page 277.

temperatures (Table 17–3). Forty-eight plants in the cotyledon stage were placed in each treatment condition. Artificial light with a 16-hour photoperiod was used. The test continued for 6 months.

TABLE 17–3

DESIGN OF GROWTH EXPERIMENT TO STUDY TEMPERATURE EFFECT ON JEFFREY PINE. X'S INDICATE TEMPERATURE COMBINATIONS UNDER WHICH PLANTS WERE GROWN FOR 6 MONTHS.

Day Temperature	Night Temperature				
	4° C.	10° C.	17° C.	23° C.	26° C.
26° C.	X	-	X	-	-
23° C.	X	X	X	X	X
17° C.	X	-	X	-	-
10° C.	X	X	X	X	-
4° C.	X	-	X	-	-

A plot of the average whole plant dry weight against total daily degree hours shows a pronounced optimum for growth between 300 and 400 degree-hours (Fig. 17–3). This optimal range includes

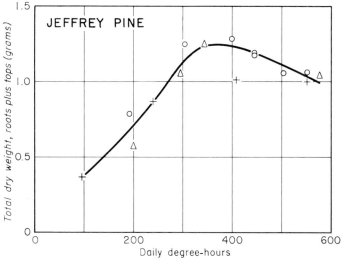

FIG. 17–3. Total dry weight, tops plus roots, of Jeffrey pine seedlings grown for 6 months under different day and night temperature conditions. Degree-hours are calculated on the basis of time in hours times the temperature in degrees centigrade during a 24-hr. period.

two points representing conditions of warmer days than nights and one point representing a growth condition where the day, 10° C., was cooler than the night, 23° C. Only the constant 17° C. day and night temperature condition is far out of line. In the light of our present knowledge, all that can be said about a constant 17° C. is that it has appeared to be inhibitory for the growth of plants in many but not all species studied under controlled temperature conditions (Went, 1957; Hellmers and Ashby, 1958).

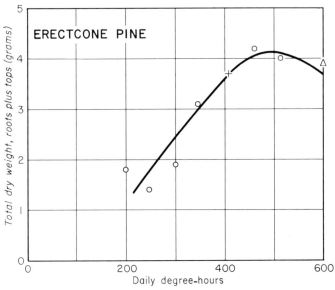

+ Day temperature equals night temperature
○ Day temperature higher than night temperature
△ Day temperature lower than night temperature

FIG. 17–4. Total dry weight, tops plus roots, of erectcone pine seedlings grown for 6 months under different day and night temperature conditions. Degree-hours are calculated on the basis of time in hours times the temperature in degrees centigrade during a 24-hr. period. Data from Hellmers and Ashby (1958).

Evidence of a total daily degree-hour control over tree growth can be found in two previously published papers (Hellmers and Ashby, 1958; Olson *et al.*, 1959). In both of these studies, the trees were grown under various day and night temperature combinations.

The growth of erectcone pine (*Pinus brutia* Ten), a variety of Aleppo pine, was studied by Hellmers and Ashby (1958). A plot of the average dry weight data for the whole plant indicates a growth peak at approximately 450 to 500 degree-hours (Fig. 17–4).

Olson *et al.* (1959) made an extensive study of eastern hemlock (*Tsuga canadensis* (L.) Carriere). For one of their growth-temperature experiments, the plants were grown from seed that had been collected in regions with different lengths of frost-free season. The experiment was conducted under a variety of temperature conditions. A plot of their data on stem elongation for the plants grown from seeds collected in the region with the longest frost-free season, 181 to 195 days, shows a good correlation with the daily heat sum (Fig. 17–5). Optimum growth occurred between 400 and 500 daily

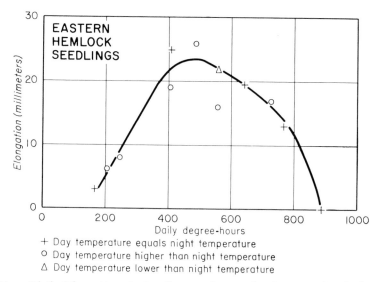

+ Day temperature equals night temperature
O Day temperature higher than night temperature
△ Day temperature lower than night temperature

FIG. 17–5. Elongation during first year's growth of eastern hemlock seedlings grown under different day and night temperature conditions. Degree-hours are calculated on the basis of time in hours times the temperature in degrees centigrade during a 24-hr. period. Data from Olson *et al.* (1959).

degree-hours. Data on plants from seed representing regions with shorter frost-free periods also show a peak. However a slight shift in the peak to higher daily heat sums for the plants representing the shorter and shorter frost-free season regions is indicated.

Olson *et al.* (1959) also presented data on stem elongation for 1-year-old seedlings of hemlock grown under controlled temperatures. Presumably, these plants were all from the same seed source. The same temperature-growth relations existed as for the seedlings, namely, a definite increase in growth with an increasing daily heat sum to an optimum at approximately 500 daily degree-hours and then a decline in growth with additional heat increases (Fig. 17–6).

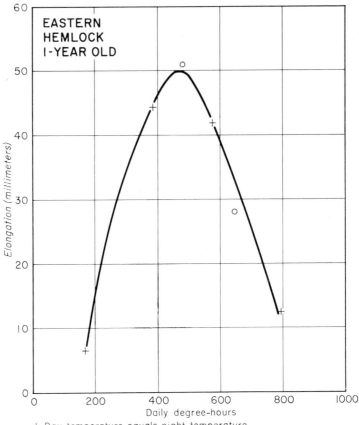

FIG. 17–6. Elongation of 1-year-old seedlings of eastern hemlock during their second growing season while under different day and night temperature conditions. Degree-hours are calculated on the basis of time in hours times the temperature in degrees centigrade during a 24-hr. period. Data from Olson *et al.* (1959).

This was true irrespective of the time of day during which heat was applied.

Discussion

Trees have been classified into species on the basis of their morphological differences. Furthermore, plants of different species are known to be biochemically different and to have different tolerance limits for temperature. Therefore, it is not surprising to find differences in heat requirements for optimum growth.

Heat requirements between the upper and lower lethal limits for the various representatives of a species may affect (1) the range of the species, (2) the distribution of the species within the range, (3) the site classification for the species, (4) the growth rate of the individuals during a growing season, and (5) the induction of summer dormancy.

Control of the range of a species and its distribution within the range are limited by the plant's ability to grow under the existing environmental conditions. These environmental conditions include competition from other plants as well as the physical factors of the site. For instance, a tree on a given site may not be able to compete successfully if the conditions are far from the tree's optimal temperature requirements, but not at the point of being lethal. This would be especially significant if the competing plants had optimal temperature requirements similar to those existing on the site (Salisbury, 1926).

Site productivity is usually classified by foresters in terms of tree heights. Thus height growth integrates the effects of many factors, one of which is temperature. As more knowledge is obtained about the heat requirements for optimum growth of trees of different species, this factor should be considered in the determination of site potential and in the selection of species for afforestation and reforestation programs.

Temperature also can be an important factor causing year to year growth differences. Such differences are often observed between individual trees. However, the effect on total production of a forest stand or the direct relation of the growth to temperature, with few exceptions, has not been determined. The work of Mikola (1960) is one of the exceptions. He studied the growth of trees near the northern tree line where temperature is limiting. Radial growth and needle length were affected by the temperature of the current season while height growth was primarily affected by the temperature of the previous summer.

Reduction in growth rate with the onset of unfavorable growth conditions in a summer season was referred to earlier. Kramer (1957a) pointed out that in the range of loblolly pine the warming of the nights as summer advances probably causes a reduction in growth rate. The results reported here (Table 17–1) show that this situation is accentuated by the tendency for loblolly pine to form terminal buds under high temperatures.

Determining temperature effects upon optimum tree growth is a complex problem. However, with the development of controlled-temperature greenhouses and growth chambers, it is now feasible to study these effects and possibly to untangle the temperature effect from the effects of other environmental factors. The data presented in this paper only touch upon the mass of information needed before the temperature effects upon trees of different species can be understood. The responses of root, shoot, and cambial meristems to temperature will have to be studied in greater detail. The interaction of shoot and root growth of forest trees in relation to soil and air temperatures should be investigated. Information on these various temperature effects will be of practical as well as theoretical value, especially in tree nursery and planting programs.

Summary

Data were presented to show that certain species of conifers vary in their heat requirements for optimum growth. The controlling factors and the species favorably affected by them are as follows:

1. Optimal growth of loblolly pine and Douglas-fir occurred with a day-night temperature differential.
2. Growth of redwood was affected primarily by day temperature.
3. Night temperature significantly controlled the growth of digger pine.
4. Daily heat sum was the dominant factor in growth of Jeffrey pine, erectcone pine, and eastern hemlock.

The discussion points out that temperature probably affects the range of a species and the distribution of the plants within the range. It also indicates that temperature, through the control of tree growth, affects site classification. In addition, evidence was presented to show that different physiological processes in a tree respond to particular seasonal temperature patterns.

LITERATURE CITED

BALDWIN, H. I. 1942. Forest tree seed. Chronica Botanica Co., Waltham, Mass.

BILLINGS, W. D. 1952. The environmental complex in relation to plant growth and distribution. Quart. Rev. Biol. 27: 251–265.

CALLAHAM, R. Z. 1960. In these proceedings.

CLARKE, G. L. 1954. Elements of ecology. John Wiley & Sons, Inc., New York.

CROCKER, W., and L. V. BARTON. 1953. Physiology of seeds. Chronica Botanica Co., Waltham, Mass.

DAUBENMIRE, R. F. 1959. Plants and environment. 2d ed. John Wiley & Sons, Inc., New York.

HELLMERS, H. 1961. Temperature effects on Jeffrey pine. Forest Sci. In press.

HELLMERS, H., and W. C. ASHBY. 1958. Growth of native and exotic plants under controlled temperatures and in the San Gabriel Mountains, California. Ecol. 39: 416–428.

HELLMERS, H., and W. P. SUNDAHL. 1959. Response of Sequoia sempervirens (D. Don) Endl. and Pseudotsuga menziesii (Mirb. Franco) seedlings to temperature. Nature 184: 1247–1248.

KRAMER, P. J. 1957a. Some effects of various combinations of day and night temperatures and photoperiod on the height growth of loblolly pine seedlings. Forest Sci. 3: 45–55.

———. 1957b. Thermoperiodism in trees. In: The Physiology of Forest Trees. K. V. THIMANN (ed.). The Ronald Press Co., New York. Pp. 573–580.

KRAMER, P. J., and T. T. KOZLOWSKI 1960. Physiology of trees. McGraw-Hill Book Co., Inc., New York.

LEVITT, J. 1951. Frost, drought and heat resistance. Ann. Rev. Plant Physiol. 2: 245–268.

LIVINGSTON, B. E. 1916. Physiological temperature indices for the study of plant growth in relation to climatic conditions. Physiol. Res. 1: 399–420.

LIVINGSTON, B. E., and G. J. LIVINGSTON. 1913. Temperature coefficients in plant geography and climatology. Bot. Gaz. 56: 349–375.

MIKOLA, P. 1960. In these proceedings.

MIROV, N. T. 1956. Composition of lodgepole X jack pine hybrids. Can. Jour. Bot. 34: 443–457.

———. 1957. Distribution of turpentine components among species of the genus *Pinus*. In: The Physiology of Forest Trees. K. V. Thimann, (ed.). The Ronald Press Co., New York. Pp. 251–268.

OLSON, J. S., F. W. STEARNS, and H. NIENSTAEDT. 1959. Eastern hemlock seeds and seedlings response to photoperiod and temperature. Conn. Agr. Expt. Sta. Bull. 620.

SALISBURY, E. J. 1926. The geographic distribution of plants in relation to climatic factors. Geog. Jour. 67: 312–335.

SAMISH, R. M. 1954. Dormancy in woody plants. Ann. Rev. Plant Physiol. 5: 183–204.

TOOLE, E. H., S. B. HENDRICKS, H. A. BORTHWICK, and V. K. TOOLE. 1956. Physiology of seed germination. Ann. Rev. Plant Physiol. 7: 299–324.

U.S. FOREST SERVICE. 1948. Woody-plant seed manual. U.S. Dept. Agr. Misc. Pub. 654.

VEGIS, A. 1956. Formation of the resting condition in plants. Experientia. 12: 94–99.

WEAVER, J. E., and F. E. CLEMENTS. 1938. Plant ecology. 2d ed. McGraw-Hill Book Co., Inc., New York.

WENT, F. W. 1943. Plant growth under controlled temperature conditions, I. Amer. Jour. Bot. 30: 157–163.

———. 1953. The effect of temperature on plant growth. Ann. Rev. Plant Physiol. 4: 347–362.

———. 1957. Experimental control of plant growth. Chronica Botanica Co., Waltham, Mass.

18

Environmental Factors in Development Stages of Trees

M. Schaffalitzky de Muckadell

Development stages in trees represent separate phases in the ontogenesis from seedling to adult tree. These stages are characterized by morphological and physiological qualities. The existence of the development stages must be due to certain changes which take place in apical meristems as they age. Such changes are probably due to one or several chemical compounds specific to the different development stages. Normally the changes are irreversible and may occur rather suddenly.

The existence of changes in meristems as they age and the existence of development stages are thus two expressions for one and the same thing. The former are best suited for gradual and indistinct transitions, whereas the latter are suitable for the so-called juvenile stages. Juvenile stages are the best known examples of development stages. They are often so well defined, that the term "juvenile forms" may be used.

Before the relation of development stages to environment is considered some examples of development stages which may underline the above definitions will be mentioned.

The classical and best known example of a plant showing development stages is *Hedera helix*, the common ivy, which passes through a juvenile stage with climbing or creeping shoots and palmately lobed leaves. When the ivy comes of age an adult flowering form with upright shoots and elliptic leaves develops.

Development stages have been discussed for several centuries by fruit growers because many fruit trees show juvenility by characteristically bearing thorns. The adult forms do not produce thorns, and as adult clones are usually propagated, the juvenile stage of many common fruit tree varieties has actually been lost.

In a number of *Pinus* species a short stage with primary needles is well known, for instance *Pinus pinea,* before the secondary, fascicled needles develop.

In experiments at the Horsholm Arboretum *Fagus sylvatica,* the European beech (Fig. 18–1), has been the main species under test.

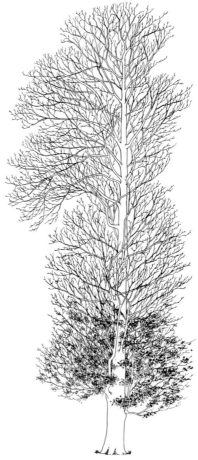

Fɪɢ. 18–1. "Straight beech," Soro Academy, 2nd Forest District. Sketched March, 1956, by Noll. From Schaffalitzky de Muckadell (1956).

It was demonstrated that the ability to retain the brown withered leaves during the winter was a true juvenile character, which disappeared with age. The experimental design in such demonstrations was based upon the view that the entire lower trunk portion of even a very old tree remains juvenile. This view is supported by the fact that basal epicormic branches appear to be juvenile.

Once the hypothesis that two different stages existed in a species was formed, a suitable test plant was selected. The main criterion for selection was that scions in both presumed development stages could be obtained from the experimental plants. This criterion was generally fulfilled by trees with low epicormic branches.

Scions from the two categories were grafted on rootstocks of identical origin, growing under similar conditions, usually in two

Fig. 18–2. Grafts from "straight beech," grafted 1954, photographed January, 1956. For the right row, scions were taken from the low leaf-retaining epicormic branches; for the left row from top of tree. From Schaffalitzky de Muckadell (1956).

adjacent rows (Fig. 18–2). Grafting and later treatment of the grafts were carried out simultaneously and by exactly the same methods, hence any differences caused by the treatment were excluded.

If the presumed development stage characters persisted in the two categories of grafts, the existence of the development stages was considered to be demonstrated.

Such sets of juvenile and adult grafts from the same tree were used in studies of reactions to environment. In beech one of the most interesting observations was that the juvenile stage came into leaf later than did the adult plant. This was investigated in a number of beech clones, always with the same result. It was known beforehand that in breeding work the writer had early-flushing and late-flushing plants, but it was not known that the same tree flushes earlier with increasing age. Similar results were obtained in *Fraxinus excelsior*, the European ash.

Fig. 18–3. Row of 12-year-old adult grafts of *Fagus sylvatica* at the Horsholm Arboretum. Arrows indicate the bark necroses, which all face southwest. Photo taken in April, 1957, by H. Vedel. From Schaffalitzky de Muckadell (1959).

In Denmark late spring frost is one of the most important dangers in young beech plantations, and it therefore is very useful that young beeches react more slowly to spring climate and leaf-out rather later than old trees. If this were not the case spring frosts would be still more dangerous.

Both in ash and beech sunscorch on south and southwest faces often causes bark necrosis on stems, especially if a closed stand is opened up from these directions (Fig. 18–3). It is not good silviculture in Denmark to open a stand from the southwest or south, but in practice it is now and then done. Our adult grafts of the two species have often suffered from such necrosis whereas the bark of juvenile grafts seems to be highly resistant to sunscorch.

Sunscorch is generally believed to occur during the summer, but the bark necroses probably are also caused by large temperature variations in early spring before leafing out occurs, as is the case with fruit trees in the north European climate. The dead brown leaves of the juvenile beeches protect the stems against these temperature variations, and may thus contribute to the resistance of juvenile forms to bark necrosis.

Results of a number of small-scale and rather short-term experiments with juvenile and adult forms of *Fagus sylvatica* and *Fraxinus excelsior* (Fig. 18–4) point toward greater vigor in juvenile material. These observations are in accord with information in the literature.

In many species other useful characteristics found in juvenile forms include the presence of thorns, which protect against game and cattle damage, and greater shade tolerance which enables young plants to stay alive under a dark forest canopy. The juvenile forms thus possess various useful properties which make them specially adapted to exist and grow well in their natural habitat. They seem to be more or less resistant to some of the common dangers.

During recent years, forest tree breeders in Denmark have experimented to find out if direct grafting of selected clones in young plantations would be a profitable silvicultural method. As usual opinions differ greatly. There are enthusiastic advocates in favor of such a method, which is termed "clone cultivation." However, the writer does not recommend further expansion of clone cultivation in silvicultural practice, primarily because the adult material which is grafted may have lost many of the precious qualities that enable juvenile stock to grow well. Secondly, the results depend upon how much better selected trees are than average trees, i.e., how clever the tree breeder is in selection.

The clones ought to be so much better that they can pay for the cost of grafting and for the special care they demand during the early years of growth. However, the writer believes that these selections do not fulfill these demands, because the methods of selection are not yet satisfactory. The selected clones may be adequate for a general elevation of the forest crop standards when the clones are placed in seed gardens, but too little is known about the value of individual clones to use them directly in forests on a large scale. Nevertheless the experiments with clone cultivation are interesting and should be closely watched by silviculturists.

Having mentioned the reaction of juvenile and adult forms to different environmental conditions, the question of environmental influence on the duration of the stages will be considered. It is emphasized that this influence is extremely strong, which is the main reason that literature on development stages has been given

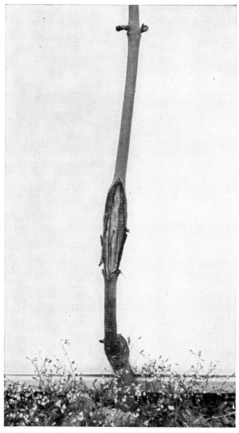

Fig. 18–4. *Fraxinus excelsior.* Adult 2-year-old budding with bark necrosis. Photographed April, 1957, by H. Vedel. From Schaffalitzky de Muckadell (1959).

so little attention in forestry. If the demonstration experiments at the Horsholm Arboretum had not been carried through under strictly similar conditions for the two sets of grafts, the results would have been impossible to interpret.

The most striking example of the influence of environment on ontogenetic development was found in beech. In very heavy shade young beeches become leaf-shedding, i.e., environment causes the disappearance of even their main juvenile character, leaf retention.

In order to study the extent to which shade influences leaf retention, the following experiment was made:

In a natural regeneration under a 120-year-old beech stand fifteen leafless seedlings, which were undergoing severe shade and root competition, were selected. Because of the slender stems of these 20–80-centimeter-high plants it was possible to determine their approximate age by counting the annual shoots.

The minimum age appeared to vary from 17 to 37 years when in May, 1953, they were transplanted with wide spacing to favorable

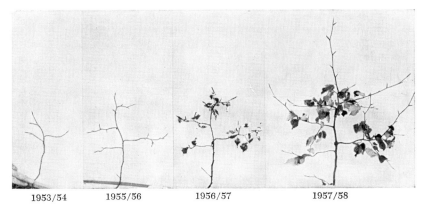

1953/54   1955/56   1956/57   1957/58

Fig. 18–5. Photographs in four winters of an approximately 30-year-old beech tree which until May, 1953, grew in very heavy shade. Note the gradual recovery of the plant after removal in 1953 to light shade. The incipient leaf retention shows that the plant has been kept back in the juvenile stage. From Schaffalitzky de Muckadell (1959).

shade conditions. Light intensity measurements were made with an electric photometer in bright sunshine on June 13, 1957. The light intensity averaged 5 per cent of full light under the beech stand as compared to 25 per cent in the new environment.

It is interesting to note that the working hypothesis in 1953 was that these beeches had left the juvenile leafy stage, and it was therefore expected that they would continue leaf-shedding. However, Fig. 18–5 shows how the extremely great ability of shade to prolong the juvenile stage was demonstrated. During the period from 1953 to 1958 all surviving plants gradually became leaf-retaining.

A number of similar experiments also indicated the effect of shade in maintaining fairly old beech plants in the juvenile stage. These observations suggest that foresters should not give up the use of chronologically old natural regenerations, as has been the tendency in Denmark and elsewhere. By careful tending such regenerations may develop into good stands.

On the whole the existence of development stages or meristematic aging in trees and the interplay between this phenomenon and environment are of some importance to the silviculturist. A knowledge in this field will contribute to a better understanding of the behavior of trees, hence to better silviculture.

Discussion

EDWIN B. KURTZ, JR.

De Muckadell's provocative paper has raised the problem of senescence in plants, if we assume that an adult plant is more senescent than a juvenile plant. He showed that the change from juvenile to adult forms can be controlled by environmental factors, such as shade. Thus the juvenile form can be maintained in shade. However, gibberellic acid can cause an adult ivy plant to revert to the juvenile form (Robbins, 1957), a developmental change of the meristem which appears to be the reverse of senescence. Apparently some reversible biochemical system determines whether the meristem will produce the adult or juvenile form. The question next arises as to the nature of this biochemical system. The following brief discussion presents some evidence and ideas concerning the nature of this system, and also proposes an experimental approach utilizing juvenile and adult forms for the study of the developmental changes of the shoot tip.

In a series of publications Kessler et al. (Kessler, 1956, 1957, 1958; Kessler et al., 1959; Kessler and Monselise, 1959) have shown that there are marked changes in the concentration of ribonucleic acid (RNA) and deoxyribonucleic acid (DNA) as the plant matures and that the RNA/DNA ratio increases when a plant becomes fruitful. Furthermore, these workers showed that flowering of olive trees and grape vines, for instance, can be promoted by spraying the plants with uracil, xanthine, or caffeine. They also found that the concentration of uracil in fruiting trees is much greater than in non-fruiting trees, which seems to agree with the finding of Salisbury and Bonner (1958) that 5-fluorouracil inhibits flowering. It therefore appears that there is an intimate relationship among the concentrations of purines, pyrimidines (particularly uracil), RNA, and DNA, and maturation and flowering of plants.

Returning now to juvenile and adult forms of plants, it would be of interest to know whether the RNA/DNA ratios of juvenile and adult forms are different and characteristic of each morphological state. Since De Muckadell has shown that shade maintains juvenility, does shade also maintain a constant RNA/DNA ratio? The use of chemicals to induce juvenile-adult changes also could be studied, and any effects on the RNA/DNA ratio noted. That is, because the spraying of plants with uracil, xanthine, or caffeine increases the RNA/DNA ratio and also promotes flowering, will these compounds also change the relative concentrations of RNA and DNA in a juvenile shoot and therefore cause the shoot to become adult? Conversely, because gibberellic acid can cause reversion from adult to the juvenile state in ivy, there may be a concomitant decrease in the RNA/DNA ratio. Kessler (1956) and Kessler and Monselise (1959) showed that there is a direct correlation between RNA content and protein synthesis, which suggests the possibility of using RNA extracted from an adult shoot to induce a juvenile shoot to change to the adult form, or vice versa. In these and any similar studies, the morphological change of the shoot from the juvenile to adult state, or the reverse change, provides a simple yet precise indicator of internal biochemical changes.

Concerning the use of RNA to transfer characteristics from one plant to another, it should be mentioned that RNA from leaves of fruiting pear trees has been used successfully to induce changes in the protein content and composition of non-fruiting pear trees (Kessler, 1958).

If any of the foregoing suggestions concerning aging of plants should prove correct, or if some other mechanism of senescence should be found, a great many practical applications would be possible. For example, will it be possible to "age" seedlings more rapidly by spraying them with certain purines or pyrimidines? Could such a procedure be used to shorten the time now needed in a tree breeding program? In any event, the senescence of plants is worthy of much more study than it now receives and even a partial understanding of the process would be of great value in forestry and related fields.

LITERATURE CITED

KESSLER, B. 1956. Effect of methyltryptophan and thiouracil upon protein and ribonucleic acid synthesis in certain higher plants. Nature 178: 1337–1338.

———. 1957. Effect of certain nucleic acid components upon the status of iron, deoxyribonucleic acid, and lime-induced chlorosis in fruit trees. Nature 179: 1015–1016.

———. 1958. Effect of transmitted ribonucleic acid from healthy pear trees upon synthesis and composition of protein. Nature 181: 201–202.

KESSLER, B., R. BAK, and A. COHEN. 1959. Flowering in fruit trees and annual plants as affected by purines, pyrimidines and triiodobenzoic acid. Plant Physiol. 34: 605–608.

KESSLER, B., and S. P. MONSELISE. 1959. Studies on ribonuclease, ribonucleic acid and protein synthesis in healthy and zinc-deficient citrus leaves. Physiol. Plant. 12: 1–7.

ROBBINS, W. J. 1957. Gibberellic acid and the reversal of adult *Hedera* to a juvenile state. Amer. Jour. Bot. 44: 743–746.

SALISBURY, F. B., and J. BONNER. 1958. Effects of uracil derivatives on flowering of Xanthium. Plant Physiol. 33, Sup.: xxv.

SCHAFFALITZKY DE MUCKADELL, M. 1956. Skovtraernes udviklingsstadier og deres betydning for skovdyrkningen. (Development stages of forest trees and their importance in silviculture.) Dansk Skovfor. Tidsskr. 41: 385–400.

———. 1959. Investigations on aging of apical meristems in woody plants and its importance in silviculture. Det Forstl. Forsøgsv. i Danmark 25: 309–455.

19

Wind, Transpiration, and Tree Growth

Taisitiroo Satoo

Wind is an environmental factor of considerable importance. It is generally believed that it affects the growth and form of trees by increasing transpiration and by causing various kinds of mechanical injury. It is not rare to find dwarfed trees on ridges at higher elevations which demonstrate the effect of wind on tree growth. Although the effects of wind on forest trees have long been recognized and wind has been considered a cause of unsuccessful afforestation, most of the information available is in the form of field observations made by ecologists and foresters. Only a few measurements of an experimental nature have been made on effects of wind on growth of plants, and most of the reported observations were not concerned with forest trees. This paper will discuss some aspects of the influence of wind on growth and water relations of forest trees.

Growth

It is well known that windbreaks favor the yield of field crops. Afforestation also is often unsuccessful on sites which are exposed to prevailing wind. Wada (1937) reported that height and diameter of stems and the number and length of branches of *Chamaecyparis obtusa* in a plantation exposed to prevailing wind were greater where brush was left in strips between planting rows than where brush had been removed. He attributed the improved tree growth to the protection of these trees from wind by brush. Unfortunately, however, study of the direct effect of wind on growth in the field is complicated by the fact that in nature exposure to wind usually is accompanied by increased evaporation of soil moisture. Decrease of growth thus could be due to an insufficient supply of soil moisture. Controlled experiments are necessary to separate the indirect effect of wind, through its effect on soil moisture, from the direct effect of wind on growth of trees.

The author (Satoo, 1948d) has studied the effect of wind and soil moisture on the growth of black locust (*Robinia pseudoacacia* L.) seedlings in the greenhouse. Metal containers were filled with sand mixed with fertilizer and covered with paraffined cardboard to prevent excessive evaporation from the soil. Three germinated seeds were planted in each container. All containers were kept in water tanks to prevent the soil from overheating by solar radiation and from cooling by wind. The containers were divided into

TABLE 19–1

EFFECT OF WIND AND SOIL MOISTURE ON GROWTH OF BLACK LOCUST SEEDLINGS.

Growth Measurements	Wind	No Wind	Wind	No Wind
Soil moisture				
(Per cent of water capacity)	80	80	40	40
Dry weight of top (mg.)	367.7	688.2	117.6	357.6
Dry weight of root (mg.)............	68.8	111.3	23.1	67.0
Height (mm.)	144.0	258.2	43.0	156.2
Diameter at base (mm.)	2.02	2.27	1.41	1.85
Number of compound leaves	13.8	15.4	10.0	13.0
Number of leaflets	79.8	102.2	40.3	69.2
Number of leaflets per leaf	6.8	7.8	4.7	6.3
Length of compound leaf (mm.)	64.4	81.4	29.1	65.8
Length of internode (mm.)..........	12.45	20.04	5.15	14.3
Length of root (mm.)	231	296	124	244

four sets of five each. The soil moisture of two sets of five containers was adjusted to 80 per cent of water-holding capacity while that of the other two was adjusted to 40 per cent. After the cotyledons were fully developed, one plant from each container was selected on the basis of uniformity and all others were removed. Each one of the sets of plants from the two soil moisture levels was exposed to wind. Wind velocities measured at the middle of the plants varied between 3.7 and 3.5 m./sec. Average daily evaporation as determined from evaporimeters having a 10 cm. diameter filter paper evaporating surface was 30.5 g. in wind and 18.0 g. without wind. The results of the final seedling growth measurements, made after 4 weeks of exposure to the wind, are given in Table 19–1. The depressing effect of wind on growth was noted at both soil moisture levels but was most conspicuous in the set of plants having low soil moisture. It was observed also that stems of the plants grown in wind were bent to the leeward.

Depression of growth in height, dry weight, leaf area, etc. of plants grown under artificial wind is reported for marigold by Finnel (1928), for sunflower by Martin and Clements (1935) and by Wrenger (1935), and for Italian millet by Rao (1938). The results reported by these authors are in general agreement with those cited above, but they grew plants only under nearly optimum soil moisture conditions. Haas (1939), however, could not find any consistent trend in the effects of wind of low velocity on growth of avocado seedlings with various concentrations of sodium chloride in the soil. In contrast, Wadworth (1959) recently reported that wind of low velocity accelerated the growth rate of stands of young plants of *Brassica naps,* and that there was an optimum wind velocity. Wind of low velocity accelerated growth by improving the carbon dioxide supply and resulted in increased photosynthesis. Deneke (1931) indicated that the rate of carbon dioxide absorption by leaves increased with the velocity of air movement over the leaves. Heinicke and Hoffman (1933) and Decker (1947) observed that rate of air supply affects photosynthesis. It is probable that wind of low velocity improves growth by increasing the carbon dioxide supply and thus increasing photosynthesis. However, photosynthesis is also affected by wind through its effect on increasing transpiration and altering plant-water relations.

Since it was too difficult to measure photosynthesis in strong wind by means of gas analysis, the author (Satoo, 1955a) studied the influence of wind on dry matter increase and stomatal aperture in leaves of *Quercus acutissima.* Acorns were planted in metal containers filled with soil of volcanic-ash origin having a field capacity of 64.5 per cent and a permanent wilting percentage of 33.5 per cent. The seedlings were grown in a greenhouse until late June when the surfaces of the containers were sealed and the adjustment of soil moisture was started. Soils in the containers were allowed to dry until the soil moisture was about 44 per cent of dry weight. At this point about one-third of the water available at the field capacity was present. Four sets of five containers, then, were selected randomly. The day before the experiment two sets of plants were watered until excess water drained through the hole in the bottom of the containers. The following day six leaf discs, each 1 cm. in diameter, were taken from each plant at 10 A.M. Then, one set of each of the plants in moist soil and of the plants in dry soil was exposed to artificial wind of 3.0 m./sec. at the center of the plants. The other plants at high and low moisture were not exposed to the wind. At 2 P.M. six leaf discs were taken again from the other half of the leaves sampled at 10 A.M. The oven-dry weights of the leaf discs were determined with a torsion balance having a sensitivity of 0.01 mg., and increases in dry weight between the first and second samples were considered as dry matter increase in the leaves.

Stomatal aperture was determined with Monsi's (1938) quantitative infiltration method after taking the second disc samples. As shown in Table 19–2, increases in the dry matter of leaves and of stomatal

TABLE 19-2

EFFECT OF WIND AND SOIL MOISTURE ON DRY-MATTER INCREASE AND STOMATAL APERTURE IN LEAVES OF *Quercus acutissima*.

Soil condition	Dry-Matter Increase in Leaves (Relative)		Stomatal Aperture (Relative)	
	No Wind	Wind	No Wind	Wind
Moist soil........	100	78	100	78
Dry soil	28	17	66	48

aperture were depressed by wind in dry soils as well as in moist soils.

In another experiment the influence of wind duration was studied. Four sets of five plants similar to those in the former experiment were watered and two of these sets were exposed to artificial wind from 8 A.M. to 10 A.M., at which time leaf disc samples were taken as in the previous experiment. Then one set of the two previously exposed to wind and one of the two not exposed to wind were simultaneously exposed. At 2 P.M., leaf disc samples were again taken and increase in dry matter per unit area of leaves and stomatal aperture were determined. The effects of wind on dry matter increase of leaves and on stomatal aperture are shown in Table 19–3. The influence of wind increases with the duration of exposure.

TABLE 19-3

EFFECT OF DURATION OF EXPOSURE TO WIND ON DRY-MATTER INCREASE AND STOMATAL APERTURE IN LEAVES OF *Quercus acutissima*.

Wind Condition	Dry-Matter Increase (Relative)		Stomatal Aperture (Relative)	
	No Wind 10 A.M.-2 P.M.	Wind 10 A.M.-2 P.M.	No Wind 10 A.M.-2 P.M.	Wind 10 A.M.-2 P.M.
No wind, 8 A.M.-10 A.M.	100	87	100	77
Wind, 8 A.M.-10 A.M.	77	50	78	61

Bernbeck (1920a) reported that photosynthesis in *Vitis vinifera* and *Zea mays* decreased with increasing wind velocity. Skvortzov (1931) exposed oat plants to dry wind for several hours and then measured photosynthesis by the gas-analysis method. He found a depression in the rate of photosynthesis and a decrease in leaf water content after exposure to wind. Soil moisture was not controlled in his experiments. However, Deneke (1931), after experimenting with models as well as with plant materials at wind velocities so low that the leaf water balance was not disturbed, concluded that wind accelerated photosynthesis by increasing the carbon dioxide supply to the leaves. In the writer's experiment, stomatal aperture was found to be markedly affected by wind. It was assumed that increasing transpiration by wind resulted in a water deficit in leaves and a partial closure of stomates, thus depressing the rate of photosynthesis and the rate of dry matter increase in leaves.

Water Relations of Trees *in Situ*

Field investigations of the effect of wind on water relations of trees are few and the results complicated. Stocker (1932) could not find any relation between wind and transpiration of trees at the arctic timber line. However, on the Hungarian steppes, Stocker (1933) measured more transpiration on windy days than on windless days. Briggs and Shantz (1916) could not correlate transpiration with wind velocity. Schratz and Fritsche (1932) reported that on windy days a change in transpiration did not coincide with a change in evaporation. Michaelis (1934) found higher osmotic pressures, and lower water content in needles on the windward side than on the leeward side of dwarfed Norway spruce at a timberline of the Alps. Compton (1936) also reported that the water content of orange leaves is lower when the wind blows.

The writer studied water relations of *Chamaecyparis obtusa* in a windbreak, as a simple case of wind effect on trees (Satoo, 1952). The windbreak was located in the northwest of Tokyo, where a dry northwest wind of 3 m./sec. mean velocity usually prevails throughout the winter. The windbreak trees were planted in two single rows, one running north to south and the other running west to east, connecting and forming a northwestern corner. The trees were 18-years-old and their heights were 2.5 to 3 ms. The average diameter breast high was 6.4 cm., and the average distance between trees was about 0.6 ms. Transpiration, water content of leaves, evaporation, and wind velocity at 1.3 m. above ground were determined on both sides of the windbreak in late March. Transpiration was measured by means of a rapid leaf weighing method and evaporation by weighing wet blotting paper, 3 by 4 cm., hung from branches.

The results of this experiment are shown in Fig. 19–1. The water content of leaves was always higher on the leeward side,

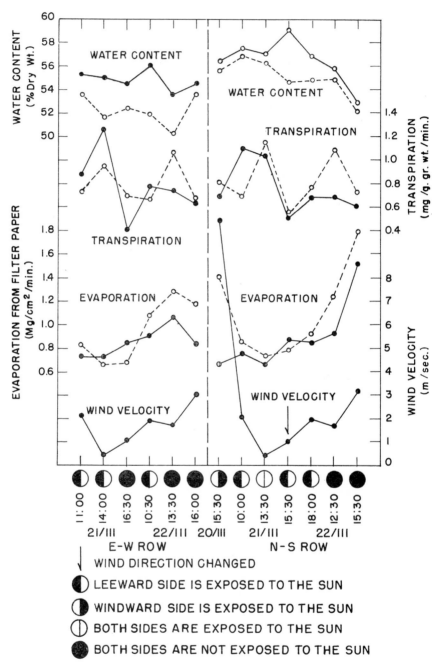

FIG. 19–1. Transpiration and water content of leaves of *Chamaecyparis obtusa* in a windbreak, evaporation from wet blotting papers, and wind velocity (average of each four determinations). Solid line with dots: leeward side of the windbreak; broken line with open circle: windward side of the windbreak.

but transpiration rate did not appear to show any consistent trend. Detailed examination of the data, however, showed that the transpiration rate was higher on the windward side except when the leeward side was exposed to direct sunlight. This difference is very slight. The transpiration rate was not related to wind velocity and evaporation rate. In controlled experiments, as shown in Fig. 19–2, transpiration rate usually is not proportional to the wind

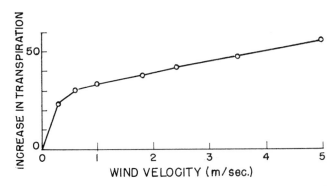

FIG. 19–2. Increase in transpiration rate of *Chamaecyparis obtusa* as a function of wind velocity (relative values, average of seven determinations).

velocity (Stålfelt, 1932; Wrenger, 1935; Martin and Clements, 1935; Satoo, 1955b). Controlled experiments also generally show that transpiration increases suddenly when plants are first exposed to wind and then decreases gradually, sometimes to below the original rate before exposure to wind (Wrenger, 1935; Martin and Clements, 1935; Griep, 1940; Satoo, 1955b) (Fig. 19–3). These facts illustrate that the relationships between transpiration and wind velocity are not simple.

Relation Between Transpiration and Water Absorption

From the above-mentioned experiments, it may be supposed that wind affects tree growth through its effect on the internal water balance of trees. It is generally believed that transpiration is accelerated by wind, and since Wiesner (1887), many experimental studies (Firbas, 1931; Stålfelt, 1932; Wrenger, 1935; Martin and Clements, 1935; Griep, 1940) have substantiated this opinion, except those of Seybold (1929, 1931–32, 1933).

Studies of the effect of wind on transpiration have been carried out from a variety of viewpoints. Some studies were prompted by a scientific curiosity to learn more about the process (Brown, 1910;

Gäumann and Jaag, 1939; Martin, 1942; Hygen, 1954; and others mentioned earlier). Other studies were stimulated by the realization that a better understanding of physiological processes, such as transpiration and its relationship to environmental conditions, is necessary to explain the ecological relations of plants and to develop sound agricultural and forestry practices (Bernbeck, 1920b, 1924; Fritsche, 1929; Gail and Long, 1935; Rao, 1938; Satoo, 1948b, 1948c, 1951, 1953, 1955b). Information is available from these

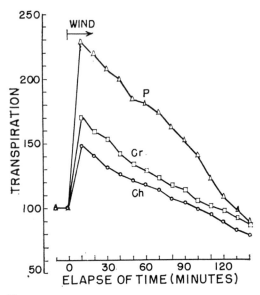

FIG. 19–3. Change in transpiration with lapse of time after the beginning of the exposure to artificial wind (relative values, average of six determinations). P: *Pinus densiflora;* Cr: *Cryptomeria japonica;* Ch: *Chamaecyparis obtusa.*

studies on the influence of wind on transpiration and its relation to other factors such as light, air humidity, leaf temperature, species, age of leaves, growing conditions of plants, etc.

Rapid transpiration caused by wind may not be harmful in itself, if absorption of water is rapid enough to balance the water losses. Therefore, the internal water balance which is an expression of the relative rates of absorption and transpiration, may be fundamental in the study of the influence of wind on growth and water relations of plants. Although studies on the influence of wind on transpiration are numerous, and the influence of wind on water absorption has been studied by Wilson and Livingston (1937), Satoo (1948a), Nakayama and Kadota (1948, 1949), and Kato (1951), very few simultaneous determinations of the two processes have been made on intact plants. Experiments of this nature were made by the author (1948b, 1949) on intact plants and by Knight (1917) on cut shoots.

Satoo (1949) measured simultaneously the rates of transpiration and water absorption of water-cultured seedlings of *Cryptomeria japonica* under controlled laboratory conditions. As shown in Fig. 19–4, when exposed to artificial wind, the transpiration rate suddenly increased and then decreased gradually, while the rate of absorption increased gradually. At the end of 2.5 hours of exposure

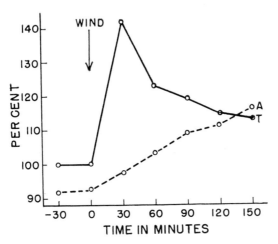

FIG. 19–4. Change in the rates of absorption and transpiration of intact seedlings of *Cryptomeria japonica* after exposure to wind (relative to the transpiration rate before exposure to wind, average of seven determinations). A: Absorption; T: Transpiration.

to wind, the absorption rate exceeded the transpiration rate. Changes in absorption rate lagged far behind the change in transpiration rate.

Similar experiments were also carried out with seedlings, the roots of which had been cut off beforehand. The change in transpiration rates caused by wind acting on the rootless seedlings was similar to those occurring in intact seedlings, but the change in the rate of absorption was not similar (Fig. 19–5). The rate of absorption by seedlings without roots reached its maximum after one hour of exposure to wind and thereafter it decreased slightly. Although the change in rate of absorption of water by seedlings without roots resembled the change in rate of transpiration, absorption lagged behind transpiration. The absorption lag was shorter in the seedlings without roots than in intact seedlings. This difference may be attributed to root resistance (Kramer, 1937, 1938) in the intact seed-lings. The lag of absorption behind transpiration probably results from the fact that the rate of transpiration responds immediately to the change in environmental condition but absorption does not increase until the effect of leaf-water deficit caused by suddenly increased transpiration is transmitted to the absorbing root surfaces. Although an absorption lag may be caused chiefly by root resist-ance, resistance in leaves and stems is not negligible. In case of

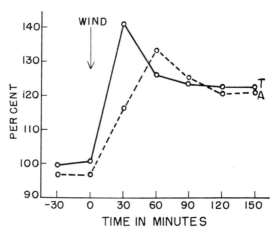

Fig. 19–5. Change in the rate of absorption and transpiration of rootless seedlings of *Cryptomeria japonica* after exposure to wind (relative values to the transpiration rate before exposure to the wind, average of six determinations). A: Absorption; T: Transpiration.

seedlings without roots, a change in absorption rate followed the change in transpiration but with some lag. This suggests that, after a sudden increase in transpiration and leaf water deficit, some-thing (perhaps partial closure of stomates) occurs in the leaves. Transpiration then decreases, the water deficit in leaves is lessened, and decreased water absorption follows.

It is apparent that a sudden increase in transpiration caused by wind is not accompanied by sufficiently rapid absorption of water to balance plant water losses, and a long-continued water deficit develops. The water deficit in leaves may cause closure of stomates and a depression in the rate of photosynthesis, and this will ulti-mately have a limiting effect on growth. In the present study, plants were used whose roots were supplied with an abundance of water. The water deficit in leaves may be more serious in cases of plants growing under field conditions, where the soil moisture sup-ply is often limited. In fact, growth and dry matter increases in leaves were more seriously depressed by wind when plants were grown in a soil of low moisture content (Satoo, 1948d, 1955a). In the practice of forestry species differences relating to the effect of wind on internal moisture deficits also may be of great importance.

LITERATURE CITED

BERNBECK, O. 1920a. Wind und Pflanze. Tharandter Forstl. Jahrb. 71: 130–193.

———. 1920b. Die Wasserversorgung der Pflanzen im Winde. Naturw. Ztschr. f. Forst- u. Landw. 18: 121–141.

———. 1924. Wind und Pflanze. Flora 117: 293–300.

BRIGGS, L. J., and H. L. SHANTZ. 1916. Daily transpiration during the normal growth period and its correlation with weather. Jour. Agr. Res. 7: 155–212.

BROWN, M. A. 1910. The influence of air currents on transpiration. Proc. Iowa Acad. Sci. 17: 13–15.

COMPTON, C. 1936. Water deficit in citrus. Proc. Amer. Soc. Hort. Sci. 34: 91–95.

DECKER, J. P. 1947. The effect of air supply on apparent photosynthesis. Plant Physiol. 22: 561–571.

DENEKE, H. 1931. Über den Einfluss bewegter luft auf die Kohlensäureassimilation. Jahrb. Wiss. Bot. 74: 1–32.

FINNEL, H. H. 1928. Effect of wind on plant growth. Jour. Amer. Soc. Agron. 20: 1206–1210.

FIRBAS, F. 1931. Die Wirkung des Windes auf die Transpiration. Deut. Bot. Gesell. Ber. 49: 433–452.

FRITSCHE, K. 1929. Physiologische Windwirkung auf Bäume. J. Neumann, Neudam.

GAIL, F. W., and E. M. LONG. 1935. A study of site, root development, and transpiration in relation to the distribution of *Pinus contorta*. Ecol. 16: 88–100.

GÄUMANN, E., and O. JAAG. 1939. Der Einfluss des Wind auf pflanzliche Transpiration. I. and II. Schweiz. Bot. Gesell. Ber. 49: 176–238, 556–636.

GRIEP, W. 1940. Über den Einfluss von Aussenfaktoren auf die Wirkung des Windes auf die Transpiration der Pflanzen. Ztschr. f. Bot. 35: 1–54.

HAAS, A. R. C. 1939. Growth and transpiration in avocado seedlings as affected by artificial wind of low intensity. Calif. Avocado Assoc. Yearbook 1939: 92–96.

HEINICKE, A. J., and M. B. HOFFMAN. 1933. The rate of photosynthesis of apple leaves under natural conditions. Cornell Univ. Agr. Expt. Sta. Bull. 577.

HYGEN, G. 1954. The effect of wind on stomatal and cuticular transpiration. Nutt Mag. f. Bot. 3: 83–94.

KATO, T. 1951. On the transpiration peaks of some shoots appearing in the beginning of wind blow. Trans. 59th Mtg. Jap. Forestry Soc. 112–114.

KNIGHT, R. C. 1917. "Relative transpiration" as a measure of the intrinsic transpiring power of the plant. Ann. Bot. 31: 351–359.

KRAMER, P. J. 1937. The relation between rate of transpiration and rate of absorption of water in plants. Amer. Jour. Bot. 24: 10–15.

———. 1938. Root resistance as a cause of the absorption lag. Amer. Jour. Bot. 25: 110–113.

MARTIN, E. V. 1942. Studies of evaporation and transpiration under controlled conditions. Carnegie Inst. Wash. Pub. 550.

MARTIN, E. V., and F. E. CLEMENTS. 1935. Studies of artificial wind on growth and transpiration in *Helianthus annuus*. Plant Physiol. 16: 613–636.

MICHAELIS, P. 1934. Oekologische Studien an der Alpinen Baumgrenze. IV. Zur Kenntnis der winterliche Wasserhaushaltes. Jahrb. Wiss. Bot. 80: 189–247.

MONSI, M. 1938. Eine theoretische Betrachtung über die Infiltrationsmethode. Bot. Mag. (Tokyo) 52: 300–312.

NAKAYAMA, M., and M. KADOTA. 1948. The wind influence on the transpiration of some trees. I. Bull. Physiographical Sci. Res. Inst., Tokyo Univ. 1: 17–34.

———— and ————. 1949. The influence of wind on the transpiration of some trees. II. The difference in the amounts of transpiration of pine leaves by length of wind duration. Bull. Physiographical Sci. Res. Inst., Tokyo Univ. 2: 10–17.

RAO, V. P. 1938. Effect of artificial wind on growth and transpiration in the Italian millet, *Setaria italica*. Bull. Torrey Bot. Club 65: 229–232.

SATOO, T. 1948a. Factors affecting the change in rate of water absorption by shoots of *Cryptomeria japonica* with respect to the exposure to artificial wind. Jour. Jap. Forestry Soc. 30: 26–32.

————. 1948b. Effect of wind and temperature surrounding roots on transpiration of plants in dormant season. Bull. Tokyo Univ. Forests 36: 19–28.

————. 1948c. Effect of wind on transpiration of new and old leaves of some trees. Bull. Tokyo Univ. Forests 36: 29–34.

————. 1948d. Effect of wind and soil moisture on growth of seedlings of *Robinia pseudoacacia*. Bull. Tokyo Univ. Forests 36: 35–40.

————. 1949. Relation between rate of transpiration and rate of absorption of water in seedlings of *Cryptomeria japonica* exposed to artificial wind. Bull. Tokyo Univ. Forests 37: 19–30.

————. 1951. Leaf temperature in relation to the influence of wind on transpiration of plants. 1–3. Bull. Tokyo Univ. Forests 39: 31–38, 39–47, 49–54.

————. 1952. Notes on the water relations of trees in windbreaks. Misc. Inform., Tokyo Univ. Forests 9: 25–30.

————. 1953. Influence of wind on transpiration of seedlings of *Cryptomeria japonica* grown under different soil moisture conditions. Bull. Tokyo Univ. Forests 44: 1–6.

————. 1955a. The influence of wind on dry matter increase in leaves of *Quercus acutissima*. Bull. Tokyo Univ. Forests 50: 21–26.

————. 1955b. The influence of wind on transpiration of some conifers. Bull. Tokyo Univ. Forests 50: 27–35.

SCHRATZ, E., and G. FRITSCHE. 1932. Über die Bedeutung pflanzlicher Temperatur-messungen bei Transpirationsuntersuchungen am Standort. Beih. Bot. Centbl. 49. Erg. Bd. (Drude Festschr.) 438–455.

SEYBOLD, A. 1929. Physikalische Komponente der pflanzlicher Transpiration. Monog. an den Gesamtgeb. der Bot. 2. Julius Springer, Berlin.

————. 1931–32. Weitere Beiträge zur Kenntnis der Transpirationsanalyse. Planta 13: 18–28; 14: 77–93, 386–410; 16: 518–525.

————. 1933. Zur Klärung des Begriffes Transpirationswiderstand. Planta 21: 353–367.

SKVORTZOV, S. S. 1931. On the influence of desiccating winds on the photosynthesis. Bull. Appl. Bot., Genet., and Plant Breeding 25: 45–68.

STÅLFELT, M. G. 1932. Der Einfluss des Windes auf die kutikuläre und stomatäre Transpiration. Svensk Bot. Tidskr. 26: 45–69.

STOCKER, O. 1932. Transpiration und Wasserhaushalt in verschiedenen Klimazonen. I. Untersuchungen an der arktischen Baumgrenze in Schwedisch-Lappland. Jahrb. Wiss. Bot. 75: 494–549.

————. 1933. Transpiration und Wasserhaushalt in verschiedenen Klimazonen. II. Untersuchungen in der ungarischen Alkalisteppe. Jahrb. Wiss. Bot. 78: 751–856.

WADA, T. 1937. Wind and forestry. Jour. Jap. Forestry. Soc. 19: 97–103.

WADWORTH, R. M. 1959. An optimum wind speed for plant growth. Ann. Bot. N. S. 23: 194–199.

WIESNER, J. 1887. Grundversuche über den Einfluss der Luftbewegung auf die Transpiration der Pflanzen. Sitzber. Keiserl. Akad. Wiss. Wien, Math.-Naturw. Kl. 96: 182–197.

WILSON, J. D., and B. E. Livingston. 1937. Lag in water absorption by plants in waterculture with respect to change in wind. Plant Physiol. 12: 135–150.

WRENGER, M. 1935. Über die Einfluss des Windes auf die Transpiration der Pflanzen. Ztschr. f. Bot. 29: 257–320.

20

Geographic Variability in Growth of Forest Trees

ROBERT Z. CALLAHAM

Introduction

Tree growth, like all plant characters, is a product of the interaction of genes and environment; however, the genes, environment, and interaction are not the same for every individual of a species. Genes exert master control over the plant's growth mechanisms. They control mechanisms for responding to environment and for utilizing environment in growth. Usually many genes control growth, and their individual effects are thought to be additive. The contributions of the individual genes establish the genetically fixed range of tolerance of a tree. The environment supplies the raw material essential to the tree's manufacturing plant. All component parts of the environment—climate, soils, biota—must provide their share to the manufacturing process called growth. Deficiency or excess in any part can limit the process.

For growth to occur, the range of variation in environmental factors must fall within the range of tolerance of the genotype. Individual trees of a species grow in diverse environments, and to expect all individuals of a species to be genetically alike and to be adapted to all environments would be illogical. Rather, each tree should be expected to be peculiarly adapted to the extreme variations in its environment. Each tree arrives at its balance with its environment on its own genetic basis.

Populations of trees can be described in terms of average values, and these averages can be closely related to characteristics of local environment. Investigations of genetic variation within species show the relation between these characteristics of trees and their environments.

311

Much evidence is available to support the foregoing and following statements. The purpose of this paper is not to present a bibliography on one of the largest subjects in the field of forest genetics. Review and summaries of the world knowledge on this subject already abound. Only selected references will be cited in support of statements and viewpoints. Primarily, reference will be made to research on *Pinus ponderosa* Laws. in which the writer has participated.

Genetic Controls of Growth Demonstrated in Progeny Tests

Progeny tests are the main tool which scientists have employed to demonstrate genetic variation in growth. A progeny test exposes genetic differences by bringing different genotypes together under one set of environmental conditions. Replication under a variety of environments brings forth each tree's genetically-fixed range of tolerance for factors of its environment, and replication exposes interactions between genotype and environment in growth control.

Genetic control over growth differs extensively between widespread populations of trees. Even crude tests comparing progenies from remote areas make this genetic change most obvious. Whenever seeds from many widespread sources are planted in one or more localities, genetically controlled growth differences catch the eye. The observer is struck by genetic differences in seeds, in germination behavior, in morphology of foliage, stems, and roots, in the periodicity, rate, and amount of shoot and root growth, and in many other characters (Langlet, 1938; Critchfield, 1957).

The closer two populations are to one another, the more obscure differences between them generally become. The growth differences between local populations close to one another are quite subtle. To uncover these differences, critical tests must employ rigid statistical or physical controls over environmental variation. Ponderosa pine progeny tests at the Institute of Forest Genetics at Placerville, California, illustrate this point. The purpose of these tests was to determine genetic differences between individuals and populations along a 50-mile transect covering 7,000 feet elevational rise on the west face of the Sierra Nevada. Replication and randomization were incorporated into the design of the tests. Hence, the investigator could estimate closely the environmental variation and split out the genetic variance.

Genetic growth potential does not vary much between neighboring trees on this transect. Callaham and Hasel (1961) recently completed analyses of a test of progenies of eighty-one individual ponderosa pines in California. Growth was analyzed after 15 years. Some populations and individuals exceeded expected growth considering both the elevation of their parents and their nursery performance. Other individuals and populations fell well below expectation (Fig. 20–1). The factors related to such significant departures from normality are not known, but site factors undoubt-

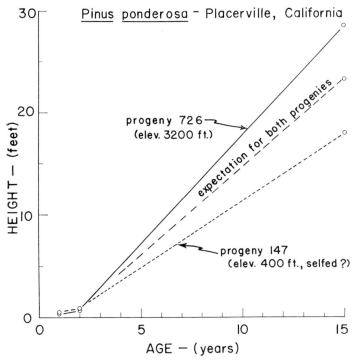

FIG. 20–1. Growth of the best and next to poorest of 81 progenies. The same 15-year heights were expected for both based on second-year height growth, elevation, and elevation [2].

edly have played a dominant role in evolution of local genetic growth variations (Squillace and Bingham, 1958a). In no case did the progeny of any seed tree differ significantly in height at fifteen years from the progenies of two to eight neighboring trees.

Of course, this does not mean that outstanding trees cannot be found. Many "elite" trees have been found which pass on to their progenies unusual genetic growth potentials. The quest for such super trees is world-wide, yet only rarely does the seeker find extraordinary germ plasm. Close neighbors in the forest usually have evolved similar genetic growth controls. Two evolutionary forces both act to equalize individuals within populations. Cross-fertilization provides gene exchange, and environmental selection weeds out the nonadapted individuals.

In addition to the foregoing conclusions on growth, progeny tests have produced another item of basic information. Estimates of the heritability of height growth come from two ponderosa pine studies (Callaham and Hasel, 1961; Squillace and Silen, 1960). Heritabilities of height growth in the broad sense were 0.39 and 0.36. These values, although not high, indicate that a significant 36 to 39 per cent of the variations in height growth can be attributed to genetic differences.

Many genes contribute to genetic control over growth. Tests of progenies produced by controlled breeding show this through the pattern of inheritance of growth characters. The growth of off-spring most often is intermediate between growth of parents. This is true whether crosses are analyzed between adjacent populations, or between races or subspecies, or between species themselves. Such intermediacy indicates multiple factor control of growth characters.

Crossing one tree with itself or a close relative, called selfing or inbreeding, further illustrates genetic control of growth. In progeny tests selfed or inbred lines are compared with their outcrossed parents; typically, vigor is depressed (Orr-Ewing, 1957; Squillace and Bingham, 1958b). The genetic interpretation is that deleterious genes become homozygous. One point of importance to growth discussions is that progenies from selfing do not give a true measure of the genetic worth of a seed tree. Seeds from isolated trees should be taken with caution; they are likely to be the fruits of self-pol-lination and to produce slow-growing seedlings (Callaham and Hasel, 1961) (Fig. 20–1). In stands of forest trees, self-pollination might be a general problem. However, evidence has accumulated that outcrossing is favored and that selfing is disfavored through a process called selective fertilization (Squillace and Bingham, 1958b).

Juvenile Growth: Preview to Mature Growth

Long-term progeny tests elucidate the link between juvenile and mature expressions of growth. From 49 to 72 per cent of the variation in height growth at 15 to 40 years can be related to height growth during 2 years in the seed bed (Callaham and Hasel, 1961; Squillace and Silen, 1960) (Fig. 20–1). Hence, early heritable growth differences forecast later growth differences, and much can be learned from a progeny test in a few years.

Several non-genetic factors play a dominant role in early growth and can obscure heritable differences. Seed size partially determines germination time, and both strongly influence early growth (Callaham and Hasel, 1961; Squillace and Bingham, 1958b; Righter, 1945). The scientist has to account for environmental variation from these and other non-genetic causes when analyzing genetic variations in early height growth.

Climate Partly Determines Growth

Features of the climate are other non-genetic factors regulating all growth. Climate influences growth within a genetically fixed framework. Within this framework the plasticity of the phenotype can be seen as climatic factors vary.

Every introductory plant physiology textbook points out the partial control of growth by temperature, daylight, and moisture. Each has a strong influence on tree growth from the first division of the embryo to reproductive maturity. Temperature governs the rate of all growth processes, and extreme temperatures can determine survival. Growth generally occurs under a broad range of temperatures, but the best growth occurs at an optimum temperature between lethal high and low temperatures. Light varies in intensity, quality, and duration; in all its aspects light influences the growth process. Water is required for all plant life, of course. While a tree cannot exist without this trinity—heat, light, and water —research has demonstrated genetic differences within species in requirements for each of them. A few examples of genetic differences within ponderosa pine in requirements for these elements of climate will be examined.

GERMINATION RATE. The rate of germination of tree seeds is governed primarily by temperature, given adequate moisture and light, of course. Germination proceeds most rapidly at some optimum temperature. This optimum differs from the optimum temperature for other growth characters. Furthermore, the genetically-fixed optimum temperature for germination is not the same for all trees or for all populations of a species (Critchfield, 1957; Olson et al., 1959).

Studies of ponderosa pine illustrate this genetic variation in germination response to temperature (Callaham, 1959). Speed of germination was determined for lots of 10 seeds (Fig. 20–2). Each lot represented up to five wind-pollinated progenies from each source. Incubation was at five constant temperatures—8°, 16°, 24°, 30°, and 36° C.

Broad geographic differences were noticeable immediately. Within one week, germination was under way at 24°, 30°, and 36° C. for progenies from sources east of the Rocky Mountains. The optimum temperature was somewhere between 24° and 30° C. Progenies from the Southwest behaved in the same manner except

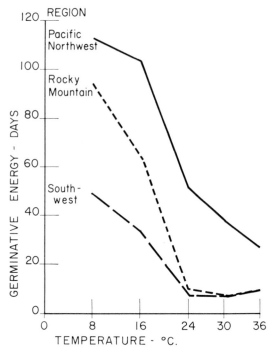

Fig. 20–2. Mean germinative energy at five incubation temperatures for ponderosa pine progenies from a number of field plots in three regions.

for one significant difference. Only a very few of the Southwest seeds germinated at 8°; yet, at 16° germinative capacity and energy were high. Progenies from the Pacific Northwest, including California, Oregon, and Washington, germinated three to six weeks later; their temperature optimum was at 36° C. or higher.

Variations among progenies within sources, although subtle, showed that optimum temperatures differed for individuals (Fig. 20–3). The cumulative germination for each of two trees growing near Corvallis, Oregon, shows a high temperature optimum for one tree (No. 5) and a low temperature optimum for the other tree

(No. 2). This one example suffices to illustrate the genetic diversity present within local populations.

Moisture relations during germination also illustrate genetic differences. Squillace and Bingham (1958a) found differences between progenies in their ability to take up water from a sugar solution during germination. Progenies from trees "as little as one-half mile apart in continuous *Pinus monticola* stands" showed dis-

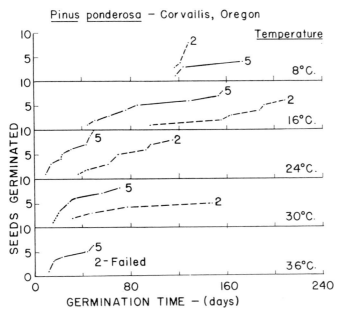

FIG. 20–3. Cumulative germination at five incubation temperatures for lots of ten seeds from each of two ponderosa pines near Corvallis, Oregon.

tinct genetic differences in this character. This was one of the first demonstrations of an inherent distinction between local populations on the basis of uptake of water needed for germinative growth.

SEEDLING GROWTH. Following germination, seedling development is dominated by temperature and light conditions, providing moisture is adequate. Their independent effects on growth can be ascertained by the use of controlled environment facilities. Such "growth chamber" studies are limited in the size of plants they can contain; hence, basic work on light and temperature effects has utilized seedlings in their first few seasons of growth. Tremendous inter- and intraspecific differences are found in seedling growth response to controlled change in lighting and heating.

Photoperiod can affect the inception and cessation of growth, establishing the duration of the growth period. This regulatory effect of daylength and, more important, nightlength has been demonstrated repeatedly. The onset and cessation of growth may be genetically fixed in relation to a particular photoperiod. Similarly, the length of the growth period may be fixed by some inherent "time clock." Such mechanisms probably have evolved in response to a particular length of growing season (Critchfield, 1957). Vaartaja (1959) and many others have shown that all individuals or

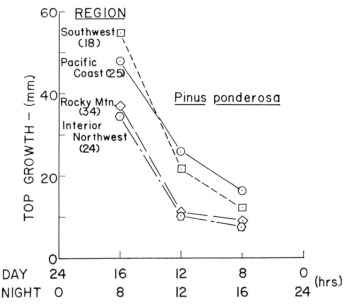

Fig. 20–4. Top growth of progenies of a number of ponderosa pines from four regions after 14 weeks of exposure to three daylengths.

populations of a species do not respond similarly to change in photoperiod. Evolution has led to a variety of genetic adaptations enabling plants to use the native photoperiod at their source as the clock by which to time their growth.

Studies of growth in relation to photoperiod for ponderosa pine from a variety of sources were conducted by Hellmers and Callaham in 1956. Progenies from 26 localities were grown under 16-, 12-, and 8-hour days at regulated optimum temperatures at the Earhart Plant Research Laboratories of the California Institute of Technology. During a 14-week period, average height growth increased with increasing day length for trees from all sources (Fig. 20–4). Progenies from trees growing in the Southwest—Arizona and New Mexico—showed the greatest response to lengthening days. These Southwest trees are definitely different in their inherent growth controls from their neighbors to the north and east in the Rocky Mountains. Similar differences can be shown for other regions.

Temperatures primarily influence the rate of growth, although they sometimes influence growth period (Irgens-Möller, 1957; Kramer, 1957; Olson et al., 1959). Kramer (1957) only recently made the first demonstration that trees have a thermoperiodic requirement for growth. Very little is known about the thermal requirements for growth of forest tree species, and even less is known of intra-specific variation in such requirements. Olson and his colleagues (1959) mention only briefly their tests of thermal requirements of Tsuga canadensis (L.) Carr. from fifteen sources.

Hellmers and the writer have unpublished data on thermal requirements for growth of ponderosa pine. Studies in 1956 of intra-specific variation in this species included progenies from 26 localities (in part different from the 26 referred to earlier). Growth was measured under nine combinations of three day temperatures, 30°, 23°, and 17° C. and of three night temperatures 22°, 14°, and 7° or 10° C.; daylength was an optimum 16 hours. The data (Fig. 20–5) lead to two conclusions. First, ponderosa pine grew best under relatively hot nights, 22° C. or higher, and under cool to warm days 17° to 23° C. Thus, ponderosa pine differs markedly from P. taeda L. which grows best under hot days and cool nights, according to Kramer (1957). Second, ponderosa pines from diverse parts of its range showed significantly different responses to variation in temperatures. Seedlings from east of the Rocky Mountains (Fig. 20–5 E, F) must have high night temperatures for good growth. The seedlings from the Southwest (Fig. 20–5 D) grew at a remarkable rate under cold days and hot nights. In contrast, Pacific Coast seedlings grew reasonably well at lower (14° C.) night temperatures (Fig. 20–5 A, B).

In the future, scientists will explore more of these inherent growth characters. As scientists discover what makes a tree "tick," they find that growth mechanisms of trees have evolved to be in harmony with the environment in which trees grow. Growth can be closely related to climate as many empirical studies have found. This reflects not a chance relationship but rather the product of an evolutionary process.

TREE GROWTH. According to the elementary texts, growth is related to temperature, light, and moisture. But how is growth related to climate? Only empirical studies of growth in a variety of climates will give the answer. Such studies have been under way since the close of the nineteenth century. Langlet (1959, p. 16) reemphasizes this and points with just pride to his countrymen who were first to pursue their studies to fruition more than forty years ago. What is the relative importance of seasonal climate versus annual climate?

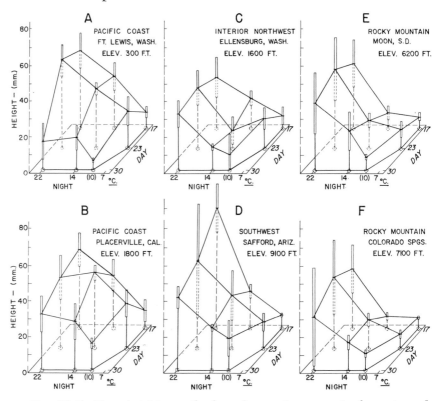

Fig. 20–5. Mean height growth of ponderosa pine progenies from six seed sources in four regions. Treatment included 16-hr. days and nine combinations of three day and three night temperatures. (Broad vertical bars show the range of the mean ±2 standard errors of the mean.)

When the plant is dormant during the winter, the day-to-day climate might be irrelevant. Yet, at the peak of production in the spring a slight climatic change, like an overnight temperature drop, could be crucial. Climate is an ever-changing combination of weather elements. Certain of these elements must be most critical for growth; Glock (1955) summarized what was known on this problem.

A very recent analysis of an old study illustrates the close correlation existing between inherent height growth and certain climatic factors (Squillace and Silen, 1960). Analysis of *Pinus ponderosa* plantations in Idaho, Oregon, and Washington established significant correlations between height growth at the plantations and these features of climate at the source of the trees:

Precipitation	*Mean Temperature*
Annual	Annual
January through June	April–May
September through June	July minus January
$\dfrac{\text{September–June}}{\text{Annual}} \times 100$	

Areas which received most of their precipitation in fall, winter, and spring produced trees that usually grew faster; areas which received less moisture during those seasons produced slower growing trees. With respect to temperature, warmer areas produced trees that usually grew faster than trees from cooler areas. April–May temperature was more important in this regard than average annual temperature. In the multiple correlation, the proportion of rainfall occurring in the fall, winter, and spring plus the April–May temperature accounted for 33 to 76 per cent of the variation in progeny growth on the six plantings.

Recently, Langlet (1959) has correlated tree growth over a 17-year period to daylength. Inherent growth differences between trees from different sources were highly correlated with the length of day at the start of the "vegetation period," when average daily temperatures exceed $+6°$ C. Further analysis of his data shows a significant correlation between height growth and duration of the "vegetation period" (Fig. 20–6). Daylength at the onset of the growing season and length of the growing season may be added to the list of critical climatic factors.

Many more factors probably can or will be added to this list, but this point stands out: tree growth is adapted inherently to climate. Probably a tie-up exists between growth and edaphic factors of the environment as well. However, little is known in this area. Until the significance of genetic adaptations to soils is appreciated, caution should be exercised in extrapolating from growth data obtained on one soil series to radically different soils.

Continuous Variation in Climate

The mass of climatic data can serve as a guide to better understanding of geographic variation in tree growth. Topographic variation in critical climatic factors may indicate topographic variation in inherent growth characters. A pattern for climate may be the pattern for growth.

Fortunately, available atlases of climate and detailed weather summaries simplify the chore of analyzing weather patterns. Scru-

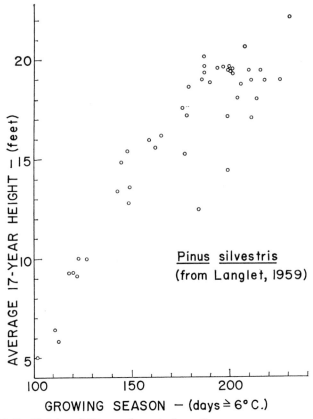

Fig. 20–6. Height of *Pinus silvestris* from forty-six sources, in relation to length of the "vegetation period" at the seed source. Data taken from Langlet (1959, Table 1).

tiny of these references brings forth regular relations between climate and topography. In ascending mountainsides, one encounters lower absolute temperatures, less diurnal and seasonal fluctuation in temperature, shorter growing seasons, and more precipitation. Going toward the earth's poles, one finds falling temperatures and increasing seasonal fluctuations in temperature and daylength, and progressively shorter growing seasons. Together, the facts add up to regular predictable change in a continuum of climate.

Clinal Variation in Tree Growth

Climate has a continuous and predictable variation, and tree growth is related to climate. The logical deduction follows: Tree growth varies continuously in predictable patterns. Individuals of

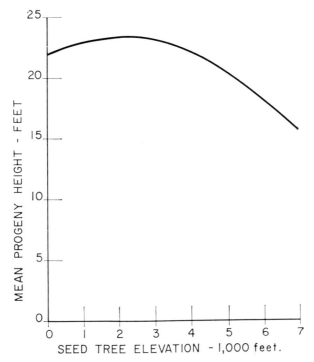

FIG. 20–7. Height of 15-year-old ponderosa pine progenies growing at 2,730 feet in the Sierra Nevada.

a widespread, uninterrupted species should show continuous variability (Langlet, 1934) or clines (Huxley, 1938) of inherent climatic adaptation. Interruptions in distribution of trees, as by water or mountains, might break such clines, of course. However, man should not come to the naïve conclusion that patterns of genetic variation are discontinuous because he has limited perception. He can neither study all populations of a species nor visualize inherent adaptation to the multidimensional interaction of all environmental variables. Discontinuities in factors of the environment, like abrupt change of soil type, may result in abrupt genetic change, producing ecotypes. Reasons for such changes usually are quite apparent. As Langlet (1959, p. 16) stated, "Discontinuities may thus very well occur—where the conditional ecological factors vary discontinuously." However, discontinuities or abrupt changes do not negate the basic premise of continuous variation.

Irregularities in the clinal pattern of variation certainly will occur. To forbid their occurrence would be to forbid evolution. These irregularities represent fluctuations in the rate of genetic change.

The California progeny test cited earlier illustrates this point well (Callaham and Hasel, 1961). Genetic variation in height growth takes the form of an ecocline (Gregor, 1939), related to elevational change in climate (Fig. 20–7). Certain progenies at lower elevation, possibly self-pollinated, showed significant reduction in growth from the ecocline. Nine progenies of another low-elevation population grew exceptionally well. They may be on the road to improved genetic adaptation. The important point is this: All individuals or populations need not fit an ideal statistical model of a cline. Certainly, statistics can be used to generalize on patterns of genetic change, but a waving free-hand curve or plane will fit data better and will be more meaningful in a biological sense.

Finally, the evidence for continuous genetic variation in tree growth mounts ever higher. Starting from the nineteenth century, to Langlet's (1934) presentation of overwhelming experimental evidence, to recent studies (Irgens-Möller, 1958; Olson et al., 1959), the record leaves little doubt.

LITERATURE CITED

CALLAHAM, R. Z. 1959. *Pinus ponderosa*: Geographic variation in germination response to temperature. Proc. 9th Internatl. Bot. Cong. 2: 57–58.

CALLAHAM, R. Z., and A. A. HASEL. 1961. *Pinus ponderosa:* Height growth of wind pollinated progenies. Silvae Genetica 10: 33–42.

CRITCHFIELD, W. B. 1957. Geographic variation in *Pinus contorta*. Harvard University, Maria Moors Cabot Found. Pub. 3. 118 pp.

GLOCK, W. S. 1955. Tree growth. II. Growth rings and climate. Bot. Rev. 21: 73–188.

GREGOR, J. W. 1939. Experimental taxonomy. IV. Population differentiation in North American and European sea plantains allied to *Plantago maritime* L. New Phytol. 38: 293–322.

HUXLEY, J. 1938. Clines: An auxiliary taxonomic principle. Nature 142: 219–220.

IRGENS-MÖLLER, H. 1957. Ecotypic response to temperature and photoperiod in Douglas-fir. Forest Sci. 3: 79–83.

————. 1958. Genotypic variation in the time of cessation of height growth in Douglas-fir. Forest Sci. 4: 325–330.

KRAMER, P. J. 1957. Some effects of various combinations of day and night temperatures and photoperiod on the height growth of loblolly pine seedlings. Forest Sci. 3: 45–55.

LANGLET, O. 1934. Om variationen hos tallen (*Pinus silvestris* L.) och des samband med Klimatet. Skogsvårdsför. Tidskr. 32: 87–110.

————. 1938. Proveniensforsok med olika Tradslag. Skogsvårdsför. Tidskr. 36: 55–278.

————. 1959. A cline or not a cline: A question of Scots pine. Silvae Genetica 8: 13–22.

OLSON, J. S., F. W. STEARNS, and H. NIENSTAEDT. 1959. Eastern hemlock seeds and seedlings: Response to photoperiod and temperature. Conn. Agr. Expt. Sta. Bull. 620. 70 pp.

ORR-EWING, A. L. 1957. Further inbreeding studies with Douglas-fir. Forestry Chron. 33: 318–332.

RICHTER, F. I. 1945. *Pinus:* The relationship of seed size and seedling size to inherent vigor. Jour. Forestry 43: 131–137.

SQUILLACE, A. E., and R. T. BINGHAM. 1958a. Localized ecotypic variation in western white pine. Forest Sci. 4: 20–33.

——— and ———. 1958b. Selective fertilization in *Pinus monticola* Dougl. I. Preliminary results. Silvae Genetica 7: 188–196.

SQUILLACE, A. E., and R. R. SILEN. 1960. Racial variation in ponderosa pine. Forest Sci. In press.

VAARTAJA, O. 1959. Evidence of photoperiodic ecotypes in trees. Ecol. Monog. 29: 91–111.

21

Selection of Superior Forest Trees

François Mergen

The majority of forest tree populations are composed of numerous heterozygous genotypes. The heterozygous condition is especially pronounced in wind-pollinated species, such as the gymnosperms. Because there is a heterogeneous gene pool it is possible to select desirable phenotypes for a considerable number of generations without exhausting the existing gene pool. The great range in existing variations, or the amount of inherited differences within certain species, promises to make the selection of outstanding variants a sound approach to the improvement of forest trees.

Why then have the results from past selection programs not been as spectacular as one might expect? The main reasons for the lack of more positive results probably include the short time that selection of superior forest trees has been in progress, lack of proper understanding as to how the trees should be selected, and, in most cases, lack of adequate knowledge concerning the amount of variation present in the species concerned. In the literature there are numerous examples of successful selection programs with forest trees, especially if the horticultural variants that are on the market are included. Horticulturists have been quick to commercialize "abnormal" forest trees, while foresters have failed in many instances to propagate outstanding specimens.

As long as good trees were plentiful in the natural forests, little thought had to be given to future generations, and selection of better trees to serve as parents for future crops was regarded as academic. However, with increased interest in artificial regeneration by planting, the selection of superior trees to serve as a seed source has been placed in focus. By planting large quantities of nursery-grown seedlings, it fortunately is possible to circumvent one of nature's principles, namely "the survival of the fittest." Foresters select the trees that will form the next generation; these selections may, or may not, be fitted to the particular site. If the selection has been wise a satisfactory crop results, but if a mistake has been made in matching the trees and the site the latter is often blamed. In excess of 2 billion seedlings were planted during 1959 in the United States. This places a heavy responsibility on the foresters who procure seed for these large planting programs.

The approaches that are being used to assure a supply of seed from good trees vary in the level of superior-tree selection depending partly on the time of selection: (1) at the time the trees are chosen to reseed an area naturally, (2) when seed is collected from forest trees for artificial reforestation, (3) when stands or trees are selected to establish seed production areas, and (4) when superior trees are selected for intensive breeding work and for establishment of seed orchards. Each of these levels will be discussed in detail.

Objectives of Selection

Under natural forest conditions, trees that survive and reproduce themselves are those that are best suited to compete and reproduce under the local natural environments. They are good competitors, but these trees often are not those most desired by foresters. In an intensively managed forest less emphasis is placed on the ability to survive and thrive under unfavorable conditions, and more thought is given to the qualities of the product that is being grown.

Until a few years ago forest geneticists had to rely on examples from agriculture to illustrate the gains that are obtainable by selection; now a considerable number of examples with forest trees can be cited. It is known, either from controlled progeny tests or from extensive studies of variation patterns in forest trees, that there are genes or gene combinations that affect the degree of resistance to a particular disease (Toole and Hepting, 1949; Zak, 1955), chemical content of trees (Pryor and Bryant, 1958; Schutt, 1958), resistance to certain insect pests (Wollerman, 1955), rate and type of height growth (Barber and Dorman, 1951; Squillace and Bingham, 1954; Toda, 1958), form of the tree (Mergen, 1954b), and the anatomical characteristics of the trees (Echols, 1955; Johnsson, 1950). Foresters will not be using the full potentialities of their profession if they fail to recognize and use these inherited qualities in the tending of existing forests, or when they establish new forests for coming generations.

When and How To Select

When trees are selected for shelterwood cuttings or for seed tree systems, considerations should certainly be given to the inherited qualities of the remaining trees. Although the tallest and most valuable trees should not be left in a seed tree system unless they can be harvested economically later on, at least the poorest trees, or those that are infested by insect or disease, should not be left standing. Under these systems little or no upgrading of the forests is possible, while degrading of the stand and pauperization of the desirable genes can be achieved rather rapidly if only the poorest trees are left to regenerate the area. The main objective in selecting seed trees in the high-forest silvicultural systems will not be to upgrade the resulting forests above the average of their parents, but to maintain a genetic and economic *status quo*.

When trees are selected for seed collection, there exists an opportunity to carry out eugenic selection and insure good parentage for the resulting plantations. Several of the larger seed brokerage firms are discouraging selection of seed from poorly formed trees, and require careful labeling as to type and condition of the trees from which the cones were picked. This is certainly a step in the right direction. Another factor should also be taken into consideration, namely that of collection from isolated trees. In inbreeding studies with conifers and with some hardwoods, inbreeding depressions were observed (Bingham and Squillace, 1955; Cram, 1955; Johnson, 1945; Mergen, 1954c). Therefore, seed should not be collected from isolated trees for fear of inadequate cross-pollination that might result not only in a smaller yield of seed per unit volume of cones, but also in poorer seedlings. Above all, when trees are chosen for seed collection one should select against, rather than for, the poorer phenotypes.

It has become widely accepted practice in both the eastern and western parts of the United States to establish seed production areas to alleviate the seed supply problem. For these seed production areas desirable trees are selected either in even-aged natural forest stands or in plantations, and the selected trees are favored and cultivated so that they will yield large quantities of high-quality seed (Easley, 1954; Mergen and Pomeroy, 1953). Potential seed trees are selected on the basis of their past performance, such as rapid growth, good form, and freedom from disease and insects (Fig. 21–1). They are selected solely on the basis of their outward appearance (phenotype), and their genetic potential (genotype) is not known. Tree selection for seed production areas is fairly simple, and depending on the species and age of the stand, ten to fifty

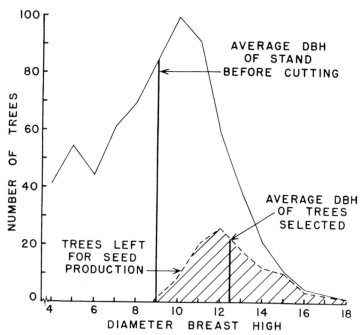

AGE 20 YRS.   HEIGHT 60-80'   VOLUME 36.4 CDS/ACRE

VOLUME OF AVERAGE TREE
      IN STAND   0.134 CDS.

VOLUME OF AVERAGE TREE
RESERVED FOR SEED PRODUCTION   0.270 CDS.

Fig. 21–1. Frequency distribution of diameter classes in a natural even-aged slash pine stand that was converted into a seed-production area. The frequency distribution before cutting is illustrated by the solid line, and after cutting by the hatched area. The undesirable and slow-growing trees were removed, and the largest and most vigorous trees were left to develop into large-crowned seed producers. Courtesy U.S. Forest Service.

trees are left per acre at a fairly uniform spacing, allowing each tree to develop a large live crown for maximum seed development.

Although often nothing is known about the hereditary qualities of the superior trees thus selected for seed production, there is a good likelihood that the resulting seedlings will be at least equal in vigor to the average of the trees in the original stand and possibly above that average. In this type of selection the trees that were chosen had survived competition in the forest, were well fitted for that particular site, and had utilized the site and local environments most efficiently. The writer helped to set up several seed production areas in slash pine and longleaf pine forests in north Florida. One of the areas is eighty-six acres in size, and it is expected that the pulpwood company which owns and manages the stand will collect 2,000 bushels of cones in a good year (Pomeroy and Mergen, 1954). It will assure seed of known origin from selected parents and at a cost lower than seed bought from cone brokers. Careful handling of the seed from the seed production areas resulted in a viability that was 50 per cent above average, and the yield of plantable seedlings was three times the number that was obtained under standard practices (Harkin, 1957).

The greatest future for superior tree selection, however, lies not in selecting the best trees within a given stand or within a county, but in the selection of the very best individuals within a state, or possibly within the entire range of a species. These trees are to be used in seed orchards for the mass production of superior seed, and as the framework in selective breeding programs. Various terms, such as *plus* tree, *superior* tree, or *elite* tree, have been used in describing the selected trees. As suggested by Swedish geneticists the term *elite* should be reserved for genetically superior trees, while the other terms describe phenotypically outstanding trees (Gustafsson, 1958).

Considerable time and money are being spent on selection of outstanding trees for selective breeding work (Anonymous, 1959; Perry and Wang, 1957; Rudolf, 1959). Whether this is the right approach, or whether gains would be forthcoming more rapidly if a species hybridization or a mutation approach is used cannot be answered simply. The outcome and benefits of a particular type of selection need to be appraised for each case because they depend on the approach used and on the particular objectives. It has been shown that in certain instances the selection of outstanding trees with subsequent mass propagation was quite successful, while in other instances no beneficial results were obtained. The possibilities of genetic improvement, the rate at which the improvement will be forthcoming, as well as the total amount of improvement that is possible through selection depend on a number of factors such as (1) the amount of genetic variation present in the species, (2) the characters selected for improvement, (3) the intensity of selection,

(4) the method of selection, (5) the heritability of the character under selection, and (6) the method of propagation.

AMOUNT OF GENETIC VARIATION PRESENT. In any selection program, the first objective should be to obtain an estimate of the existing range in variation of the trait that is being selected. Superior tree selection does not add any new genes to the species, but merely selects the outlying variants and furthers their multiplication. It is meaningless to state that the objective of a selective breeding program is breeding for trees with decay-resistant xylem, if the decay resistance factor does not occur in at least one tree of the species concerned. It can be generally stated, that the wider the range in the variation pattern, the greater can be the superiority of the selected individuals above the mean of the population (Fig. 21–2).

CHOICE OF CHARACTERS FOR IMPROVEMENT. The greatest genetic gains will be obtained if artificial selection deals with characteristics that are different from those that were favored by natural selection. Artificial selection is not recommended for certain traits that are reflected directly in the fitness of a tree to thrive under a particular environment, unless one is selecting within introduced species. Such traits as fruitfulness, frost hardiness, drought hardiness, height growth in an intolerant species, and resistance to the common local pests have probably been favored by natural selection through perhaps thousands of generations. Since the Pleistocene there have been possibly 200–800 generations in some of the northern pines, and one additional generation of artificial selection will have only a small effect on the change of some traits.

Therefore, characters of importance to the forester that have no direct adaptive or survival value might give quicker results and they should be favored. Some of these traits are anatomical features of the wood, yield of organic compounds (oleoresin, sugar, tannin, etc.), straightness of the bole, natural pruning, and size of branches. The type of character one is selecting not only influences the genetic rate of improvement, but also has an effect on the physical effort spent during field selection. For certain outward morphological traits, thousands, or possibly millions, of trees can be checked in a day, while for certain chemical or anatomical traits often only one or two trees can be verified in a day. A good example of this is the selection for high oleoresin yield in slash pine, where the oleoresin yield of certain trees had to be checked over a period of one year (Mergen *et al.*, 1955).

FIG. 21–2. Extreme variation in early growth of 18-year-old longleaf pine in a progeny test at Olustee, Florida. Tree A is still in the grass stage, tree B just out of the grass stage, tree C has a height of 38 feet and a diameter at breast height of 7 inches, and tree D had started height growth several years ago. Courtesy U.S. Forest Service.

INTENSITY OF SELECTION AND SELECTION CRITERIA. Intensity of selection, or selection differential, is an expression of the number of trees selected in relation to the number of trees sampled. This selection differential can be expressed in various ways if the mean and variation pattern of the species are known. It can be expressed in terms of the best tree in a forest of 100, 1,000, 10,000, or 100,000 trees; in terms of standard deviations from the mean; or it can be expressed in terms of percentage superiority, e.g., trees whose height growth is 100 per cent greater than that of the average of the stand. However, when selections are made for insect or disease resistance, trees are chosen that were exposed to the disease and were not affected, or trees that were affected and were able to throw off the attack before they were impaired.

METHOD OF SELECTION. If one is selecting for characters that are only apparent at the rotation age, or if there is a weak correlation between the traits in the juvenile stage and at maturity, selection must be confined to forest stands that are at, or close to, the rotation age. However, if a strong parent-progeny correlation exists as was found for height growth in western white pine, selection can be carried out in nursery beds or in young plantations (Squillace and Bingham, 1954). It should also be realized that the selection of superior trees is more efficient if the selected phenotypes can be compared to trees of the same age that had been growing under the same environment, or if compared to trees that had been subjected to the same treatments. This almost ideal condition is found in nursery beds where the seedlings are of the same age, and are growing under fairly uniform spacing under the same fertilizing and watering regime. In addition, the seed comes from several thousand parents, and several million seedlings can be checked in one day. This method was used quite successfully in one of the state nurseries in Florida to select slash pine trees with exceptional and abnormal growth, and longleaf pines with a short grass stage (Mergen, 1954a; 1958a) (Fig. 21–3). Selection for frost hardiness and disease resistance in nursery beds should be possible whenever there is a strong correlation between juvenile and mature traits. If selection is for superior height or vigor, nursery bed selection will be more reliable if the seed is graded by size before sowing, so that selection can be made among more uniform seedlings.

HERITABILITY OF THE CHARACTER UNDER SELECTION. The term *heritability* in the narrow sense, as accepted in genetic literature, refers to that part of the total phenotypic difference that is caused by the additive effect of genes. According to Lush (1940), heritability is calculated as follows:

$$H = \frac{\sigma_G^2}{\sigma_G^2 + \sigma_D^2 + \sigma_I^2 + \sigma_{EH}^2 + \sigma_E^2}$$

where σ_G^2 = additive genetic variance, σ_D^2 = variance due to dominant genes, σ_I^2 = variance due to epistasis, σ_{EH}^2 = variance caused

FIG. 21–3. Slash pine seedlings selected in a nursery bed for their extremes of natural variation. The seedlings are 1 — 0 stock. Courtesy U.S. Forest Service.

by non-linear interactions of environment and genotype, and σ_E^2 = variance caused by environment. Lerner (1958) also defined heritability as the regression of the genotype on the phenotype, or as the square of the correlation between the genotype and phenotype. It is an index of the transmissibility of the selected characteristic, and is mathematically expressed as the effect of the genes in relation to the total amount of phenotypic variability. Consequently, the greater the additive gene effect, the larger the index of transmissibility. In view of the fact that heritability is composed of two components, the effect of the environment and that of the genes, the numerical value for heritability can also be changed by changes in the environment. Therefore, the more uniform the environment under which the trees are growing, the greater will be the value for heritability.

In conjunction with the use of a numerical value for the *selection differential,* the potential gain in superior tree selection can be estimated by the formula:

$$\text{Estimated gain} = \text{Heritability} \times \text{Selection differential.}$$

METHOD OF PROPAGATION. The rate at which selected superior genotypes will find their way into commercial forestry will largely depend on the method of propagation. If, on one extreme, the selected trees have to be reproduced sexually and flower only after they have reached a considerable age, and the genetic improvement per generation is small, more than a hundred years might elapse before practical benefits could be realized. If, on the other hand, the desirable traits are under rigid genetic control, and the trees can be multiplied economically by vegetative propagation, superior stock can be made available at once.

Approaches to Selection

Depending on the objective of the forest tree improvement program, trees are selected either for being superior in only one outstanding trait, or for a combination of several or many desirable characters. With the tandem method of selection, only one character is considered at a time, and additional desirable traits are either selected for in successive generations, or they are introduced into succeeding generations by crossing with trees that are superior in these traits. When several characters are considered simultaneously, either the total score method or the method of independent culling levels can be used. For the total score method, index values are assigned to the various traits, and the trees with the highest scores are selected. Depending on the heritability and economic importance of the traits, weighted values should be assigned in calculating an aggregate phenotypic index. When the method of independent culling levels is used, each characteristic is required to meet a critical minimum level, and the trees are culled if one of the characteristics does not come up to this minimum level.

If trees are selected for only one desirable trait at a time, maximum selection pressure can be applied to this characteristic, and possible negative correlation between the selected characters will not be a concern. As more factors are considered concurrently, the degree of progress per character will decrease in a geometric progression unless there is positive linkage between the selected char-

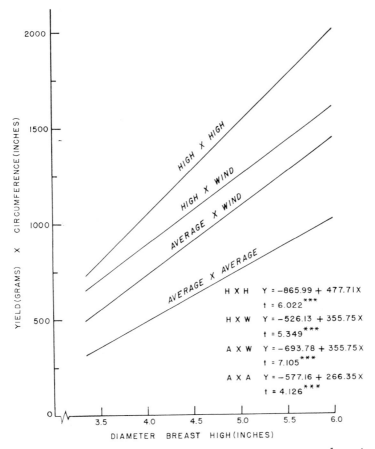

Fig. 21–4. Regression lines for four progeny groups in an oleoresin yield inheritance test of slash pine. The progeny whose male and female parents were both high yielders produced the greatest amount of oleoresin. When open-pollinated cones were collected from high yielders, the resulting progeny produced higher yields than the natural progeny of average trees, or of controlled crosses between two average parents. Courtesy U.S. Forest Service.

acteristics. This is probably why the most outstanding results with forest trees have been achieved when the selection objective was limited to one objective, e.g., selection for high oleoresin yield in slash pine (Mergen *et al.*, 1955), or disease resistance in Mimosa (Toole and Hepting, 1949) (Fig. 21–4). However, if *correct* weights can be assigned to the auxiliary traits and selection is carried out in very large populations, ultimate progress will be greater with the total score method than with the tandem method.

Selection Standards for Superior Trees

Adequate progeny testing is the backbone of all programs concerned with superior tree selection and selective breeding. Numerical values may be obtained from such tests, thus permitting estimation of genetic gains, as well as providing a basis for preparation of meaningful selection guides. The study of forest trees has advanced sufficiently so that rigid standards for selection of superior trees of the most important forest tree species can be prepared. These standards, along with methods of selection, should take into account the results obtained with other tree species as well as those from agricultural crops and from animal breeders. They should be worked out in close cooperation between the silviculturist, wood technologist, and forest geneticist. These standards can then be modified as the results from progeny tests become available. It will probably be best to limit the goals of superior tree selection to individual traits or to a small number of auxiliary ones, or give them proper weights. In the past, foresters were tempted to include in the specifications for superior trees all the traits that could possibly be conceived, even though some had little or no bearing on the main objective.

To facilitate selection in natural forests, plantations or nursery beds, illustrated guides are being prepared for various tree species (anonymous, 1952; Dorman, 1952; Isaac, 1955; Rudolf, 1956). These guides will help foresters and wood workers to be on the lookout for outstanding trees (Fig. 21–5). In addition, frequency distributions of the variation patterns are being established (Zobel and McElwee, 1958a; 1958b), and, as they are identified, superior trees can be described in statistical terms.

The intensity of selection, or the amount of time and money devoted to the selection phase of forest tree improvement programs, should depend on utilization objectives. If it is planned to make controlled pollinations along with clonal progeny tests, considerable effort should be invested in selection. A good system of keeping records is essential to go along with selection for it is important to describe, measure, and catalogue each selected superior tree. Various systems for cataloguing are used, including cards that can be sorted with a needle or with a mechanical sorter (Hoffman, 1958). If the selected trees are located on publicly owned land, or on

Fig. 21–5. Illustrations of selected superior phenotypes. A: Outstanding 17-year-old slash pine tree, 60 feet tall, growing in a natural stand in Nassau County, Florida; B: example of good phenotype of white spruce, selected by the staff of the Northern Institute of Forest Genetics, Rhinelander, Wisconsin. Fig. 5A Courtesy Universtiy of Florida, School of Forestry; Fig. 5B Courtesy U.S. Forest Service.

land of a private owner, written agreements for its use will have to be made. It is most distressing to return to a superior tree, hoping to collect cones from a previous controlled pollination, and then find that the tree was either cut down, or that half the crown is missing because someone else collected scions for grafting from the same tree.

Since selection for superior forest trees has started, the number of catalogued "plus" trees has grown into the thousands. An excess of 1,000 "plus" trees have been located in the United States alone (Fig. 21–6). In Sweden, about 3,000 trees have been selected for a combination of good form and exceptional height and diameter growth (Streyffert, 1958). When Finnish foresters released their data in 1953, they had selected, measured in detail, and mapped approximately 500 pines, 200 spruces, and 100 birch trees, along with some 300 trees of minor forest tree species (anonymous, 1953).

When selection is carried out for a specific anatomical or chemical characteristic, or for a by-product such as oleoresin from pines, one should keep in mind the fact that the large-scale results of such a selective breeding program will not be forthcoming until at least 30 to 50 years have passed. In the wood-using industries, and in the industries that use the by-products of trees, changes in utilization standards and conversion practices are rapid. It is very likely that some of the specific tree requirements can be taken care of more easily by technological methods in the mill, rather than by biological control in the forest. Therefore, these factors should be considered and selection should be for traits that will still be of importance some 30 to 50 years hence (Mergen, 1958b). Rapid growth at a uniform rate will undoubtedly always be a desired characteristic in most tree species, and selection for it will always be economically sound.

As phenotypic selection for superior traits takes place in the forest, results from research on biochemistry and biophysics of forest trees that is being carried out concurrently will supply helpful diagnostic tools for facilitating field selection. These tests will help elucidate cause and effect relationships, and they might well provide insight to the underlying causes of desirable characteristics. The tannin content of bark in chestnut trees can give an indication of resistance to chestnut blight (Nienstaedt, 1953), the viscosity of oleoresin can be used as an index of the yield capacity of slash pine (Mergen et al., 1955), the resin on pine branches can serve as an indication of the resistance to the resin midge (Austin et al., 1945, and the thickness of white pine bark can serve as an index of susceptibility to white pine weevil (Kriebel, 1954). As results of

FIG. 21–6. Western white pine tree selected for resistance to the white pine blister rust. Although standing in the open, the tree has a narrow crown with thin branches. At the time the photograph was taken the tree was 55 feet tall, had a dbh of 13 inches, and was 30 years old. Courtesy U.S. Forest Service.

these and other tests became available, they will facilitate field selection, as well as allow progeny testing at an early age.

It should be realized that selection for superior trees is just as feasible in hardwoods, as it is in conifers. However, very little selection for good form or rapid growth is currently being carried out with hardwood species. The reasons for this are partly biological and partly economic. A large proportion of the hardwood forests are of coppice origin, and this sprouting has established clonal stands that can be up to one acre in size, e.g., in poplars. This clonal origin makes it virtually impossible to select for trees with outstanding growth. In addition, the commercial outplanting of hardwoods in the United States is only a very small fraction of that of conifers, due to planting difficulties and problems in plantation management. In the past, selection in hardwoods was concerned with polyploid individuals, such as the "giant aspen" in Sweden (Johnsson, 1947), for resistance to insects and disease (Wollerman, 1956; Diller, 1956), for specific anatomical characteristics of the wood (Johnsson, 1950), for chemical composition of the sap (Spaven, 1949), or for rubber yield (Paardekooper, 1956).

Summary

In superior tree selection the objective is to achieve direct effects on gene combination and frequency in forest trees. The impact or progress that can be achieved depends on the existing variation in the gene pool and on the degree to which the forest geneticist can capitalize on this. There are great genetic differences in many of our commercial forest tree species. It is up to the forest geneticist to describe these, establish their genetic pattern, and make recommendations for their selection. Selection should be based on sound genetic principles, and the experience gained in other phases of plant and animal selection should be consulted. As most selection will be based on outward appearance, well-designed progeny tests are needed to evaluate the selection. From these progeny tests recommendations may be made that will allow a modification of current selection practices.

Selection of superior trees should not be the only approach to obtaining genetic improvement in forest trees, nor will it be the cure-all for existing silvicultural difficulties. However, if used in conjunction with other techniques, such as the recognition of ecotypical and clinal variations, and inter- and intraspecific hybridization, selection will contribute greatly to the more efficient management of existing and future forests.

LITERATURE CITED

ANONYMOUS. 1952. A guide for the selection of superior trees in the Northern Rocky Mountains. U.S. Forest Serv. North. Rocky Mount. Forest Res. Expt. Sta. Misc. Pub. 6. 7 pp.

―――. 1953. Forest tree breeding in Finland. Finn. Paper and Timber 6: 73–74.

―――. 1959. Third annual report, N. C. State: Industry cooperative forest tree improvement program. School of Forestry, N. C. State Col., Raleigh, N. C.

AUSTIN, L., J. S. QUILL, and K. C. BRECHEEN. 1945. Use of shoot characters in selecting ponderosa pines resistant to resin midge. Ecol. 26: 288–296.

BARBER, J. C., and K. W. DORMAN. 1957. Slash pine progeny tests indicate genetic variations. 4th South. Forest Tree Improvement Conf. 44–46.

BINGHAM, R. T., and A. E. SQUILLACE. 1955. Self-compatibility and effects of self-fertility in western white pine. Forest Sci. 1: 121–129.

CRAM, W. H. 1955. Self-compatibility of Caragena arborescens Lam. Can. Jour. Bot. 33: 149–155.

DILLER, J. D. 1956. "Screening" the American chestnut for blight resistance. 3d Northeast. Forest Tree Improvement Conf. 2–4.

DORMAN, K. W. 1952. Hereditary variation as the basis for selecting superior forest trees. U.S. Forest Serv. Southeast. Forest Expt. Sta. Paper 15. 88 pp.

EASLEY, L. T. 1954. Loblolly pine seed production areas. Jour. Forestry 52: 672–673.

ECHOLS, R. M. 1955. Linear relation of fibrillar angle to tracheid length, and genetic control at tracheid length in slash pine. Trop. Woods 102: 11–22.

GUSTAFSON, A. 1958. Plus- och elitträd. Skogen 9, 10: 282–283, 314–315.

HARKIN, D. A. 1957. Every seedling from selected seed. Jour. Forestry 55: 842–843.

HOFFMANN, K. 1958. Die Aufnahme von Auslesebäumen als Grundlage für ihre genetische und physiologische Beurteilung. Züchter 28: 257–262.

ISAAC, L. A. 1955. Tentative guides for the selection of plus trees and superior stands in Douglas fir. U.S. Forest Serv. Pacific Northwest Forest Range Expt. Sta. Res. Note 122. 9 pp.

JOHNSON, L. P. V. 1945. Reduced vigour, chlorophyll deficiency, and other effects of self-fertilization in Pinus. Can. Jour. Res. C23: 145–149.

JOHNSSON, H. 1947. Forest tree breeding in Sweden. Pulp and Paper Res. Inst. Canada. Rpt. 5 pp.

―――. 1950. Avkommor av masurbjörk. For. f. Vaxtfor. an Skogstrad, Ann. Rpt. 18–29.

KRIEBEL, H. 1954. Bark thickness as a factor in resistance to white pine weevil injury. Jour. Forestry 52: 842–845.

LERNER, I. M. 1958. The genetic basis of selection. John Wiley & Sons, Inc., New York.

LUSH, Y. L. 1940. Intra-sire correlations or regressions of offspring on dam as a method of estimating heritability of characteristics. Proc. Amer. Soc. Anim. Prod. 293–301.

MERGEN, F. 1954a. Improving the early growth of longleaf pine. Forest Farmer 13(11): 8, 9, 16, 17, 19.

―――. 1954b. Inheritance of deformities in slash pine. South. Lumberman 190(2370): 30–32.

―――. 1954c. Self-fertilization in slash pine reduces height growth. U.S. Forest Serv. Southeast. Forest Expt. Sta. Res. Note 67. 2 pp.

―――. 1958a. Natural polyploidy in slash pine. Forest Sci. 4: 283–295.

―――. 1958b. The forest biologist's stake in the TAPPI Forest Biology Committee. Tappi 41(4): 746.

MERGEN, F., P. E. HOEKSTRA, and R. M. ECHOLS. 1955. Genetic control of oleoresin yield and viscosity in slash pine. Forest Sci. 1: 19–30.

MERGEN, F., and K. B. POMEROY. 1953. Some practical suggestions for better slash pine seed. South. Lumber Jour. 57(11): 88–89.

NIENSTAEDT, H. 1953. Tannin as a factor in the resistance of chestnut, *Castanea* spp., to the chestnut blight fungus, *Endothia parasitica* (Murr.) A. and A. Phytopath. 43: 32–38.

PAARDEKOOPER, E. C. 1956. Results of the testing of *Hevea* seedlings obtained by hand pollination during 1927–1944. Arch. Rubber Cult. 33: 61–139.

PERRY, T. O., and C. W. WANG. 1957. Cooperative forest genetics research program. Univ. Fla., School Forestry Res. Rpt. 4. 27 pp.

POMEROY, K. B., and F. MERGEN. 1954. Better forests a reality. Natl. Container Digest 8(4): 5.

PRYOR, L. D., and L. H. BRYANT. 1958. Inheritance of oil-characters in Eucalyptus. Proc. Linn. Soc. N. S. Wales. 82: 55–64.

RUDOLF, P. O. 1956. Guide for selecting superior forest trees and stands in the Lake States. Lake States Forest Expt. Sta. Paper 40. 32 pp.

———. 1959. Forest tree improvement research in the Lake States. Lake States Forest Expt. Sta. Paper 74. 56 pp.

SCHUTT, P. 1958. Schwankungen im Zellulose- und Ligningehalt bei einigen in Westdeutschland angebauten *Pinus contorta* Herkunften. Silvae Genetica 7: 65–69.

SPAVEN, J. 1949. The secret of the maple. New England Homestead 122(8): 6, 8.

SQUILLACE, A. E., and R. T. BINGHAM. 1954. Breeding for improved growth rate and timber quality in western white pine. Jour. Forestry 52: 656–661.

STREYFFERT, T. 1958. Forestry in Sweden. Oregon State College, Office of Publications, Corvallis, Ore.

TODA, R. 1958. Variation and heritability of some quantitative characters in *Cryptomeria*. Silvae Genetica 7: 87–93.

TOOLE, E. R., and G. H. HEPTING. 1949. Selection and propagation of *Albizzia* for resistance to *Fusarium* wilt. Phytopath. 39: 63–70.

WOLLERMAN, E. H. 1956. Strains of black locust resistant to borer. 3d Northeast. Forest Tree Improvement Conf. 35–36.

ZAK, B. 1955. Inheritance of resistance to littleleaf in shortleaf pine. Southeast. Forest Expt. Sta. Res. Note 88. 2 pp.

ZOBEL, B. J., and R. L. MCELWEE. 1958a. Natural variation in wood specific gravity of loblolly pine, and an analysis of contributing factors. Tappi 41(4): 158–161.

——— and ———. 1958b. Variation of cellulose in loblolly pine. Tappi 41(4): 167–169.

22

Evidence of Hybrid Vigor
in Forest Trees

F. I. RIGHTER

Hybrid vigor relates to quantitative characters such as growth rate, size, or fruitfulness. As most tree characters of economic importance are of this kind, they are of the greatest interest and importance to tree-breeders, and the exploitation of heterosis in such characters, when it is beneficial, is, of course, of special importance in forest-tree breeding. Therefore, in addition to adducing some of the abundant evidence for hybrid vigor in forest trees, this paper will discuss its exploitation.

The term *heterosis* is a convenient and euphonious contraction of *heterozygosis*, coined by Shull (1914) to connote increase in size and other characteristics resulting from crossing. It is used as synonymous with hybrid vigor, and will be so considered in this discussion.

The literature on heterosis is very voluminous. It would take more time than is available to read a list of references representing but a part of the literature on the subject.

Heterosis is an ambiguous term, meaning different things to different people (Mangelsdorf, 1952). Under its label, different phenomena are confused (Dobzhansky, 1952, 1955). Two principal hypotheses have been formulated to explain it. One, called *overdominance*, asserts that it arises from interaction of different alleles, and hence that heterozygosity is necessary for its expression. The other, called the *dominance of linked genes* hypothesis, implies that maximum heterosis would be expressed in an individual in which every allelic pair of genes contains at least one dominant (Crow, 1952).

Dobzhansky (1952, 1955), viewing the phenomenon from an evolutionary standpoint, has called the heterosis that arises from these causes or conditions *true heterosis* or *euheterosis*. He distinguishes the causes by calling the heterosis arising from overdominance *balanced euheterosis*, and that resulting from the interaction of linked dominant genes *mutational euheterosis*. To distinguish between euheterosis and the heterosis that occasionally results from wide outcrossing, as for example, between different species, he tentatively proposed for the latter the term *luxuriance*. Ability to survive in the parental habitats in competition with the parental forms is Dobzhansky's criterion of true heterosis. Proof that luxuriant hybrids can so compete is not established (Dobzhansky, 1955).

Gustafsson (1951) has classified heterosis into three types, namely *somatic, reproductive,* and *adaptive*. In the first type, luxuriance of vegetative systems is affected. This type corresponds to Dobzhansky's luxuriance. The second type relates to heterosis that influences the number of pistils, pollen grains, ovules, and seeds produced. The third type relates to genotypes that produce a greater number of new individuals which survive and multiply in succeeding generations under continuous competition with other genotypes. This type corresponds to the true heterosis of Dobzhansky.

Definitions of heterosis differ also, and the difference is one of meaning rather than one of merely stating the same thing in different words. One states that a hybrid is heterotic if it surpasses the better parent in vigor; the other states that a hybrid is heterotic if it surpasses the average vigor of its parents (Hayes, 1952). To promote consistency, one of the definitions should be discarded. The writer favors retention of the former.

Duffield (1954) has indicated that, in defining hybrid vigor in the growth rate of forest trees, the rotation age should be given. This is because the growth curves of different species may be different. Hence, hybrids between species differing in that respect might be heterotic at one stage, or during one period, of development, but not at another stage, or during another period, of development.

Heterosis is not limited to F_1 hybrids. Indeed, it may even be increased in the F_2 and later generations. Clausen and Hiesey (1958) refer to an impressive case in which 50 per cent of the F_2 of a cross between subspecies of *Achillea borealis* exceeded the F_1 in vigor. Such increase in vigor in the F_2 is in sharp contrast to the usual loss of vigor in the F_2 of interspecific hybrids as well as hybrid corn.

Corn hybrids F_1 and F_2 are superior in vigor to the inbred lines from which they are derived. Hence they are commonly referred to as being heterotic, though the F_2 hybrids actually are not heterotic by definition.

Examples of Use of Hybrid Vigor in Agriculture

Although the hypotheses formulated to explain hybrid vigor have not been verified by experiment, practical breeding procedures for producing it in corn were devised long ago by Shull (1909, 1910) and Jones (1918). The use of these methods in corn improvement in the Corn Belt of the United States has been the most successful, and hence the most famous, of all applications of genetics to crop improvement, despite the fact that, as noted by Fisher (1948), the work of corn improvement was very largely the product of empiricism, enterprise, and strong public support. According to Stebbins (1958), it brought about an increase in yield of 25 per cent. Moreover, hybrid corn has acted in the Corn Belt as a catalyst in bringing about adoption of improved cultural methods which themselves have produced an additional increase equal to, if not greater than, that resulting from the use of hybrids (Mangelsdorf, 1951).

As previously noted, hybrid vigor may also be obtained through wide outcrossing. Perhaps the most famous case is that of the mule which, for many centuries, has been a highly valued animal because of its proverbial vigor, hardiness, and disease resistance. It is reported (Lush, 1945) that mules were produced in ancient Sumer by mating the horse to the onager. According to statistics presented by Rice et al. (1951), the value per head of mules was higher than the value per head of horses on farms in the United States over the 69-year period from 1880 to 1949. In 1949, the values per head for horses and mules on farms in the United States were $52.30 and $117.00 respectively. At that time there were 5,921,000 horses and 2,353,000 mules on farms in the United States. Thus, hybrid vigor in corn and in the mule illustrates the great importance of the phenomenon to man. Theoretically, heterosis in forest trees, whether obtained through inbreeding and crossing or through wide outcrossing, has similar potentialities.

Hybrid Vigor in Forest Trees

Theoretically, hybrid vigor is impounded in sexually reproducing and cross-fertilizing species, awaiting only the breeder's art to give it conspicuous expression through inbreeding, followed by crossing. The writer knows of no crosses between inbred lines of such forest trees. Experimental evidence of this phenomenon in forest tree species consists solely in the contrasted behavior or properties of S_1 progenies in comparison with the behavior or properties of natural, or crossed, progenies from the same seed-parents. Such evidence, though incomplete and, perhaps, inconclusive, indicates that crossing of inbred lines of such a species will give rise to hybrids that surpass both parents in vigor of growth and other characters.

The ill effects of inbreeding in corn and other cross-fertilizing species are well known. Similarly, such effects of inbreeding have been reported in the early development of progenies derived from selfing various species of forest trees. Thus, to cite a few instances, depression in juvenile growth rate has been reported in *Pinus* by Mergen (1954), Bingham and Squillace (1955), Wright and Gabriel (1958), and others; in *Liriodendron tulipifera*, by Carpenter and Guard (1956); in *Larix* and *Picea*, by Langner (1951, 1959a); in *Picea*, by Langlet (1940–41) who reported on work done by Sylvén.

All sorts of abnormalities appear in inbred forest trees as well as in other organisms early in life; and, as the trees grow older, they are likely to be a very scraggly lot. It is quite evident in nursery tests of *Pinus ponderosa* and of *Pinus taeda*, as well as in field tests of 19- and 27-year-old *Pinus jeffreyi* at Placerville that the inbreds could not survive in competition with the normal cross-bred trees (Fig. 22–1). Thus, heterozygosity appears to be obligate in those species, and it probably is in most other tree species having a similar method of reproduction. Figures 3 and 4 in the article by Carpenter and Guard (1956) strongly suggest that such is the case in *Liriodendron*, and the data presented by Bingham and Squillace (1955) are equally suggestive on this point. Thus, selfing of normally cross-fertilizing forest trees produces phenomena that in general are parallel to those that result from selfing corn. Hence, both theoretical considerations and experimental results indicate that the tree breeder can evoke hybrid vigor from inbred lines of forest trees of many species, provided they are self-fertile. According to Syrach Larsen (1956), self-fertility has been reported also in species of *Betula, Fraxinus, Pseudotsuga, Quercus, Thuja, Tilia*, and *Ulmus*.

In several instances reported by Duffield (1950), Orr-Ewing (1957), and Blinkenberg *et al.* (1958), self-fertility was reported as being low or lacking. However, relatively few selfing studies have been made in any forest-tree species. Therefore, such results may be regarded as tentative because variation in self-fertility from tree to tree is to be expected. In fact, such variation was observed in *Pinus monticola* by Squillace and Bingham (1958).

Because corn-breeding procedures have been so successful in increasing yield, several authors have suggested the possibility of applying these procedures to the improvement of forest tree crops (Sherry, 1947; Gustafsson, 1950; Matthews, 1955; Langner, 1959a). Since, theoretically, crop improvement is possible in many species of forest trees through use of such procedures, the only point that

FIG. 22–1. The seedling on the left is a typical specimen. It would be very difficult to select a typical "self." Both are from the same seed parent and both are the same age.

needs consideration is the economic feasibility of such applications. The breeding procedure used in the Corn Belt of the United States to produce hybrid corn may serve as a point of departure in discussing the exploitation of heterosis in forest trees through inbreeding followed by crossing.

The breeding procedure originally proposed by Shull (1909, 1910) consists in the development of highly homozygous, or pure, lines through successive selfings and concomitant selections, followed by crossing two selected, homozygous lines. A series of five or more selfings is required to produce the requisite degree of homozygosity in the inbred lines. Because the inbred lines are reproductively weak, this single-cross method is not economically feasible for the production of field corn, though it is so for the production of sweet corn, which sells at a higher price. A modification proposed by Jones (1918) made production of hybrid field corn economically feasible. This modification consists of producing two F_1 hybrids from four selected, inbred lines, followed by crossing the F_1 hybrids. As reproductive vigor is fully restored in the F_1 hybrids, an abundance of F_2, or double-cross, seed is readily obtained at the cost of an acceptable reduction in uniformity and yield.

In practice, this process is not as simple and easy as might be supposed from the foregoing account of it. In corn breeding, many inbred lines must be produced and tested in various crossing combinations in order to obtain the four lines needed for the production of a single double-cross hybrid (Mangelsdorf, 1951). In silviculture, several hybrids might be needed to supply enough genetic diversity in the stand to insure against total loss of a crop, unless a single hybrid has been thoroughly tested for adaptability.

Various other difficulties, particularly that of controlling pollination, would have to be overcome. Thus, it is evident that the procedure would be lengthy and troublesome, even when applied to tree species that come into flowering early in life. Nevertheless, the experimental and practical utility of its products, both inbred and crossed, would be very great.

As Langner (1959a) has suggested, highly inbred lines could be used in both inter- and intraspecific hybridization. F_1 hybrids between highly inbred lines of closely related species might be particularly vigorous and much more uniform than are ordinary F_1 hybrids between species. The F_2 progenies of such crosses would, of course, be of exceptional interest.

According to Matthews (1955) and Matthews and McLean (1957) respectively, projects have been started in England for crossing inbreds of European and Japanese larches and for applying corn-breeding methods to the improvement of *Pinus sylvestris*. Such projects hold great promise for species, such as *Pinus sylvestris*, which flower early in life. Moreover, it may be expected that plant physiologists will devise methods for controlling, or regulating, flower production in many kinds of forest trees so that such procedures may become practicable in non-precocious species. Such control probably will include prevention, as well as stimulation, of flowering.

Various modifications of the Corn Belt procedure are possible. As foreseen by Gustafsson (1950), weakly homozygotized lines might produce satisfactory hybrids for use in forestry; hence fewer successive selfings would be required and much time and trouble would be saved. A rather drastic modification, tested by Wellhausen (1952) in improving corn in Mexico, where genetic uniformity is less important than it is in the Corn Belt of the United States, might prove highly effective and practicable in forest tree breeding. Working in a virgin population, Wellhausen obtained very good double-cross hybrids from S_1 lines. Indeed, he found that testing for combining ability can begin with selected, open-pollinated plants. Thus, intermediate improvement may be effected very quickly by such procedures. Moreover, successive, "intermediate" improvements could be exploited throughout the inbreeding phase, assuming that inbreeding is to continue until a high degree of homozygosity is obtained. Thus, Wellhausen presented data showing that, without any testing for combining ability whatever, the average yield of fourteen single-crosses of S_2 and S_3 lines, selected from their ancestral S_1 lines, was about 9 per cent greater than the average yield of the S_1 lines. The use of single-cross forest trees might prove practicable, despite the reduction in reproductive vigor that is to be expected in inbred lines. Isolation of pairs of inbreds would make it possible to collect seed from both lines—this would also apply in F_1 hybrids—and the harvest from both S_1 trees might be as great as that from a single F_1 hybrid. The application of such breeding procedures to elite trees would probably be much more effective in tree-crop improvement than using the progenies from intercrossing among them. Thus, the great uniformity of single and double crosses would contribute much to crop yield, whereas segregation in the progenies of elite trees would bring about greater tree to tree variation, and hence, lower crop yield than would result if the full superiority of the elite trees were expressed in each unit of their progenies.

The literature of forest genetics contains numerous reports of heterosis in artificially produced interspecific hybrids. Most of the reports relate to growth rate, but data in some reports of hybrids between species show, as should be expected, that other characters are heterotic, even though growth rate in the hybrids is not heterotic. Reports of heterosis in growth rate in artificial hybrids which have been adequately tested relate to seedlings and immature trees. Some reports are based on the criterion of superiority over both parents; others are based on the criterion of superiority over the average vigor of the parents. Some are heterotic in one location, but not in another. Taking these reports at their face value, it is evident that much time and space would be required to discuss many of these reports, even briefly. Therefore, this paper touches on only a few of them.

Heterosis in seedling growth has been reported in the hybrid *Pinus monticola* × *Pinus strobus* by Righter (1945) and Bingham *et al.* (1956). Righter's report dealt with the performance of the hybrid derived from the Sierra Nevada race of *Pinus monticola* as the seed parent. His tests were made at the Institute of Forest Genetics, near Placerville, California, under environmental condi-

Fig. 22–2. Left to right: *Pinus nigra,* hybrid, *Pinus resinosa.* Age: 4 years. Hybrids and parental species marked by stakes.

tions that are strikingly different from those of the habitats of the parental species. The report of Bingham *et al.* dealt with the performance of the hybrid derived from the northern Idaho race of *Pinus monticola* as the seed-parent. Their tests were made at Spokane, Washington and Wisconsin Rapids, Wisconsin. In the tests at Placerville and Spokane, the hybrids outgrew both parental species during the first three years. At Wisconsin Rapids, however, *Pinus strobus* outgrew the hybrid.

Another instance of superiority of a pine hybrid in early growth rate was reported by Duffield and Snyder (1958). A comparison of this hybrid, *Pinus nigra* × *Pinus resinosa,* and progenies derived from the parental trees is shown in Fig. 22–2.

Johnsson (1949), working with three birch hybrids, reported that each hybrid exceeded the average size of the parental species at 7 years of age.

Buchholz (1945) reported embryonic heterosis in the cross between *Pinus contorta* and *Pinus banksiana*. In this case, the embryos of the hybrids were, stage for stage, intermediate between the parents in size, but the hybrid embryos grew faster and reached comparable stages of development more quickly than did the embryos of the parental species. The hybrid has maintained its superiority in growth rate over the parental species throughout 19 years at Placerville, where environmental conditions are very different from those of the native habitats of the parental species.

Langner (1959b) reported heterosis in hybrids between *Picea sitchensis* and *Picea omorika* at 2 years. In this instance, the hybrids surpassed both parents in growth rate. He reported, however, that older hybrids from former crossings in which different individual parents were used, did not all show such heterosis.

Heterosis has been reported in other characters of hybrids between forest tree species. Thus, data presented by Ching (1959) indicate that the hybrid between Douglas-fir and bigcone Douglas-fir surpasses both parental species in needle length and number of stomata per band. Similarly, data presented by Bannister (1958) show needle length to be greater in the hybrid between *Pinus attenuata* and *Pinus radiata* than it is in the parental species. Therefore, although F_1 hybrids usually are intermediate in most quantitative characters, heterosis in many such characters may be expected though it cannot be predicted. Moreover, it may be expected in some F_2 individuals.

Methods of exploiting improvements displayed by hybrids between forest tree species have been discussed by numerous authors. If mass production through vegetative propagation is economically feasible, individuals of outstanding inherent superiority among hybrid populations may be selected and quickly multiplied for use. If such propagation is not feasible, mass production of seed through some form of controlled pollination may be possible. The latter method is being used to mass produce interspecific hybrids in Korea (Hyun, 1956), Europe (Syrach Larsen, 1956), and the United States (Libby, 1958). The hybrid now in mass-production in Korea is *Pinus rigida* Mill. $\times$ *P. taeda* L.; it is heterotic in juvenile vigor in the place of its use (Hyun, 1956). *Populus tremula* L. $\times$ *P. tremuloides* Michx. is heterotic in early growth rate in the places in Europe for which it is commercially produced (Syrach Larsen,

1956). Thus, the possibility of producing heterotic forest trees carries implications of the greatest importance to forest-tree breeders and forest owners in many countries.

LITERATURE CITED

BANNISTER, M. H. 1958. Variations in samples of two-year-old *Pinus attenuata*, *P. radiata*, and their hybrids. Trans. Roy. Soc. New Zeal. 85: Part 2: 227–236.

BINGHAM, R. T., and A. E. SQUILLACE. 1955. Self-compatibility and effects of self-fertilization in western white pine. Forest Sci. 1(2): 121–129.

BINGHAM, R. T., A. E. SQUILLACE, and R. F. PATTON. 1956. Vigor, disease resistance and field performance in juvenile progenies of the hybrid *Pinus monticola* Dougl. × *Pinus strobus* L. Ztschr. f. Forstgenetic u. Forstpflanzenzüchtung 5(4): 104–112.

BLINKENBERG, C., H. BRIX, M. SCHAFFALITSKY DE MUCKADELL, and H. VEDEL. 1958. Controlled pollinations in *Fagus*. Silvae Genetica 7(4): 116–122.

BUCHHOLZ, J. T. 1945. Embryological aspects of hybrid vigor in pines. Sci. 102(2641): 135–142.

CARPENTER, I. W., and A. T. GUARD. 1956. Some effects of cross-pollination on seed production and hybrid vigor of tuliptree. Jour. Forestry 48(12): 852–855.

CHING, KIM K. 1959. Hybridization between Douglas-fir and bigcone Douglas-fir. Forest Sci. 5(3): 246–254.

CLAUSEN, J., and W. M. HIESEY. 1958. Phenotypic expression of genotypes in contrasting environments. Scot. Soc. Res. Plant Breeding Rpt. 1958: 41–51.

CROW, J. F. 1952. Dominance and overdominance. In: Heterosis. J. W. GOWEN (ed.). Iowa State College Press, Ames, Iowa. Pp. 282–297.

DOBZHANSKY, T. 1952. Nature and origin of heterosis. In: Heterosis. J. W. GOWEN, (ed.). Iowa State College Press, Ames, Iowa. Pp. 218–223.

———. 1955. A review of some fundamental concepts and problems of population genetics. Cold Spring Harbor Symposia Quantitative Biol. 20: 1–15. The Biological Laboratory, Cold Spring Harbor, N. Y.

DUFFIELD, J. W. 1950. Techniques and possibilities for Douglas-fir breeding. Jour. Forestry 48(1): 41–45.

———. 1954. The importance of species hybridization and polyploidy in forest tree improvement. Jour. Forestry 52(9): 645–646.

DUFFIELD, J. W., and B. SNYDER. 1958. Benefits from hybridizing American forest tree species. Jour. Forestry 56(11): 809–815.

FISHER, R. A. 1948. Modern genetics. Brit. Sci. News 1(10): 2–4.

GUSTAFSSON, Å. 1950. Conifer seed plantations: their structure and genetical principles. Proc. 3d World Forestry Cong.: 117–119.

———. 1951. Induction of changes in genes and chromosomes. II. Mutations, environment and evolution. Cold Spring Harbor Symposia Quantitative Biol. 16: 263–281. The Biological Laboratory, Cold Spring Harbor, N. Y.

HAYES, H. K. 1952. Development of the heterosis concept. In: Heterosis. J. W. GOWEN (ed.). Iowa State College Press, Ames, Iowa. Pp. 49–65.

HYUN, S. K. 1956. Forest tree breeding Korea. Inst. Paper 1, Inst. Forest Genet., Cent. Expt. Sta., Suwon, Korea 35. 19 pp. plus 16 in English.

JOHNSSON, H. 1949. Studies on birch species hybrids. I *Betula verrucosa* × *B. japonica*, *B. verrucosa* × *B. papyrifera*, and *B. pubescens* × *B. papyrifera*. Hereditas 35: 115–135.

JONES, D. F. 1918. The effects of inbreeding and crossbeeding upon development. Conn. Agr. Expt. Sta. Bull. 207.

LANGLET, O. 1940–41. Om utvecklingen av granar ur frö efter självbefruktning och efter fri vindpollinering. Meddel. f. Statens Skogsförsöksanstalt 32: 1–22. Summary in German.

LANGNER, W. 1951. Kreuzungsversuche mit *Larix europaea* D. C. und *Larix leptolepis* Gord. Ztschr. f. Forstgenetic u. Forstpflanzensuchtung 1: 2–17.

———. 1959a. Selbstfertilität und Insucht bei *Picea Omorika* (Pančič) Purkyne. Silvae Genetica 8(3): 84–93.

———. 1959b. Ergebnisse einiger Hybridisierungsversuche zwischen *Picea sitchensis* (Bong.) Carr. und *Picea Omorika* (Pančič) Purkyne. Silvae Genetica 8(5): 138–143.

LIBBY, W. J. 1958. The backcross hybrid jeffrey × (jeffrey × coulter) pine. Jour. Forestry 56(1): 840–842.

LUSH, J. L. 1945. Animal Breeding Plans. 3d ed. Iowa State College Press, Ames, Iowa. 443 pp.

MANGELSDORF, A. J. 1952. Gene interaction in heterosis. In: Heterosis. J. W. Gowen (ed.). Iowa State College Press, Ames, Iowa. Pp. 320–329.

MANGELSDORF, P. C. 1951. Hybrid Corn. Sci. Amer. 185(2): 39–47.

MATTHEWS, J. D. 1955. Forest Genetics. In: Report on Forest Research by the Forestry Commission, London, for the Year Ending March 1944. Pp. 27–29.

MATTHEWS, J. D., and C. McLEAN. 1957. Improvement of Scots Pine in Britain by selection and breeding. 7th Brit. Commonwealth Forestry Conf., Austral. and New Zeal. 1–14.

MERGEN, F. 1954. Self-fertilization in slash pine reduced height growth. U.S. Forest Serv. Southeast. Forest Expt. Sta., Res. Note 67. 2 pp.

ORR-EWING, A. L. 1957. A cytological study of the effects of self-pollination on *Pseudotsuga menziesii* (Mirb.) Franco. Silvae Genetica 6(6): 179–185.

RICE, V. A., and F. N. ANDREWS (with chapter on selection in meat animals by E. J. Warwick). 1951. Breeding and improvement of farm animals. 4th ed. McGraw-Hill Book Co., Inc., New York. 787 pp.

RICHTER, F. I. 1945. *Pinus:* The relation of seed size and seedling size to inherent vigor. Jour. Forestry 43(2): 131–137.

SHERRY, S. P. 1947. The potentialities of genetic research in South African Forestry. Brit. Empire Forestry Conf., Gt. Brit. 1947. 11 pp.

SHULL, G. H. 1909. A pure line method in corn breeding. Rpt. Amer. Breeders' Assoc. 5: 51–59.

———. 1910. Hybridization methods in corn breeding. *Amer. Breeders' Mag.* 1: 98–107.

———. 1914. Duplicate genes for capsule-form in *Bursa bursa*-pastoris. Ztschr. f. Abstam.-und induktive Vererbungslehre 12(2): 97–149.

SQUILLACE, A. E., and R. T. BINGHAM. 1958. Selective fertilization in *Pinus monticola* Dougl. Silvae Genetica 7(6): 188–196.

STEBBINS, G. LEDYARD. 1958. The use of plant breeding to increase the world's food supply. Indian Jour. Genet. and Plant Breeding 17(2): 120–128.

SYRACH LARSEN, C. 1956. Genetics in silviculture. Oliver & Boyd, Ltd., Edinburgh. 224 pp.

WELLHAUSEN, E. J. 1952. Heterosis in a new population. In: Heterosis. J. W. Gowen (ed.). Iowa State College Press, Ames, Iowa. Pp. 418–450.

WRIGHT, J. W., and W. J. GABRIEL. 1958. Species hybridization in the hard pines, Series Sylvestres. Silvae Genetica 7(4): 109–115.

23

Ecological Variability and Taxonomy
of Forest Trees

OLOF LANGLET

Forest research work has generally been regarded as a purely functional occupation in which basic scientific results are applied to specific problems. The pure science in its ivory tower expected nothing in return and particularly not from such directly practical disciplines as yield studies and reproduction research.

It was perhaps for this reason that Cieslar and Engler, pioneers of provenance research, remained remote from the world of botanical science or, to characterize the situation more concisely, never were acknowledged by it.

For centuries, taxonomists have counted stamens and pistils, noted the shapes of leaves and the color of flowers. Cieslar (1899) introduced in good earnest a new term, *physiological variety:*

"Among the botanical species, and even among the recognized morphological varieties, there are physiological varieties which for their existence have to thank hereditary characteristics acquired under the influence of special environmental conditions during an infinite space of time."

Cieslar noticed his physiological varieties in Norway spruce and Scots pine. He compared spruce seedlings derived from Swedish seed with seedlings from Tyrolean seed, the former being small alongside the latter. He studied spruce grown from seed from different altitudes. Seed from higher altitudes produced small plants which flushed early in the spring but which also ceased growth early in the summer, while the greater plants from seed from low altitudes were late in flushing and also late in terminating their period of growth. This was a case of physiological differences. Had Cieslar been able to foresee future terminology he most certainly would have used the term "ecological variety."

Engler, in Switzerland, was not far behind with his experiments. Switzerland and the Tyrol are Alpine country and seed need not be moved very far in a horizontal direction before it arrives at an altitude with a completely different temperature range. Engler had the advantage of knowing about Cieslar's earlier experiments, and he seems to have been more eager to get a synopsis of the relevant circumstances. To this end he obtained seed not only from a series of different altitudes but, in the case of pine, also from a series of plants from different parts of Europe. The material was tested on a series of experimental plots at different altitudes.

Cieslar and Engler made good use of the material at their disposal. They overlooked nothing, and in fact they noted much that proved to be irrelevant. They also came to practically all the conclusions to which their studies could lead. Cieslar, for example, stated that plants from seed from low altitudes produced a greater weight of trunk and branches per unit weight of needles than plants from seed from high altitudes. He found that lowland plants could not withstand autumn frosts and the winter cold on a high-altitude experimental plot, and he came to the conclusion that they were adapted to longer growing periods than available to them at the higher elevation. Cieslar (1895) concluded that "the various physiological varieties were hereditarily adapted to the length of the vegetation periods in their respective native habitats."

Emphasizing the relation between physiological variability and climate Cieslar soon introduced the term "climatic variety," a designation approved by Engler. It should be noted, however, that Engler did not attach any fixed taxonomic rank to the term variety. On the contrary, in 1905 he wrote:

"The terms 'species', 'variety', 'race', etc., have been created by man to map the infinite variety of the organic world. In reality there are neither species nor varieties, but only *individuals* and the more we learn about living nature the greater the difficulty in defining these terms and the greater the confusion."

Engler (1908) summarized the climatic variability of pine in the following words:

". . . The varieties of this species occurring from south to north, and from the lowlands of Central Europe to the upper tree limits in the Alps, form two continuous series that are very similar, and the initial and ultimate sections of which are linked together by a large number of intermediate types. The North German pine can no more be distinguished from the South Swedish pine by any distinct morphological or biological characteristics than the latter can be distinguished from the Lappland pine, just as the Baltic and Livonian pines are nothing but climatic forms of transition between the East Prussian and the Finnish pines. The characteristics of all Scots pines in the different

European regions vary always only in quantity. There are no sharply defined borders anywhere."

Despite their accurate observations and their clear comprehension Cieslar and Engler have not received the credit due them. Nevertheless, they were the first to demonstrate physiological variability, and the continuous change of characteristics in well-defined Linnean species. This ought to be admitted and known at least within the realms of the science of genetics. Surely they made their observations at a time when Lamarckism was flourishing. They found the provenances of pine and spruce to bear the stamp of their natural habitats and they turned to the most obvious explanation quite as the Darwinists did: environmental conditions had exerted influence on the populations. Then arose the schism. The Darwinists considered this environmental influence to be the cause of modifications which would disappear after transfer to other environments. Cieslar and Engler, realizing the situation and convinced as a result of their researches that the question was one of genetically-fixed properties, found it quite natural that the environment would exert direct influence on hereditary characters over very long periods of time.

Gradually Lamarckism gave way to Darwinism and Mendelism. Environment was no longer considered to exert a direct influence on the heritability of the characters. The influence was considered to be indirect and solely through natural selection. This change of attitude took time to develop. As late as 1919 Baur (1919 p. 336), referring to individuals of *Melandrium* belonging to what Turesson (1922) was to call two different ecotypes, said that he could equally well claim that they occurred as a result of natural selection as that they arose through a direct influence by environment (neither having been proved).

Engler (1908) was fully aware of the fact that the important thing was to fix the existing variability, while the question as to how it had arisen was of secondary interest. He makes this quite clear:

"All available facts clearly indicate that the life functions of the pine and the spruce are minutely related to the climate in their natural habitats and that many of these adaptions are passed on to their offspring. However, we cannot state with certainty how these climatical varieties arose, whether by mutation as explained by Hugo de Vries and natural selection, or by selection of individual variability as per Darwin or by direct adaption as indicated by Lamarck or even in some other way. But *one thing is quite certain*, and that is that the climate is the cause of a climatic variety dominating within its particular area."

Is there any justification in disqualifying the clear and correct conception of the "climatic races," the intraspecific ecological variability as expressed by Engler on the basis that, in the light of present knowledge, he was not able to explain the intricate mechanisms of the process by which environment can influence and change the genetical adaptation of the populations? Are we to neglect everything that was written about atoms before we found that they could be split?

Cieslar and Engler knew well what they were expounding. Furthermore, they have not been contradicted by more recent knowledge. Engler's presentation of the variability of the pine is perfectly correct regardless of the way in which the origin of this variability is interpreted. It is almost scandalous that they have not been acknowledged in the botanical literature and credited with having discovered and described the variability which is characteristic of Scots pine. The variability, which is more or less evident in the case of all plants spread over regions with different climatic conditions and which arises automatically when populations are genetically selected in accordance with the essentials in the environment in which they find themselves, is their *ecological variability*.

The extent to which the contributions of Cieslar and Engler have been overlooked is exemplified by the fact that they are neither quoted by Turesson (1922), when he defined the term "ecotype" nor by Huxley (1938, 1939) when he proposed the term "cline."

The physiological variability of the pine has been the subject of considerable research since the days of Engler. One method is to examine the dry matter content of plants in the autumn at the time when they undergo changes before enduring the winter climate. If pine provenances grown at a sufficiently northerly latitude are examined in this way a textbook example of a continuous smooth cline results. The dry matter content increases progressively the colder and more northerly is their native habitat (Langlet, 1934, 1936, 1943).

An example of this cline is demonstrated in the international provenance test of 1938, with 52 provenances of Scots pine. These provenances originated from various sections of Europe, from the north of Norway and Finland down to Rumania and the Pyrenees, from Scotland in the west to the then eastern Poland (Fig. 23–1). They came from altitudes between 5 and 1,570 ms.

Through adjusted mean monthly temperatures the part of the year with a mean day-and-night temperature of at least $+6°$ C was determined. Also, the daylength of the first day of this period was noted. Of course, this daylength has no special significance. It only represents one daylength at or near the beginning of the vegetation period and combines in one the two factors temperature and light. Above all, this method enables graphic representation in a clearer way than a multiple correlation with length of vegetation period and latitude (which give the same correlation coefficient) as the two variables.

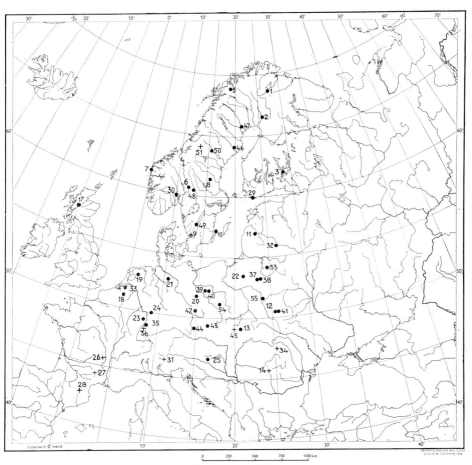

●, altitudes below 500 meters; +, altitudes above 500 meters.

Fɪɢ. 23–1. Provenances of Scots pine—IUFRO international test, 1938.

Regardless of the implication of these daylengths, the fact remains that they show a very close correlation with the analyzed dry-matter contents of the 2- and 4-year pine plants (Fig. 23–2). The correlation coefficient R is no less than $+$ 0.98 or, in other words, about 97 per cent of the original variance is removed by eliminating the influence of the daylength during the first $+6°$ C day (Langlet, 1959a). From this statement it follows that the variability is continuous according to the variation of the determining ecological factors. As latitude always, and temperature mostly, varies continuously this results in an ecological variability within the species, that is continuous also geographically.

A similar, but negative, correlation is found between the same daylengths and the mean heights at 17 years of the same provenances

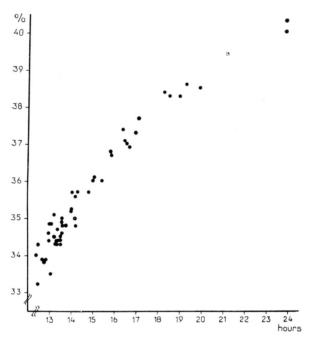

Fig. 23–2. Relationship between dry-matter content and the length of daylight of the first day in the year with an average normal temperature of +6° C. at the native habitats of the 52 provenances. Correlation coefficient R> + 0.98.

of Scots pine growing in New Hampshire as measured by Wright and Baldwin (1957) (Fig. 23–3).

The variability of Norway spruce differs from that of Scots pine. True, the spruce also forms clines from the south to the north and from low to high altitudes—the general adaption to seasonal changes which it cannot avoid. For spruce, however, there should be considered another ecological variability which the pine mainly seems to lack. While the pine is adapted to the seasonal changes of temperature and to some extent also to daylength, the spruce is minutely adapted also to the local habitat. The spruce acquires this adaption because of its great sensitivity to locally-varying, late spring frosts. The time of flushing in spruce fluctuates from year to year depending only upon the warmth of the spring. The growth of different pine provenances also depends on the climate of the growing place. The eventual influence of daylength, if existing at all is outweighed by the influence of temperature (Langlet, 1960).

If the variability of the pine can be represented by a sloping or sinuous area with a smooth surface, then the variability of the spruce will have the same general outline but the surface will often be very rough.

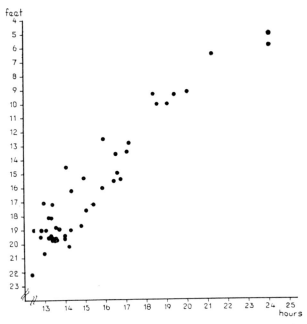

FIG. 23–3. Relationship between the average 17-year height of the 46 provenances in New Hampshire and the daylight period as in Fig. 23–2.

This is the present-day picture of the variability of the spruce and the continuous series of pine populations all over Europe mentioned by Engler in 1908–the *ecological variability*. However, Engler also dealt with morphological variability when he stated that the south-Swedish pine cannot be distinguished from the Lappland pine in northern Sweden.

Sylvén (1916) sought to clarify this question by studying and measuring a large number of samples submitted from 59 forest districts in northern and central Sweden, thus anticipating the method recommended by Anderson and Turrill (1935). The differences observed confirmed his opinion that Scots pine in Sweden could be divided into two distinct subspecies. Of the nine characteristics which Sylvén then considered to be distinguishing features at least five have since proved to be modifications, viz., seed color, seed-wing color, age of needles, crown ratio, and the relative height to which the coarse bark extends. This leaves four characteristics which, to a greater or lesser extent, appear to be hereditary, viz., the length of the needles (and certain other needle properties), cone color, thickness of the cone scales at the apophyses, and the relative width of the crown.

In order to evaluate the variability of the various characteristics on the basis of the data provided by Sylvén, each characteristic was divided into six intensity grades (Langlet, 1959b). The intensity grade of each of the nine properties has been determined for each of the 59 districts. The sums of these grades for each district were, in their turn, distributed into six groups. The sum of all nine characteristics, genetic and modifiable, represents the phenotype of pine, its actual appearance at the place where it grows (Fig. 23–4, *left*). The limits drawn by Neger (1913) and by Sylvén for the extent of the north-Swedish pine southwards are indicated. Figure 23–4 shows how the pine changes successively, how it becomes more and more north-Swedish from south to north, from the coast up to the mountains and to the coldest regions of the country. Even the milder climate along the extension of the Norwegian fjords is clearly evident.

In principle, the five modifiable properties present the same picture (Fig. 23–4, *center*). However, the agreement with the climate is not as good as on the map in Fig. 23–4, *left*. The agreement is still poorer on the map (Fig. 23–4, *right*) showing the variability of the at least partly genetic properties. However, there are only four of these and when they exert their influence together with the five modifiable properties, the agreement with the climate becomes considerably closer. In principle, the tendency is clear: The genetic properties change successively with the climate. The lines on the map indicate the number of days when the temperature was $+6°$ C or more and they are more or less related to the intensity differences on the map, at least as much as the limits of Neger and Sylvén.

It will thus be seen, in the first place, that the morphological difference between Scots pines in northern and in southern Sweden consists largely of modifications. In the second place, the phenotype reflects the climate. Thirdly, even the more-or-less hereditary characteristics show a variability which, in principle, agrees with that of the phenotype and must be regarded as a consequence of the selectional activity of the climate. There is a series of morphological varieties, a continuous series of quantitative differences, *exactly such as are of no taxonomical value* (Lindquist, 1948; Stebbins, 1950). There is a typical continuous cline, as defined by Huxley.

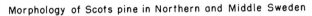

Morphology of Scots pine in Northern and Middle Sweden

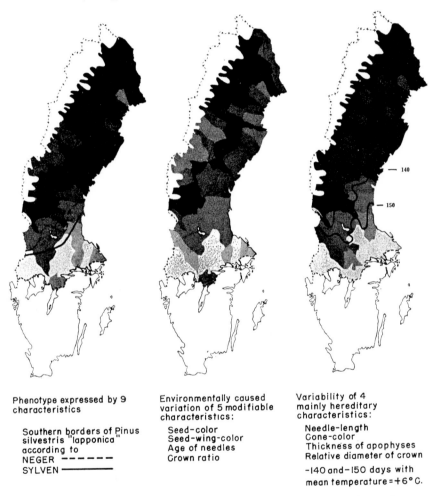

Phenotype expressed by 9 characteristics

Southern borders of Pinus silvestris "lapponica" according to
NEGER − − − − −
SYLVEN ————

Environmentally caused variation of 5 modifiable characteristics:
Seed-color
Seed-wing-color
Age of needles
Crown ratio

Variability of 4 mainly hereditary characteristics:
Needle-length
Cone-color
Thickness of apophyses
Relative diameter of crown
−140 and −150 days with
mean temperature = +6° C.

FIG. 23–4. Morphology of Scots pine in northern and central Sweden.

As regards practical forestry, no doubt there is justification in distinguishing between pine in southern Sweden and pine in northern Sweden. Thus, different log scales are required in these two regions (Näslund, 1940–41). In the case of spruce, such differences are even greater (Näslund, 1947). This is also true from the physiognomical aspect (Malmström, 1949). It is for this reason that sometimes the claim may be made that the major criticism against the division of the pine into one northern and one southern subspecies in Sweden is that the spruce has not been subdivided in the same way!

But Engler was right again. It is not possible to refer the pine in the north of Sweden and the pine in the south of the country into two distinct subspecies or into any separate taxonomical unit. It should not be done for the reason presented by Huxley (1939): "*A name confers a false sense of importance on the named groups.*" This statement is particularly applicable to a Latin name. It not only confers a false sense of importance on the named group, it also often creates an equally false impression that the group is uniform, that it is decidedly different from other named groups and from the rest of the species. Citing Huxley again, "When gradation exists within a group, the mere conferring of a subspecific or specific name gives a false impression of the homogeneity of the group."

Of course, not all ecological variability is geographically continuous. There may be more or less definite limits and discontinuities. These may result, for example, from different kinds of genetical or environmental isolation, from abrupt changes in environment, a sharp limit to a high plateau, sharp boundaries between edaphic conditions, scarcity of suitable ecological niches or simply haphazard geographical distribution.

Huxley (1939) has systematized his clines: continuous and discontinuous ones, horizontally—and obliquely—stepped clines, as well as continuous smooth clines corresponding to what is termed continuous variability of characters. However, since Huxley regards clines as an auxiliary method in taxonomy he makes careful notes of such cases where the clines are stepped and "the sections then represent subspecific groups." But why distinguish the exceptions in this way? Why put this false sense of importance on them? If the general principle is valid, that ecological variability arises as a "response" to environmental influence through selection and isolation, the rate of mutations or other "genetical" changes resulting in smooth or stepped clines, then why should the more-or-less chance creation of a discontinuous differentiation result in endowing part of an "ecocline," in the sense of Gregor (1944), with a special Latin name—as some kind of a subspecies or other taxon?

What is gained by such splitting of species? An incorrect impression results, a narrow-minded insistence on special cases of isolation, a false label, which is all too readily accepted as a guarantee of genetical uniformity to a greater extent than is justified by the character or characters offered as motivation for distinguishing a taxonomic unit. Anatole France, writing in *L'île des pingouins,* stated how easy it was to write the history of very ancient times when there existed only a single source and how it became more and more difficult when an increasing number of historians expressed an increasing number of opinions. Much the same applies here: increased knowledge of variability makes it increasingly difficult not only to define taxonomic units as such, but to decide their extent and the way in which they should be used in a given case, and when they are used, what they really mean. Unfortunately, a mean Nature has not created any direct counterparts to all of our conventional taxonomic terms. In the long run the stage foreseen by Engler, more and more confusion, is reached.

Let there therefore be agreement once and for all that, as regards the ecological variability of forest trees, nothing is gained by establishing subspecific taxonomic "units," by unnecessary splitting of species of the type *Pinus contorta-Pinus Murrayana,* or by designating subspecies of *Pseudotsuga* as Peace (1949) states. There should be hesitation to use even the term ecotype so as not to introduce non-existent limits and create the false impression that variability in general is a kind of "stepped" variability.

As regards the study of provenances, the study of ecological variability within species, the relation between this variability and the influence of environment, and the reactions of different populations to transfer to an environment foreign to them, it is unnecessary and confusing to have the species crisscrossed by a jungle of taxonomical subspecific verbiage. It is sufficient to indicate the native locality, the provenance. Then what is referred to is clearly identified. The variability may preferably be described in the non-coloured terms of clines. Names and terms that say more than they mean, and that may be interpreted in a number of different ways, should be avoided.

Thirty years have elapsed since Turesson (1930) reported at the Fifth International Botanical Congress at Cambridge, presenting practically the same ideas as are presented here. Referring to "Genecological units and their classificatory value" he pointed out the necessity for considering the ecology of the plants and stressed the value of the ecotype concept. This paper takes a step further than Turesson, but in the same direction, in proposing that the ecotype concept should be replaced by the concept of ecologic—not ecotypic —variability, be it continuous or discontinuous. *Ecotypes* and *ecotypic* are properly used only when the discontinuity of the ecological adaption has been proved.

Once again Engler (1908) is cited:

"I see it as futile, under the pretext of doing science a service, to force at any price these forms of our forest trees into an artificial system."

In summing up, there are people unable to see the wood for trees. It is just as bad if we cannot see the true variability for Latin names!

LITERATURE CITED

ANDERSON, E., and W. B. TURRILL. 1935. Biometrical studies on herbarium material. Nature 136: 986.

BAUR, E. 1919. Einführung in die experimentelle Vererbungsforschung. 3–4. Aufl., Borntraeger, Berlin. 410 pp.

CIESLAR, A. 1895. Über den Einfluss der Grösse der Fichtensamen auf die Entwickelung der Pflanzen nebst einigen Bemerkungen über schwedische Fichten und Weissföhrensamen. Centbl. f. das Gesam. Forstw. 13: 149–153.

———. 1899. Neues aus dem Gebiete der forstlichen Zuchtwahl. Centbl. f. das Gesam. Forstw. 25: 99–117.

ENGLER, A. 1905. Einfluss der Provenienz des Samens auf die Eigenschaften der forstlichen Holzgewächse. Mitt. der Schweiz. Centralanst. f. das Forstl. Versuchsw. 8: 81–236.

———. 1908. Tatsachen, Hypotesen und Irrtümer auf dem Gebiete der Samenprovenienz-Frage. Forstwiss. Centbl. 30: 295–314.

GREGOR, J. W. 1944. The ecotype. Biol. Rev. 19: 20–33.

HUXLEY, J. S. 1938. Clines: An auxiliary taxonomic principle. Nature 142: 219–220.

———. 1939. Clines: An auxiliary method in taxonomy. Bijdr. tot de Dierk. 27: 491–520.

KARSCHON, R. 1949. Untersuchungen über die physiologische Variabilität von Föhrenkeimlingen authochtoner Populationen. Mitt. der Schweiz. Centralanst. f. das Forstl. Versuchsw. 26: 205–244.

LANGLET, O. 1934. Om variationen hos tallen (*Pinus silvestris* L.) och dess samband med klimatet (Über die Variation der Kiefer und deren Zusammenhang mit dem Klima). Svenska Skogsvårdsför. Tidskr. 32: 87–110.

———. 1936. Studier över tallens fysiologiska variabilitet och dess samband med klimatet. Ett bidrag till kännedomen om tallens ekotyper (Studien über die physiologische Variabilität der Kiefer und deren Zusammenhang mit dem Klima. Beiträge zur Kenntnis der Ökotypen von *Pinus silvestris* L.). Meddel. från Statens skogsförsöksanst. 29(4): 219–470. (U.S. Forest Service translation No. 239, 1937, 1–87.)

———. 1943. Photoperiodismus und Provenienz bei der gemeinen Kiefer (*Pinus silvestris* L.). Meddel. från Statens Skogsförsökanst. 33(5): 295–330.

———. 1959a. A cline or not a cline: A question of Scots pine. Silvae Genetica 8(1): 13–22.

———. 1959b. Norrlandstallens praktiska och systematiska avgränsning. Svenska Skogsvårdsför. Tidskr. 57(3): 425–436.

———. 1960. Mellaneuropeiska granprovenienser i svenskt skogsbruk (Mitteleuropäische Fichte in Schweden, nach den Ergebnissen des internationalen Provenienzversuches von 1938). Kungl. Skogs-och Lantbruksakad. Tidskr. 99: 259–329.

LINDQUIST, B. 1948. The main varieties of *Picea Abies* (L.) Karst. in Europe. Acta Horti Bergiani 14(7): 249–342.

MALMSTRÖM, C. 1949. Studier över skogstyper och trädslagsfördelning inom Västerbottens län (Studien über Waldtypen und Baumartverteilung im Län Västerbotten). Meddel. från Statens Skogsforskningsinst. 37(11). 231 pp.

NÄSLUND, M. 1940–41. Funktioner och tabeller för kubering av stående träd. Tall, gran och björk i norra Sverige (Funktionen und Tabellen zur Kubierung stehender

Bäume. Kiefer, Fichte und Birke in Nordschweden). Meddel. från Statens Skogs-forskningsinst. 32: 87–142.

——. 1947. Funktioner och tabeller för kubering av stående träd. Tall, gran och björk i södra Sverige samt i hela landet. (Functions and tables for computing the cubic volume of standing trees. Pine, spruce, and birch in southern Sweden and in the whole of Sweden.) Meddel. från Statens Skogsforskningsinst. 36(3). 81 pp.

NEGER, F. W. 1913. Die nordische oder Lapplandkiefer. (*Pinus silvestris* L. var. *lapponica,* Fr.) Tharandter Forstl. Jahrb. 64: 101–125.

PEACE, T. R. 1949. The variation of Douglas fir in its native habitat (*Pseudotsuga taxifolia* Brit. syn. *P. douglasii* Carr.). Forestry 22(1): 45–61.

STEBBINS, G. L. 1950. Variation and evolution in plants. Columbia University Press, New York. Pp. 1–643.

SYLVÉN, N. 1916. Den nordiska tallen (Die nordschwedische Kiefer). Meddel. från Statens Skogsforskningsinst. 13–14: 9–110 and I–XII.

TURESSON, G. 1922. The genotypical response of the plant species to the habitat. Hereditas 3: 211–350. 3: 211–350.

——. 1930. Genecological units and their classificatory value. Svensk Bot. Tidskr. 24(4): 511–518.

WRIGHT, J. W., and H. I. BALDWIN. 1957. The 1938 International Union Scotch pine test in New Hampshire. Silvae Genetica 6(1): 2–14.

24

Methods of Measuring the Growth of Trees as Individuals and in Stands

C. Allen Bickford

Foresters have studied and measured growth of trees in a variety of ways. The dominating motive has no doubt been related to the practical problems of forest management. However, it should be recognized that growth has also been measured to compare response to treatment, to identify the important influencing factors, and for other research purposes. Growth of stands is important because it permits a skillful forest manager to harvest forest products indefinitely. Growth of trees is summed as the growth of stands. The rate of growth also determines the time interval required for trees to reach marketable size or economic maturity.

Growth in volume usually is considered the most important measure of increment to the forest manager because it is volume of wood that he has for sale (Baker, 1953). He must relate cutting in the forest to growth of stands to be able to harvest logs and other forest products indefinitely. Volume growth also is a recognized measure in research for comparing, describing, etc. When properly measured, volume growth combines the varying responses within a tree in a useful and meaningful manner.

Diameter growth provides a ready means for comparing the performance of trees in different situations. It determines how long one must wait to harvest a tree, and it also is useful as an index of volume growth. It is easily shown that the product of diameter, height, and diameter growth is commonly the major component of volume growth of a tree. Since tree diameter often is a dominant element in determining marketability and economic maturity, the importance of diameter growth is evident.

Height growth is measured less frequently, especially in larger trees, as it contributes less to volume growth and may be quite difficult to measure. Except in research, this measurement is limited chiefly to seedlings and saplings. In these small trees height growth is easily measured and may be more sensitive to treatment and site factors than diameter or volume growth. That is, greater variation in height growth among individual trees may be seen as a result of differences in soil, dominance, available nutrients, etc.

Tree growth in diameter and height is the response of the tree to its particular combination of heredity and environment. The contribution of heredity has been pointed out elsewhere. Environment is the complex combination of soil, climate, and tree arrangement. Soil and climate have been discussed in other papers; there is some mention of tree arrangement in the discussion that follows.

The mensurationist is concerned with measuring the growth of trees. This is too broad a subject to treat adequately in detail in this space. Particular attention will be given in this paper to description of general methods of growth measurement. The treatment that follows, admittedly incomplete, is an attempt to present pertinent principles of the major alternatives in measuring growth of trees and stands. The problem with respect to trees is described first, pointing out what is measured, some related problems, and some alternatives in measuring tree growth. A discussion of growth of stands follows, with more emphasis on methods available and sampling problems.

Measurement of Tree Growth

Before considering measurement itself, it may be instructive to review the phenomena which are measured and their relation to other aspects of trees and stands. In this connection physiological considerations, distribution of growth, and trends of growth in trees will be discussed.

PHYSIOLOGICAL CONSIDERATIONS. A tree grows at the tips, where elongation occurs and at the cambial sheath, resulting in stem enlargement. In addition, buds burst to produce flowers and leaves. Growth also has a negative aspect as foliage is shed, fruits fall off, and twigs and branches die, or even whole trees die. The practical forester's interest is usually limited to changes in total, or merchantable, height, or in diameter of the bole, possibly including major forks and limbs. His principal concern is with the manner and extent that these dimensional changes affect volume.

DISTRIBUTION OF GROWTH. The distribution of growth changes often is significant because diameter increment is not always equal along the bole, around the circumference, or from one year to another. Variations along the bole apparently result from changes in the crown and from changes in crown exposure. The results of release, leaning and pruning on distribution of diameter increment are well known. In each changed situation, diameter increment is added where it will tend to strengthen the tree in an erect position. Thus a pruned tree in the open will add more to the upper stem below the live crown while a previously sheltered tree, upon exposure by release, will add more to the lower bole. As a result, growth in diameter at breast height may be temporarily depressed by pruning or exaggerated for a short time by thinning or other partial cutting (Stone, 1944).

It is for these reasons that basal area is criticized as biased or insensitive as a measure of response to partial cutting, or as a measure of stand density (Bickford *et al.*, 1957). This influence on the distribution of diameter increment, which affects tree form, exposes the bias that results from neglecting changes in tree form when estimating volume to compare responses to partial cutting treatments.

There is also variation in the distribution of diameter increment by years (Schumacher and Meyer, 1937). Some of it is associated with weather fluctuations, and the resulting patterns are utilized in dendrochronology. Some of it is related to changes in stand density, and some correlated with size or age.

TRENDS IN TREE GROWTH. Some trends are evident from observations that do not require formal measurement or analysis, while others emerge only after painstaking measurement and careful analysis. One frequently reported trend is that, on the average, large trees grow faster in diameter than small trees (Meyer, 1942). This trend has been supported by measurement and analysis.

Individual trees, past the juvenile stage, tend to grow with negative acceleration in both height and diameter. Or, what amounts to the same thing, average annual increment for an individual tree, in both diameter and height, tends to decrease with time (Holcomb and Bickford, 1952). Evidence of these tendencies is available in stumps, log ends, etc., wherever increment for several years may be observed. It may also be seen in the tendency to shorter internodes with increasing height along the bole of most conifers and some hardwoods. During the juvenile stage, very young trees may show positively accelerated height growth for a few years (Wenger, 1955).

This tendency of individual trees to grow with negative acceleration may appear to contradict the statement that large trees grow faster than small trees. These two statements are reconciled because of the many slow-growing small trees that never attain large size, which affects the averages of small trees but not large trees. The fastest growth rates for individual trees occur in young small trees and may be seen in their wide early rings or in the corresponding leader growth. Nevertheless, the average diameter growth for small trees tends to be smaller than the average for large trees.

Related to the foregoing is the greater likelihood that smaller trees will die. This may be restated this way: the probability of survival increases with size and age until senescence sets in. This tendency is evident from the fact that a tally of dead trees usually includes a disproportionately large number of small trees in spite of the fact that they degenerate more rapidly.

METHODS OF MEASUREMENT. To measure growth of trees, two principal alternatives are available: (1) measurement of the past record of each tree to obtain the desired data, or (2) remeasurement of a series of trees after a suitable length of time to obtain the desired data. Each method has merit, as well as limitations (Bruce and Schumacher, 1942; Chapman, 1924; Meyer and Nelson, 1953; Spurr, 1952).

Use of Past Record. Growth of a tree may be measured in its past record by the method of tree dissection and stem analysis or by the use of increment cores. In the first case, the tree is felled and cut up into sections, as required. Diameters are then recorded by years, or groups of years, at each cut. Longitudinal sections can be made to obtain height data in similar detail, although it undoubtedly is more common to assume uniform height growth between cuts and interpolate as may be necessary.

When increment cores are used, the tree is bored at one or more heights above ground and at one or more points on the circumference. In spite of admitted shortcomings, a single boring per tree at approximately breast height is undoubtedly the most common procedure. Cores may be measured for a standard period (such as 10 years), an inch of radius, or from pith to cambium. The observation may be total age, total radius, rings per inch, radius for 10 years, radii by years, etc., or some combination of these (Cuno, 1934; Reineke, 1941).

Use of increment cores has the advantage that the tree is left alive for future observation and measurement. It is also less expensive to obtain data from the lower bole with cores than it is to fell and cut up a tree. There is the disadvantage that the borer hole may provide entrance for spores of wood-rotting fungi. The objective of a particular growth study will ordinarily make it clear whether one should obtain much detail from a small number of trees by dissection or less detail from a large number of trees by taking increment cores.

With either dissection or cores, use of the past record requires accurate identification of each annual ring. Dissection, by providing more evidence, may have some advantage for accurate identification. However, for many species, including most conifers, this presents no problem; although, for others, especially diffuse-porous hardwoods, it often is difficult and sometimes impossible. Magnification and staining often are helpful (Kase, 1935). Special problems are created by false rings and by discontinuous (incomplete) rings. In such cases, if most rings are easily seen, it may be helpful to use a common pattern of rings as a point of reference, i.e., dendrochronology (Glock, 1937).

For example, north Louisiana was subjected to two consecutive years of drought in the mid-twenties which left a characteristic ring pattern in the trees that survived, and were sensitive to drought. This pattern was used to advantage by the writer some 10 to 15 years later when counting rings on increment cores in that area. It dispelled doubt with respect to false rings and helped to detect extremely narrow rings following a severe burn. Discontinuous rings are no problem in that area.

Increment cores may be measured either in the field or in the laboratory. Field measurement is appropriate for relatively coarse measurement when rings are easily identified. Rings per inch, total age, and 10-year radii are examples. Laboratory measurement permits finer readings, use of shorter periods, and better ring identification. It also requires that each core be identified and so preserved that it does not swell or shrink. Drying out is the greater problem.

Mortality is one of the changes that affect trees, and foresters often need to know its extent (Hervey, 1936). In working with tree data, it would be helpful to be able to ascertain when a tree died. Windfall may sometimes be associated with a particular storm such as the 1938 hurricane in New England. Fire kill may be similarly dated for the unusual fire. In most cases, however, the investigator is confronted with a dead tree in an area unaffected by spectacular fire or wind and he would like to be able to date its death.

Indicators have been developed as a basis for identifying trees which died in the last 5 years or so, based upon the rate of disintegration—bark slough, twig and limb fall, progress of decay, etc.

(Spaulding, 1937; U.S. Forest Service, 1955). Because the distinte-gration rate varies with other factors, such as tree size, cause of death, season of death, etc., its weakness has long been recognized. The magnitude of such errors is not well established. Remeasure-ment of forest-survey plots in New Hampshire indicated a mortality rate nearly four times that obtained from dead-tree data.

Use of ring patterns has been suggested to date mortality (Ghent, 1952; 1954). Such use requires that the dead trees have both a char-acteristic internal pattern and identifiable rings to time of death. Because these inner patterns may be absent, ring identification some-times is more difficult in dead trees; and, because the sapwood rots so quickly after death, this method often cannot be used.

Remeasurement of Trees. When trees are remeasured, it is not necessary to be able to distinguish rings, and the problem of dating mortality vanishes. However, other problems appear. Each tree must be individually reidentifiable, and it must be measured and remeasured in the same manner and at the same place. Even with point of measurement marked there may be measurement errors due to differences in temperature, moisture, and the technique of using the measuring instrument as well as to changes in the bark and the usual human mistakes.

Diameter tapes are commonly used to measure diameter because they measure to great consistency. With either tapes or calipers, remeasurement is customarily made after a period of 5 or more years to minimize measurement errors in comparison with diameter growth during the period. This of course results in loss of growth data for individual years. Where such data are desired, dendrom-eters, dendrographs, and growth bands are available that may be mounted on the tree, and which provide data on growth within a season as well as far one or more growing seasons (Brown *et al.,* 1947; Daubenmire, 1945; Reineke, 1932; Hall, 1944).

Administrative problems are greater when the investigator must go back to the same tree, which must also be some sort of repre-sentative sample from the desired population. Relocation and indi-vidual reidentification inflate costs appreciably in comparison with the use of increment cores. When trees are to be remeasured, it is administratively convenient to cluster them in plots (Hummel *et al.,* 1959). On the plot itself, reidentification of each tree is required to obtain data on tree growth.

For identifying individual trees, numbering is a convenient pro-cedure, and several techniques are available: paint on the bark, tags nailed to the tree, tags at the tree base, a stem map, or some com-bination of these. But painted numbers become illegible in a surprisingly short time; tags have been found tempting to rodents, vandals, and pranksters; and stem maps must be accurate to be useful. Thus there is no panacea. The forest-survey organization in the northeastern United States has had good success with inconspicuous markings to relocate plots, and by numbering trees clockwise from north in the record (U.S. Forest Service, 1955). In any event, appreciable cost may be incurred in marking trees and plots so that they can be relocated for remeasurement.

Growth of Trees in Stands

Foresters are concerned with growth of stands because in the long run by skillful manipulation they are able to harvest a large part of this growth for commercial purposes. With clearcutting, the cut from a stand is only the sum of all the trees. Following such a cutting, however, growth often is reduced to nothing until a new stand reoccupies the area. Increasingly, foresters are using partial cuttings, which leave enough smaller trees so that growth of the stand is uninterrupted and may not even be appreciably reduced. Thus foresters are interested in and demand to know the rates at which stands are growing in order to guide the management of forests (Eyre and Zillgitt, 1953).

DEFINITION OF TERMS. Study of the growth of trees in stands has been attended by much confusion. This has arisen from some possibly fuzzy concepts, inconsistent terminology, and uncoordinated attempts to write new definitions. The following discussion is intended to help clarify the situation.

If two estimates of volume are made for the same stand at different times, the difference is an estimate of net growth. To understand the composition of net growth it is necessary to recognize what happens to individual trees during the period between estimates. Some trees are alive and are measured at both times. Some are present only at the first and others only at the second time. These classes identify three significant elements of net growth: *accretion*—material added to trees measured at both occasions; *mortality*—the volume, at time of death, of trees that died during the period between measurements; and *ingrowth*—the volume of trees that grow to measureable size during the interval between measurements. Thus net growth is accretion plus ingrowth minus mortality (Society of American Foresters, 1950).

Gross growth is the total amount of material produced on an area. A skillful forest manager will harvest essentially all of gross growth in trees large enough to be marketable. Gross growth consists of accretion and ingrowth, which is the same as net growth plus mortality. Thus net growth can also be defined as gross growth minus mortality.

Growth of a stand may be expressed in any of several convenient units such as cubic feet, board feet, cords, tons, etc. Sooner or later, measurement of growth runs into the concept of merchantability. This means that merchantable volume is something less than total volume by an amount that is unusuable because of some kind of defect. Thus foresters deal with gross volume and net volume, whose difference depends upon merchantability, as possible ways of expressing gross and net growth. To avoid confusion in describing growth phenomena, volume must be expressed one way or the other. As markets change, it is likely that gross volume would be a more useful way to express growth. If this were done consistently, the adjustment to net volume could be made readily.

METHODS OF MEASUREMENT. Many alternatives are available for measuring stand growth. No doubt this diversity has contributed to the confusion as to what is meant by growth of a stand. Some of this diversity arises from the fact that growth estimates are used for many purposes and must therefore satisfy a variety of standards to suit particular circumstances. Some of it results from differences in data that are already available. There are also differences in the techniques of sampling, measurement, etc. No attempt is made here to present an exhaustive description of the many alternatives. Instead, four broad procedures are sketched below; these are (1) yield tables, (2) stand projection based on increment core data, (3) two independent sets of measurements, and (4) remeasurement.

Yield Tables. Yield tables provide estimates of volume and related data in relation to age, site, and other factors. In the United States, stands judged to be "normal" are sampled to provide basic data. It is assumed that trends over age deducted from these data describe stand development. Thus growth of a stand may be estimated from tabular differences of a yield table when it is appropriate (Haig, 1924; MacKinney *et al.*, 1937; McArdle and Meyer, 1949).

This method is particularly suited to description of fully stocked, even-aged stands of a single species. When these conditions are not met, results may be disappointing. Where appropriate, and when the above assumption is true, estimates of growth should be unbiased. It is evident that separation of net growth into accretion, ingrowth, and mortality would be difficult even if the basic data were analyzed. If there is concern with the sampling error of estimated growth, its proper estimation from yield-table data would be complex. Yield tables are useful for growth estimation in stands for which they are descriptive, when approximate results are acceptable.

Measurement at One Occasion with Increment Core Data. When something better than a yield-table estimate is desired and there is no earlier point of reference, stand projection may be used. Basic measurements provide a stand table for the present, and increment-core data are used to project the stand forward or backward in time. Remeasured sample trees could also serve in place of increment cores. Growth is then obtained from the difference in volume at the two occasions. To apply this procedure it is necessary to know or estimate (1) the distribution of trees by species and diameter classes for the particular area; (2) numbers of trees that die during the period, by these classes; and (3) diameter growth rates by these classes. The troublesome problems stem from the determination of unbiased rates of mortality and diameter growth (Meyer, 1942; Spurr, 1952; Wahlenberg, 1941).

Difficulties have been noted in accurately determining how long a tree has been dead. The usual technique for estimating mortality rate has been to tally the trees judged to have died during a specified period and use their proportion to living trees to estimate mortality rate. This rate may be expressed in relation to volume or number of trees and may be correlated with diameter and species. Various assumptions are required, but detailed consideration of them is not needed here.

Increment core data, or those from remeasured sample trees, are used to obtain the rates of diameter growth that are needed for projection. Core data must be adjusted to include wood and bark because stand tables show numbers of trees by classes of outside-bark diameter. It is common to project forward in time, which requires some assumption relating expected future growth to growth that has been measured. Some of the more important assumptions that have been made for this purpose are: average periodic diameter growth of all surviving trees is the same for the two periods; average periodic diameter growth of all surviving trees by diameter classes as tallied is the same for the two periods; average periodic diameter growth of all surviving trees by diameter class at the beginning of the period is the same for the two periods; and average diameter growth of trees expected to live through the period is given by the regression equation obtained from the two preceding periods (Holcomb and Bickford, 1952; Wahlenberg, 1941).

It is evident that growth estimated under these various assumptions will usually differ. Thus it becomes necessary to select one that is as unbiased as possible. It also is necessary to distribute growth so that numbers of trees by diameter classes may be estimated at the other time.

If the procedure is correctly applied and the proper assumptions are chosen, estimated mean and total growth should be unbiased. It admittedly is not easy to know in advance that all factors have been taken into account properly. However, there are numerous instances where the foregoing procedure has resulted in an estimate that agreed well with the facts when they become known (Meyer and Nelson, 1952). Data on mortality plus the movements of trees among diameter classes provide the means for obtaining desired data on accretion and ingrowth as well as mortality.

It usually is desirable to know how much confidence may be placed on such an estimate, and this means that the sampling error of estimated growth should be known. Under the procedure described above, the sampling error must be estimated from the variances of volume at the two occasions. One is obtained from the variation in current volume from one plot (or other sampling unit) to another; the other is a function of this variation in current volume and of the sampling errors of the rates of mortality and diameter growth.

Two Independent Sets of Measurements. If a previous estimate of volume is available, growth may be estimated from the difference in volume then and now, if volume is estimated to comparable standards. Where the previous sampling units were unmarked and impossible to relocate and a new sampling is made, there are two independent sets of measurements. Each set provides an estimate of volume at the time the measurements are taken, and the difference between these two volumes is an estimate of net growth. The two sets of measurements do not, in themselves, provide bases for separating accretion, ingrowth, and mortaility. Supplemental information is required.

The sampling error of net growth is obtained from the sum of the volume variances at the two occasions. It should tend to be smaller than with stand projection because there is no contribution from the varying rates of individual trees. It also should be noted that this method provides an unbiased estimate of growth, and its sampling error, without requiring dubious assumptions about mortality or the trend of diameter growth.

Remeasurement. If the sampling units of the earlier estimate were so marked that they could be remeasured, there is a very substantial advantage, as will be made clear. Under remeasurement, many of the problems disappear that have been noted in connection with other methods. Net growth is still the difference in volume at the two occasions and is usable as an observation for each sampling unit. The mean of these differences, expanded to desired total, becomes an estimate of net growth. Furthermore, if it is required that components be obtained, it is easy to separate accretion, ingrowth, and mortality (Bickford, 1954). The sampling error of net growth is computed from the differences for each sampling unit. It is easily shown that the variance of net growth based on remeasured plots is smaller than that for independent samples by $2r_{12}\sigma_1\sigma_2$ (Snedecor, 1956).

It is admitted that ease of concept is plagued in practice by the mistakes humans make—the errors of omission and duplication, the mistakes in reading scales and recording data, etc. But these same mistakes are also made when there is no remeasurement. Then they go undetected and inflate the unexplained error, thus lowering confidence in the results. Remeasurement forces one to recognize these mistakes as he seeks to reconcile successive tallies.

Thus remeasurement provides unbiased estimates of growth and its sampling error without making any assumptions about mortality and the trend of diameter growth. The sampling error for the same sample size is smaller than that for any of the other three methods. Thus the significant attributes of remeasurement in growth estimation are (1) no dating of mortality is needed; (2) no identification of individual growth rings is needed; (3) no dubious assumptions with respect to patterns and trends of mortality and diameter growth are needed; and (4) fewer sampling units are required to attain a specified precision.

Choice of Sampling Unit in Remeasurement. The proper size and shape of sampling unit have been studied in relation to forest inventory and require no elaboration here. Bitterlich, Grosenbaugh, and others have reported the advantages of "point" sampling, in comparison with plots, for forest inventory (Bitterlich, 1948; Grosenbaugh, 1952). There are special problems with remeasurement that may not be so well appreciated, and the writer is not aware that any study has been made.

It is considered axiomatic that in any application of sampling desired data are sought at least cost. Total cost is obviously the product of cost per unit and number of units. Should there be more than one kind of sampling unit with a different cost, the products of cost and number would be added. Thus to obtain desired data at least cost means that techniques are desirable that will reduce cost per unit, number of units, or both cost and number.

Cost per unit is determined principally by the cost of travel to the unit and the cost of procuring data once there. For a particular procedure, the latter may be fairly constant while the cost of travel from one place to another varies with distance and obstacles. For a particular application it is unlikely there is much that can be done about distance and obstacles.

If costs of forest sampling based on plots and "points" are to be compared, it must be recognized that the cost of either a plot or a "point" depends upon how many trees are tallied—which means area of the plot and basal-area factor (or equivalent) of the "point." Thus the sampling unit to prefer on the basis of least total cost depends upon both costs and variances per unit, which vary with detailed specifications as well as with the choice between plot and "point."

For purposes of volume estimation, the fact that "point" sampling selects trees in proportion to d^2 means that the larger and more variable trees are more intensively sampled and thus one intuitively expects more efficient sampling. The situation with respect to growth estimation, however, is not so neat. The more variable components of net growth are ingrowth and mortality, and they are mainly composed of small trees. Thus sampling proportional to d^2, by selecting proportionately fewer small trees, may be less efficient than plots for purposes of growth estimation based on remeasurement. Furthermore, the efficiency of remeasured plots depends on r_{12} as has been shown. The value of this r_{12} may also be affected in choosing between plot and "point."

The important point is that data are not yet available that would permit an unequivocal statement to the effect that one is better than the other. Results from remeasured plots in the northeastern United States, which so far have failed to establish that periodic growth is related to initial volume, have led the writer to the opinion that plots should be more efficient than "points."

It may be possible to obtain an unqualified answer, using simulated data in an electronic computer. There is danger that the artificial data would contain an unsuspected bias that would prejudice results. Empirical data obtained from actual remeasurements may provide the answer. Undoubtedly it will come and it could be conditional. That is, for stands and periods where ingrowth and mortality were trivial, "point" sampling might result in less cost whereas, when mortality plus ingrowth exceeded some fraction of accretion, plots might be better. In any case, the most efficient procedure is to be used if it can be identified.

Summary

Several methods of studying and measuring growth have been outlined. An attempt was also made to provide guides in helping to choose among the several alternatives. Distinction was made between growth of trees and growth of stands. It was also pointed out that growth could be measured from the record that has been made or by remeasuring trees or stands. Brief mention was made of sampling in relation to growth measurements and related problems. If sampling is to be used, the desired precision will indicate how many samples are needed. The objective of management and the data initially available will determine the method to use. As a general guide, measurement of growth should be done in such a manner as to obtain the desired result at least cost.

LITERATURE CITED

BAKER, F. S. 1953. Stand density and growth. Jour. Forestry 51: 95–97.

BICKFORD, C. A. 1954. The place of individual tree data in estimating growth. Jour. Forestry 52: 423–426.

BICKFORD, C. A., et al. 1957. Stocking, normality, and measurement of stand density. Jour. Forestry 55: 99–104.

BITTERLICH, W. 1948. Die Winkelzahlprobe. Allg. Forst. Holzwirtschaftliche Ztg. 59(½): 4–5.

BROWN, C. T., R. C. ROSE, and S. H. SPURR. 1947. The dial gauge dendrometer as a tool in silvical research. Jour. Forestry 45: 102–104.

BRUCE, D., and F. X. SCHUMACHER. 1942. Forest mensuration. 2d ed. McGraw-Hill Book Co., Inc., New York. 425 pp.

CHAPMAN, H. H. 1924. Forest mensuration. 2d ed. John Wiley & Sons, Inc., New York. 454 pp.

CUNO, J. B. 1934. Increment borer and core technic. Jour. Forestry 32: 368–369.

DAUBENMIRE, R. F. 1945. An improved precision dendrometer. Ecol. 26: 97–98.

EYRE, F. H., and W. M. ZILLGITT. 1953. Partial cuttings in northern hardwoods of the Lake States. U.S. Dept. Agr. Tech. Bull. 1076. 124 pp.

GHENT, A. W. 1952. A technique for determining the year of outside ring. Forestry Chron. 28: 85–93.

———. 1954. Treatment of decayed wood . . . for growth ring analysis. Forestry Chron. 30: 280–283.

GLOCK, W. S. 1937. Principles and methods of tree ring analysis. Carnegie Inst. Wash. Pub. 486. 100 pp.

GROSENBAUGH, L. R. 1952. Plotless timber estimates—new, fast, easy. Jour. Forestry 50: 32–37.

HAIG, I. T. 1924. Applications of normal yield tables. Jour. Forestry 22: 902–906.

HALL, R. C. 1944. A vernier tree growth band. Jour. Forestry 42: 742–743.

HERVEY, D. E. 1936. A method of measuring the current mortality of a timber stand. Jour. Forestry 34: 1003.

HOLCOMB, C. J., and C. A. BICKFORD. 1952. Growth of yellow poplar and associated species in W. Va. Northeast. Forest Expt. Sta. Paper 52. 14 pp.

HUMMEL, F. C., G. M. L. LOCKE, J. N. R. JEFFERS, and J. M. CHRISTIE. 1959. Code of sample plot procedure. For. Commn. (Gt. Brit.) Bull. 31. 113 pp.

KASE, J. C. 1935. Stain reveals growth rings. Jour. Forestry 33: 887.

McArdle, R. E., and W. H. Meyer. 1949. Rev. ed. Yield of Douglas fir in the Pac. N. West. U.S. Dept. Agr. Tech. Bull. 201. 74 pp.

MacKinney, A. L., F. X. Schumacher, and L. E. Chaiken. 1937. Construction of yield tables for non normal loblolly pine stands. Jour. Agr. Res. 54: 531–545.

Meyer, H. A. 1942. Methods of forest growth determination. Pa. Agr. Expt. Sta. Bull. 435. 78 pp.

Meyer, H. A., and F. B. Nelson. 1952. Accuracy of forest growth determination based on measurement of increment cores. Pa. Agr. Expt. Sta. Bull. 547. 25 pp.

——— and ———. 1953. Forest mensuration. Pennsylvania Valley Publishers, Inc., State College, Pa. 333 pp.

Reineke, L. H. 1932. A precision dendrometer. Jour. Forestry 30: 692–697.

———. 1941. A new increment core instrument and coring wrinkles. Jour. Forestry 39: 304–309.

Schumacher, F. X., and H. A. Meyer. 1937. Effect of climate on timber growth fluctuations. Jour. Agr. Res. 54: 79–107.

Snedecor, G. W. 1956. Statistical methods. 5th ed. Iowa State College Press, Ames, Iowa. 523 pp.

Society of American Foresters. 1950. Forest terminology. Washington. 93 pp.

Spaulding, P. 1937. Estimating the length of time that trees have been dead in northern New England. Jour. Forestry 35: 393–395.

Spurr, S. H. 1952. Forest inventory. The Ronald Press Co., New York. 476 pp.

Stone, E. L. 1944. Effect of fire on taper of longleaf pine. Jour. Forestry 42: 607.

U.S. Forest Service, Northeastern Station. 1955. Forest survey field manual. 132 pp.

Wahlenberg, W. G. 1941. Methods of forecasting timber growth in irregular stands. U.S. Dept. Agr. Tech. Bull. 796. 48 pp.

Wenger, K. F. 1955. Height growth of loblolly pine seedlings in relation to seedling characteristics. Forest Sci. 1: 158–163.

25

Measuring and Predicting Growth of All-aged Stands [*]

CHERNG-JIANN SHIUE

A forest stand is an aggregation of trees, and its growth is simply the sum of the growth of all trees in the stand. Bickford's paper in this volume covers the subject of individual tree growth. If all the trees in a stand could be enumerated, it would be a simple job to measure and predict stand growth by summing up the result from individual trees. In view of the fact that measurement and prediction of stand growth are generally done through sampling, a different approach, emphasizing sampling technique, seems more appropriate.

In the past twenty years, sampling theory and practice have advanced so rapidly that application of improved methods has not been fully made in the field of forest mensuration. Concurrently, stand growth data have been accumulated through the remeasurement of permanent plots set out by government agencies and industrial groups. A full exploration of such data to furnish a priori information will make future sampling design more efficient. Therefore, the purpose of this paper is to discuss the characteristics and growth patterns of all-aged stands and to formulate a more effective method of measuring and predicting the all-aged stand growth. Although most discussions lead to the case of all-aged stands, some of the general approaches may be applied to even-aged stands as well.

Characteristics of All-aged Stands

Within an all-aged stand, there exists a great diversity in tree size and tree height. This diversity is present throughout any period

[*] Acknowledgment is due to C. D. Chase, Lake States Forest Experiment Station, for furnishing some permanent plot data.

385

of time, even though the pattern of diversity may fluctuate slightly. In other words, an all-aged stand is more complex in stand structure than an even-aged stand at a given point in time, but the periodic change for an all-aged stand is simple, especially when the stand reaches its harvesting stage and is managed under a selection system. The following will further illustrate this point:

A STABLE STAND TABLE (TREE FREQUENCY DISTRIBUTION BY SIZE). Figure 25–1 shows the stand table of three major types of all-aged

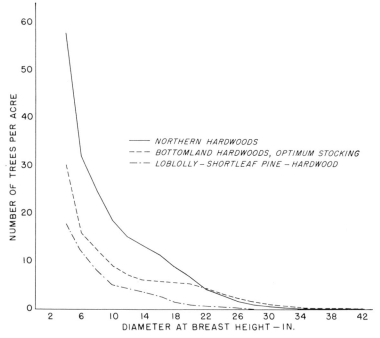

FIG. 25–1. Tree frequency distribution of all-aged stands.

stands, namely northern hardwoods (Eyre and Zillgitt, 1953), bottomland hardwoods (Putnam, 1951) and loblolly–shortleaf pine–hardwood (Reynolds, 1955). The frequency distributions characterize themselves with (1) a large range of tree sizes from four inches (the minimum size of tree tallied) up to 30 plus inches in dbh; (2) the number of trees having a monotonic decreasing trend as the size of tree increases; and (3) the declining curve resembling a truncated Poisson distribution with the truncating line through the lower limit of the size of tree to be tallied. For a given forest type, the tree frequency distribution by dbh classes will follow a certain pattern under most cases. This pattern can be changed considerably if some special type of selection cutting is practiced. For example, the number of trees in small dbh classes of loblolly–shortleaf pine–hardwood stands has been reduced after fifteen years of intensive management (Reynolds, 1953). The resultant declining trend in number of trees as the tree size increases is much less than at the beginning.

Before an all-aged stand reaches its equilibrium, the stand table curve will continue to move up and to the right. However, the frequency for the smallest dbh class may remain fairly stable while the toe of the curve extends as the stand grows. In a growing even-aged stand, the tree frequency distribution curve, which may resemble a normal curve, will shift to the right and down as the average size of trees increases and the total number of trees decreases.

A FIXED HEIGHT-DIAMETER CURVE. Even though tree size and tree height vary extremely within an all-aged stand, there exists a close and stable curvilinear relationship between tree height and dbh. For a given site, a height-diameter curve appears to be independent of time and will not change unless the all-aged condition is destroyed. In an even-aged stand, however, the height-diameter curve generally changes with time. Since the dominant tree in all-aged stands may be subjected to various degrees and periods of suppression during early stages, the height-age relationship of such trees does not give a satisfactory measurement of site. By considering the over-all pattern and elevation of the height-diameter curve, a better estimate of site may be obtained. When an all-aged stand approaches the harvesting stage and is managed under a certain method of selection cutting, the average height (weighted by basal area of the tree) remains more or less constant. Thus, it serves as an ideal index for measuring site. Furthermore, the growth of such a stand depends primarily on the increment of basal area.

SIMILAR TREE FORM IN EACH DBH CLASS. Parallel to tree height, the form of tree in all-aged stands is closely related to dbh. The size of a tree will decide its crown position in the stand and thus also determines its form. The average tree form (weighted by basal area) for a stand also remains fairly constant as the stand approaches the harvesting stage.

A CONSISTENT INGROWTH. Ingrowth of an all-aged stand is continuous although it fluctuates with time and is usually accelerated by cutting. In even-aged stands, there is copious ingrowth only in the early stage of development when the majority of stand members grow from the sapling into tree classification. After this, the ingrowth gradually decreases and finally ceases. It will not be found again until the second generation stand is established. Therefore, the variation of ingrowth due to the passage of time is much smaller for an all-aged stand than for an even-aged stand.

Measuring Growth of All-aged Stands

Sampling is a major concern in making a measurement of stand growth. The population to be sampled is the stand. It is very difficult if not impractical to consider each individual tree in the stand as a sampling unit. This is due to the tedious task of determining the size of population and selecting the sample. Total area of a stand is relatively easy to determine; therefore, it is more convenient in practice to use area for the sampling unit, either as a plot or as a point. In area sampling, the whole stand is arbitrarily divided into a number of units referred to as "plots." A plot or group of plots is considered as a sampling unit, depending on the type of sampling system employed. A single plot is used as the sampling unit in a simple random sample and in a stratified random sample, while in cluster sampling and systematic sampling (either with one or more random starts) the sampling unit usually consists of a group of plots.

The shape of a plot may be a long strip, rectangular, square or circular area. According to Cochran (Federer, 1955), a rectangular plot will have a smaller expected sampling variance; hence, it is recommended even though there is no information concerning gradiant available. Johnson and Hixon (1952) gave actual survey data showing the high efficiency of a 1 by 3 chain rectangular plot in estimating volume for old growth Douglas-fir. In the case of all-aged stands, growth is closely correlated with initial volume; therefore, a rectangular plot may reduce the sampling variance of growth. The difficulty of establishing such a plot, possible large errors in plot area and increased border effect prevent the use of rectangular plots. At the present time, the circular plot is the most popular type of sampling unit and it is used extensively for growth measurement with the size of plot varying with the product being produced from the stand. For stands in which the major products are sawlogs, ¼- or ⅕-acre plots are generally used, while one-seventh-acre plots are generally employed in pulpwood stands.

An all-aged stand usually consists of trees to be tallied varying in size from poles to sawlogs. If a fixed-size plot is used to sample an all-aged stand, there is a possibility of having some large trees near the plot boundary tallied. In this case, these large trees are partially supported by some area outside of the plot while all growth is attributed to the plot with a resulting overestimate of growth on that plot. The reverse may also happen where large trees are just outside of the plot boundary and the resulting growth would be underestimated. These two errors would be expected to be compensating when the mean of a number of plots were taken; however, it is unlikely that they would be compensating within a plot since there are a relatively small number of large trees in an all-aged stand. Consequently, some plots, with large trees, have a large volume and growth, while other plots, without large trees, show poor volume and growth. This results in a larger sampling error than in the case of even-aged stands. Increasing the size of plot may reduce the sampling variance caused by unequal numbers of large trees on the plots; however, this also increases the number of small trees to be measured which have little or no effect on the reduction of sampling error. In short, a fixed-size plot samples the trees of a stand with a probability proportional to the tree's frequency and not proportional to a tree's volume or growth. Since the objective of measurement is growth, and trees of various sizes play different roles in making up stand growth, it would be desirable to have an optimum allocation if possible by stratification of trees by size.

This leads to the other type of sampling unit mentioned earlier, namely point sampling. Bitterlich (1948) originated an idea of using an angle gauge to measure a plot radius which varied with tree size and this has been known as a variable size plot system. Grosenbaugh (1952) recognized the fact that an angle gauge is in reality a point sampling device rather than a plot sampling device. A stand, when being sampled by a point system, is stratified into a continuous series of strata on the basis of tree size. In each stratum, trees are sampled with a probability proportional to their basal area.

As previously stated, growth of individual trees in all-aged stands is closely correlated to the size of the tree and also, variation in growth is proportional to tree size. A point sample may very likely resemble a sample stratified according to tree size with optimum allocation. Therefore, it has great merit in sampling all-aged stands.

When a sampling point falls on the edge of a stand sampled, Grosenbaugh (1958) proposed tallying only a 180° or 90° sweep, then through multiplication of the result by 2 or 4, a complete observation is obtained. If a series of points fall on the edge of a stand (a systematic sample with one random start will have this possibility) and the growth is different on the edge from that in the interior, the estimate can be considerably biased. When a systematic sample with multiple random starts is taken (Shiue, 1960), the observations from a 180° or 90° sweep can be accumulated directly with those of 360° sweeps; however, the number of observations will be tallied as one-half or one-quarter for points with 180° and 90° sweeps respectively. The average observation from each random start is used to compute the sampling errors; hence, the bias due to overweighting the edge of the stands is eliminated. When the stand area is small, point sampling may give a considerable underestimate of volume as well as growth. Haga and Maezawa (1959) have developed a mathematical approximation and constructed charts to correct for edge bias when conditions seem to warrant its use.

After the sampling unit has been chosen, the next problem is to determine the method of measurement to be used from the numerous methods that have been developed. These methods generally can be classified into two types depending on whether or not the passage of time is required for the determination of growth.

The first type requires only one measurement (one sample). When a forest manager wishes to determine the past growth of a given stand and no past records are available, he has to obtain the growth information through present measurements. For each tree sampled, bark thickness and past growth in radius are determined in addition to present volume. From this information, past and present stand and stock tables are constructed and the difference between these gives the growth of the stand. This estimation consists of the growth of survivors and ingrowth, but does not take mortality into consideration and, therefore, actual growth is frequently overestimated. It is necessary to adjust the past stand and stock table by adding those trees which died during the period for which growth is measured. It is not difficult to estimate the dead trees in a stand; however, it is a real problem to determine when the tree died. The lack of accuracy in estimating mortality makes such a growth estimate unreliable, especially when the amount of mortality is comparable in size to the survivor growth. Unless mortality is negligible, as may be the case where an all-aged stand is intensively managed, such a method does not give the whole picture of stand growth.

The second type of growth estimation involves two consecutive measurements, the stand being sampled both at the beginning and the end of a time period. There are three methods under this type: temporary sample method, permanent sample without identification of sample trees, and permanent samples with identification of sample trees. All three of these methods will give net periodic growth of a given stand. However, only with the third method is it possible to partition net growth into its component parts, survivor growth, ingrowth, and mortality.

The sampling error of net growth estimate from a temporary sample always exceeds that of a permanent sample. As Cochran (1953) points out, to measure the change (growth is such a case) it is best to retain the same sample throughout all measurements. In other words, a permanent sample is preferred because there exists a high correlation between any two consecutive measurements on the same sample. This can be illustrated by the following:

Let T be the total volume estimate at the first measurement with an expected sample variance S_1^2, and T_2 be total volume estimate at the second measurement with an expected sample variance of S_2^2, and ρ be the correlation coefficient between the two measurements on the same sample unit. Then, the growth $(T_2 - T_1)$ will have a sampling variance:

$$S_G^2 = S_1^2 + S_2^2 - 2\rho S_1 S_2 \tag{1}$$

under the temporary sample method, where the selection of sampling units in two measurements is independent. This gives the value of $\rho = 0$, hence, Equation (1) reduces to the form:

$$S_G^2 \text{ (temporary plot)} = S_1^2 + S_2^2 \tag{2}$$

When a permanent sample is used, ρ is positive with a value very close to one and the sampling error will be substantially reduced as compared to the temporary sample method.

By partitioning the net growth obtained from continuous forest inventory data, evidence has been found which leads us to re-evaluation of sampling methods used at the present time on all-aged stands. Let

G_N be the net growth with an expected sampling variance S_n^2,
G_S be the survivor growth with an expected sampling variance S_s^2,
G_I be the ingrowth with an expected sampling variance S_i^2,
M be the mortality with an expected sampling variance S_m^2,
and ρ_{si}, ρ_{sm}, and ρ_{im} be the correlation coefficients between survivor growth and ingrowth, survivor growth and mortality, and ingrowth and mortality, respectively.

By definition, $G_N = G_S + G_I - M$ (ignoring cut) therefore,

$$S_n^2 = S_s^2 + S_i^2 + S_m^2 + 2\rho_{si}S_sS_i - 2\rho_{sm}S_sS_m - 2\rho_{im}S_iS_m \tag{3}$$

In an all-aged stand, ρ_{si}, ρ_{sm}, and ρ_{im} may be anticipated to be relatively small values. This is due to the fact that survivor growth, ingrowth, and mortality ratios can take all values within the range of the data. Theoretically, high mortality may induce greater ingrowth and survivor growth, and a vigorous survivor growth will cause greater mortality of suppressed trees. Plots with a large survivor growth are unlikely to have any ingrowth at all. However, the above relationships, during any given short time period, are very difficult to detect from data of a fixed size plot.

Sampling variance introduced by the arbitrary division of an area into plots will tend to mask the true relationships existing in the stand. For this reason, the sampling error of net growth will depend primarily on the sum of S_s^2, S_i^2, and S_m^2. It is tradition to measure survivor growth, ingrowth, and mortality on the same plots. However, this is not necessarily the best way to obtain net growth if the sampling variances of these components of net growth have extreme variations. For instance, in an overmature all-aged stand some of the larger trees may gradually die. Due to the large volume of these trees, the mortality is comparable in size to the survivor growth even though the number of dead trees is small. More important is that such a type of mortality, when measured with a fixed size plot, will show an extremely large sampling variance because some plots suffer a heavy loss while others have no loss. In this case, no matter how good the survivor growth estimate is, the net growth estimate is still subject to a large sample variance due to the poor estimate of mortality. Unless the mortality and ingrowth are negligible as compared to survivor growth, it is suggested that the sampling error of survivor growth, ingrowth and mortality should be approximately equal. Any attempt which is made to balance these sampling errors will improve the final results of a net growth estimate.

Since the point sampling system has the effect of reducing the sampling error caused by larger trees, net growth estimates of overmature, all-aged stands will be better than those estimates obtained from a fixed-size plot system.

Table 25–1 shows the components of net growth and their corresponding sampling errors (in terms of standard deviations), these data are from a continuous forest inventory of all-aged stands. The mean mortality and ingrowth are only 10 to 20 per cent of the size of survivor growth. Although some mortality shows an extremely high variation coefficient (over 200 per cent), the effect on sampling error of net growth is not enough to warrant consideration. In general, when an all-aged stand is managed under the selection cutting system, the mortality will be low and ingrowth will be steady; therefore, any sampling system giving a good estimate of survivor growth will also provide a good estimate of net growth.

TABLE 25–1

PARTITION OF GROWTH FOR TWO TYPES OF ALL-AGED STANDS.

		Cover Type	
		Northern Hardwoods	Bottomland Hardwoods
Location		Lower Peninsula Michigan	Lower Peninsula Michigan
Size of plots (acres)		0.2	0.2
Passage of time (years)		4-7	4-7
Number of plots		44	18
Mortality	Mean	0.043	0.110
(cords per acre per year)	S.D.	0.105	0.137
Ingrowth	Mean	0.111	0.125
(cords per acre per year)	S.D.	0.114	0.109
Survivor growth	Mean	0.549	0.871
(cords per acre per year)	S.D.	0.429	0.664
Net growth	Mean	0.617	0.886
(cords per acre per year)	S.D.	0.431	0.674
r_{im}		0.076	0.083
r_{is}		−0.197	−0.230
r_{sm}		0.269	0.012

Note: Not all r's are significant.

Predicting Growth of All-aged Stands

Prediction of future stand growth is more complicated than measurement of its past growth. The problem involves not only the selection of a sampling system but also the formulation of prediction function. There are many ways of predicting future growth depending on the factor or factors used in the prediction function:

USING PAST GROWTH AS A PREDICTION FACTOR. In some stands for which records of past growth are available, future growth may simply be predicted by a linear function such as:

$$G_f = kG_p \tag{4}$$

where G_f = future growth, G_p = past growth, and k = constant.

Although k varies with age and stocking of the stand and is modified considerably by cutting practices, the assumption, $k=1$, is always used in order to make the application of this function feasible. Such an assumption will be appropriate under a fully stocked, all-aged stand without any change in cutting practice. Since understocked and overstocked stands will accelerate and deaccelerate their growth, respectively, due to the trend of approaching normality, considering $k = 1$ will mean either an underestimate or overestimate of the future growth. Adjustment of k to fit this situation is not easy. However, if there exists a series of measurements on past stand growth, i.e., the past growth of the stand has been measured over several time periods, plotting the past growth against time and extending the curve will give a very close estimate of immediate future growth.

USING PRESENT STAND CONDITIONS AS PREDICTION FACTORS. In most cases, a forester wishes to estimate the growth of a stand on which there is no past information available. He has to rely on the present measurements to make a prediction. Methods of making such predictions include:

Stand-Table Projection. This method is described by Spurr (1952) and requires extraction of an increment core and measurement of bark thickness of each sample tree. From such data, present and future stand tables are constructed to compute the growth. In all-aged stands, the height-diameter curve, the tree-form-diameter curve and the amount of ingrowth are fairly stable with respect to time. The serious objection to the stand-table-projection method of emphasizing one predicting factor alone, dbh, may be ignored. The future ingrowth can be closely estimated by examination of trees which have a past diameter less than the minimum size to be tallied. However, the assumption of an equality between past and future diameter growths may be true only if the stand is understocked. Otherwise future growth will be considerably over-estimated. Furthermore, it is difficult to obtain reliable mortality estimates. Due to the tedious field work, complicated computing job, and crude growth estimate, the stand-table projection method is not recommended, even though it may fit the all-aged stand better than others.

Two-Way Method. Developed by Spurr (1952), this method has its greatest merit when applied to well-managed, all-aged stands in which the mortality is negligible. Extractions of increment core and measurements of bark thickness of sample trees also are necessary. However, the computation is much simplified. The method postulates that the past and future basal area growth tend to be equal, which is probably the case in an all-aged stand managed under given conditions. Since the height-diameter curve of an all-aged stand is stable with time, the average height of the stand remains more or less constant; thus Spurr's two-way predicting equation could be further simplified as:

$$V_f = V_p \, (A_f/A_p) \tag{5}$$

or

$$G_f = V_p \, (B_f/A_p) \tag{6}$$

where V_f = future volume,
$\quad V_p$ = present volume,
$\quad A_f$ = future basal area,
$\quad A_p$ = present basal area,
$\quad G_f$ = future volume growth, and
$\quad B_f$ = future basal area growth. .

Regression-Estimate Methods. Through empirical data, a regression equation can be fitted to predict the net growth of a stand based upon present stand volume, density, height or average diameter, either singly or in combination. Many prediction functions along this line have been developed for various forest stands by numerous individuals and are summarized by Spurr (1952). The availability of more permanent plot data and the application of high-speed digital computers will make this approach much easier than it has been in the past. The multiple regression function can also be extended to the cases of curvilinearity and even interacting independent variables through a proper transformation or an insertion of additional terms of high order or terms of the product of two independent variables. But in the case of all-aged stands, the prediction function may be very simple. Long (1947) theorized that the best and simplest growth predictions would be those predicting volume per unit area and based upon one measure of site (height) and one measurement of utilization of site (stand density). In an even-aged stand, the height and stand density change with age for a given site and total stand basal area. Therefore, the effect of height and basal area on growth is dependent upon age. In other words, the growth of an even-aged stand is a complicated function of height (site), basal area (stand density) and age. Since both the height-diameter curve and the tree frequency distribution by diameter of all-aged stands are independent of time after stands reach their equilibrium stage, the average height of stand (weighted average tree height by basal area) is an excellent index for measuring site. The basal area is a measurement of stocking density regardless of the time element. Hence the present volume, which is a product of basal area, average stand height and average tree form factor, may serve as the best single factor to predict the future growth of an all-aged stand. In some cases, the variation of growth is proportional to initial volume and the growth as a percentage of the initial volume remains relatively constant. A regression model, Model IA, as described by Snedecor (1956) can be used:

$$G_f = bV_p \tag{7}$$

where $G_f =$ future volume growth, $V_p =$ present volume, and $b =$ regression coefficient.

The computation of b is surprisingly different from that used in ordinary regression.

Let $X_i =$ the initial volume of ith plot,
$Y_i =$ the volume growth of ith plot, where
$i = 1, 2, 3, \ldots n,$

then
$$b = \frac{1}{n} \sum_{i=1}^{n} (Y_i/X_i) \tag{8}$$

$$s_b{}^2 = \sum_{i=1}^{n} [Y_i/X_i - b]^2 \Big/ n(n-1) \tag{9}$$

If growth is not proportional to initial vilume but b varies with initial volume having a linear trend, the following regression equation may be appropriate:

$$G_R = b' V_p \tag{10}$$

where $G_R =$ growth rate = volume growth as per cent of the initial volume
$V_p =$ initial volume, and
$b' =$ regression coefficient.

After a transformation of growth from absolute measurement to a ratio basis, its variance may be expected to stabilize. Hence the ordinary procedure to compute the regression coefficient (Model I or Model II as described in Snedecor, 1956) can be used.

A set of permanent plot data from northern hardwood stands was plotted, using survivor growth as dependent variable (x) and initial volume as independent variable (y), in Fig. 25–2. It represents a typical Model IA regression with a fan-like distribution of the points. The regression coefficient and its standard error, computed according to Equations (8) and (9), were 0.0425 and 0.0027 respectively. The net growth was not used because the variation of mortality mainly due to sampling error was so big that the true relationship between growth and initial volume might be masked.

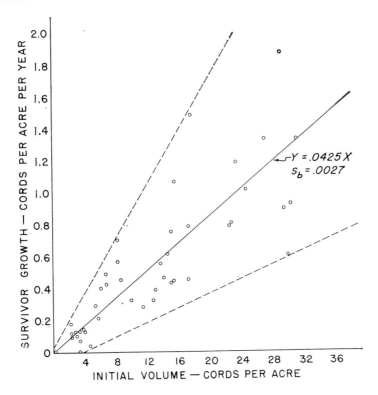

FIG. 2   THE RELATIONSHIP BETWEEN SURVIVOR
GROWTH AND INITIAL VOLUME IN
NORTHERN HARDWOOD STANDS.

FIG. 25–2. The relationship between survivor growth and initial volume in northern hardwood stands.

Reliability of the Measurement and Prediction of Growth

It is desirable to know the reliability of the stand growth estimate obtained through sample measurements or prediction. The reliability of the past growth, based on repeated measurements is primarily dependent upon the sampling system used, even though the field measuring technique of dbh, tree height, plot area, and the volume table employed may also affect the result. From the sampling error computed, confidence limits with a selected probability can be set for the growth estimate. When past growth is estimated through one measurement only, the uncertainty of the mortality estimate further reduces its reliability. Such growth measurement is of very little value unless the mortality is known to be negligible or unless it is measured by another method.

In predicting the growth, two sources of error should be considered. They are the error of sampling and the error of prediction. There is no method available for computing the prediction error when using past growth, stand-table projection or the two-way method of estimating the future growth. In view of the fact that site quality, stand composition, genetic characteristics and the past history of a given stand remain fairly stable over a short period of time, the immediate future growth (for example, for the next five years) can be very closely predicted through the methods mentioned above, if the mortality is negligible. Hence, their errors are predominantly contributed by the sampling. When past growth is used as a predicting factor, the sampling error of the future growth is generally considered to be the same as that of the past growth, which may be computed from the deviations of plot growth from the mean growth. In stand-table projection, sampling error is difficult to obtain unless a stand-table projection is constructed for each plot or each group of plots (at least two groups) in a given stand. However, for approximation, the sampling error of such a method may be obtained by using the variation in plot measurements, such as basal area or volume directly. With Equation (6) which is used in the two-way method of prediction, the sampling error consists of two parts, namely the error on present volume and the error on the ratio of growth in basal area to present basal area. The sampling error of growth is as follows (Hansen et al., 1953):

$$s_G{}^2 = G_f{}^2 \left(s_V{}^2/V_p{}^2 + s_R{}^2/R^2 + 2rs_Vs_R/V_pR \right) \qquad (11)$$

where G_f = future growth with estimated sampling variance $s_G{}^2$,
V_p = present volume with estimated sampling variance $s_V{}^2$,
R = ratio of growth in basal area to present basal area with estimated sampling variance $s_R{}^2$, and
r = sample correlation coefficient between present volume and the ratio of growth in basal area to present basal area.

This sampling error does not include the prediction error of Equation (6). However, the prediction error is negligible in the case of an all-aged stand after reaching its harvesting states.

When a regression equation is used to predict the stand growth, the prediction error can be computed. The combination of sampling error and prediction error is also feasible. Let s_b be the standard error of the regression coefficient b in Equations (7) and (10) which have been established through an analysis of empirical data. Assume that n sample plots have been measured in a stand for which an estimate of the future growth is wanted. Based on the n observations, an estimate of the present volume, V_p, and its sampling variance s_V^2 are computed. Providing the stand condition is within the range of the original data from which the prediction equation is formulated, the sampling variance for the future growth (G_f) which is expressed in absolute value for Equation (7) and in percentage of present volume for Equation (10) will be:

$$s_G^2 = G_f^2 \ (s_b^2/b^2 + s_V^2/V_p^2) \tag{12}$$

or
$$\left(\frac{s_G}{G_f}\right)^2 = \left(\frac{s_b}{b}\right)^2 + \left(\frac{s_V}{V_p}\right)^2 \tag{13}$$

When the sampling errors are expressed in terms of percentage of corresponding estimate, an additive relationship of their squares exists as shown in Equation (13). The covariance term is dropped because the random distribution of b should be independent of V_p. If this is not the case, this regression equation should not be used.

A question may be raised: "Should the n observations be put into the equation individually to obtain n predicted values from which a sampling error be computed?" By so doing, the prediction error is expected to reduce by a factor of $1/n$; hence, it can be ignored. Unfortunately, these n plots come from a stand and have a strong relationship. They should not be considered as n independent observations to be used for prediction. In other words, if one of the plots tends to have a lower value of b than the average value as expressed in the equation due to random error, another plot from the same stand will probably show the same tendency. This will not compensate as true random plots do. Thus no matter how many sample plots are taken from a stand, they should be combined as one observation for prediction. Increasing the sample size will improve the estimate of present volume, but the prediction error remains unaffected. For this reason, the limiting factor on the reliability of the future growth estimation is the prediction error (sampling error of b). In general, there seems little use in attempting to reduce sampling error to less than 25 per cent of the error inherent from the prediction equation (Grosenbaugh, 1947). Assuming $s_b/b = 1.00$ and $s_V/V_p = 0.25$, the combined standard error of future growth, s_G/G_f, would be $\sqrt{1.00^2 + 0.25^2} = 1.031$ (according to Equation 13). Even though the sampling error, s_V/V_p, is reduced to zero, the sampling error for future growth could be reduced not more than 3 per cent. Let c be the variation coefficient of a stand, the size of sample for measuring present volume to predict future growth should be:

$$n < 16\left(\frac{cs_b}{b}\right)^2 \tag{14}$$

In order to improve the prediction function, a method of treating the original data to compute the equation is also suggested, i.e., the stand or a group of plots from the same stand should be used as the sampling unit when computing the regression equation. The mean value of a group of plots certainly contains less sampling variance in mortality and ingrowth, thus the true relationship between net growth and present stand condition can be expressed more closely in the equation.

LITERATURE CITED

BITTERLICH, W. 1948. Die winkelzählprobe. Allg. Forst u. Holzwirtschaftliche Ztg. 59(½): 4–5.

COCHRAN, W. G. 1953. Sampling techniques. John Wiley & Sons, Inc., New York.

EYRE, F. H., and W. M. Zillgitt. 1953. Partial cutting in northern hardwoods of the Lake States. U.S. Dept. Agr. Tech. Bull. 1076. 124 pp.

FEDERER, W. T. 1955. Experimental design. The Macmillan Co., New York.

GROSENBAUGH, L. R. 1947. Elementary design and analysis in forest research. U.S. Forest Serv. South. Forest Expt. Sta. 44 pp.

————. 1952. Plotless timber estimates—new, fast, easy. Jour. Forestry 50: 32–37.

————. 1958. Point-sampling and line-sampling: Probability theory, geometric implications, synthesis. U.S. Forest Serv. South. Forest Expt. Sta. Occas. Paper 160. 34 pp.

HAGA, T., and K. MAEZAWA. 1959. Bias due to edge effect in using the Bitterlich method. Forest Sci. 5: 370–376.

HANSEN, M. H., W. N. HURWITZ, and W. G. MADOW. 1953. Sampling methods and theory. Vol. I. John Wiley & Sons, Inc., New York.

JOHNSON, F. A., and H. T. HIXON. 1952. The most efficient size and shape of plot to use for cruising in old-growth Douglas-fir timber. Jour. Forestry 50: 17–20.

LONG, H. D. 1947. Short period growth predictions. Pulp and Paper Res. Inst. Canada, Woodlands Sect. Res. Index 921. 5 pp.

PUTNAM, J. A. 1951. Management of bottomland hardwoods. U.S. Forest Serv. South. Forest Expt. Sta. Occas. Paper 116. 60 pp.

REYNOLDS, R. R. 1953. Fifteen years of management on the Crossett farm forestry forties. U.S. Forest Serv. South. Forest Expt. Sta. Occas. Paper 130. 27 pp.

————. 1955. Managed growth. U.S. Forest Serv. South. Forest Expt. Sta. Occas. Paper 142. 16 pp.

SHIUE, C. J. 1960. Systematic sampling with multiple random starts. Forest Sci. 6: 42–50.

SNEDECOR, G. W. 1956. Statistical methods. 5th ed. Iowa State College Press, Ames, Iowa.

SPURR, S. H. 1952. Forest inventory. The Ronald Press Co., New York. 476 pp.

26

Measuring and Predicting Growth of Even-aged Stands

DONALD W. LYNCH

Forest growth is not a simple process. It depends upon a great number of factors, many of which are highly variable and difficult to measure. Because of the complexity, predictions of growth are never exact. They tend to improve, however, as experience data from sample plots are accumulated and as techniques and abilities to measure the variables improve.

In considering forest growth, the type of growth being measured, the portion of the tree and stand being considered, and the period of time involved must be defined. From the common measurements of growth on individual trees—involving diameter, height, and form —volume growth in cubic feet is usually computed and used as the basic value from which other volume units such as board feet and cords are derived. Stand growth, either measured directly or summarized from the growth of individual trees, is the unit generally desired for management purposes.

This paper deals with growth of even-aged stands, although several of the processes described are applicable to uneven-aged stands as well. One of the major sources of information has been Spurr's (1952) *Forest Inventory,* which contains a very complete review and analysis of growth measurement and prediction methods. This paper describes and appraises the more important of these methods and discusses some of the developments since the publication of Spurr's book.

Methods of Growth Prediction

Predicting growth and yield of forest stands is not new. The Europeans have been using yield tables since the late eighteenth century, and Americans have been actively engaged in growth predictions since the days of Pinchot (1898) and Graves (1899).

The techniques of estimating stand growth include three basic steps: (1) an inventory of the existing stand or stands, (2) a projection of existing conditions into the future for a certain period, and (3) an adjustment of these projected values for such factors as mortality and ingrowth which could not be measured directly. The projection phase of the process can be classified as to whether it is *direct,* that is, based solely upon the stand whose growth is being predicted, or *indirect,* based on other stands that are assumed to be similar.

Typical of the direct approach are the continuous inventory method based on repeated measurements of the same plots, and the stand table projection method based upon stem analyses. The indirect methods can be lumped into one general term, *yield tables,* these cover a large variety of processes and conditions.

Regardless of the method used in growth predictions or the length of time considered, the vagaries of climate and the impact of unusual losses may invalidate the best efforts.

DIRECT METHODS. A knowledge of past growth of a particular stand can be obtained most accurately from the stand itself. It may come from repeated measurements over a period of years, or from increment cores extracted from trees within the stand. Both methods, however, are costly, and data for specific stands usually are not available.

Future growth estimates projected from past growth, although based on data from the stand itself, are reliable only for short-term predictions. Climatic cycles and tree mortality, two factors difficult to predict, often seriously upset future net growth estimates.

Continuous Inventory. The repeated measurement of sample plots in a forest, known in America as *continuous inventory,* is about the best practical way to assess past performance of a forest stand and to make short-term predictions of its future growth (Hall, 1959). As the level of management rises in this country, the use of continuous inventory as an essential tool will be increased. Its value, of course, increases with time, and only after many years following its installation can the system reach full utility for a particular forest property. Continuous inventory leaves no doubt about past growth, mortality, ingrowth, and changes in density and stand composition. As experience data for these factors accumulate, their usefulness in predicting growth increases. The system is not limited, of course, to even-aged stands. Obviously, the accuracy of the method for obtaining information for a forest property depends upon the number and location of the sample plots as well as accuracy in relocating the plots and making the measurements. Plots should not be conspicuously marked for fear that they will be treated in a biased manner during regular forestry activities. Grosenbaugh (1959) has suggested a plot-marking system appropriate to this electronic age.

Stand-Table Projection. A second direct method of predicting forest growth is the use of a stand-table projection based on past growth measured on increment cores. Since the increment-core technique measures only wood growth, diameter growth outside bark must be obtained by a bark growth adjustment. Growth by diameter classes is used in projecting the present stand table to a future stand table by a variety of processes. To make accurate volume growth predictions by this procedure, a forester must be able to estimate future height-diameter relations as well as future tree form, since these change with time. Gross growth computed by the stand table projection method must be adjusted for mortality and ingrowth. Despite the cumbersome aspects of the system and its several disadvantages, it can be very accurate for predicting growth of a particular stand for a short period.

INDIRECT METHODS. Because of their low cost and their suitability to long-term forecasts, indirect methods of measuring and predicting forest growth have been used extensively in American forestry. A large variety of methods has been developed to meet the diversity of forest conditions as well as to supply the wide range in uses to which growth tables are put. Falling into the general classification of yield tables, they present growth charts, tables, or formulae generally based on age and site. Yield tables can be constructed from data derived from the two methods described above, continuous inventory and stem analyses, but more commonly they are based on data from temporary sample plots covering a complete range of the desired variables. Thus, growth and yield of selected stands become the basis for predicting growth and yield for other stands with similar characteristics.

A distinct advantage of the yield-table approach to growth predictions is that data are based on stands as they actually exist with mortality and ingrowth "built in"; net growth is computed directly. Staebler (1955), however, has shown the value of gross yield tables for certain management purposes and has developed such tables for Douglas-fir.

The quality of yield tables can be improved tremendously as data from permanent sample plots become available for their construction. This is true, of course, for both managed and unmanaged stands. A major effort in forest research today is directed toward the establishment of sample plots representing a range in age, site, and stocking from which growth and yield tables for various levels of management will eventually be produced. In Europe, for example, where sample plot records provide data for full rotations, yield tables are accurate and detailed; some of the European tables also may be useful in the United States (Barnes, 1956).

The following discussion will cover the more important types of yield tables and some of the many diversifications that have been used in an attempt to increase their accuracy.

Conventional Normal Yield Tables. Most early American yield tables were based on two variables, age and site. Density was eliminated as a variable simply by basing the tables on fully stocked or "normal" stands. Normal yield tables have been developed for most major American forest types, and they have been a valuable management tool. As the level of forest management improves, however, normal yield tables have diminishing utility. The concept of "normality" is, of course, subjective. Furthermore, extensive stands of full stocking are not found under natural conditions, and the use of normal yield tables has required an adjustment for density, usually on the basis of volume or basal area. The assumption that a given stand density persists and that the same adjustment can be made for future yields is the major weakness of these tables. Experience has shown that density does change with age; understocked stands increase in density and overstocked stands decrease.

Progress is being made in many forest types to obtain reliable data on these changes (Gevorkiantz, 1937; Chaiken, 1939; Briegleb, 1942; Meyer, 1942; Wellwood, 1943; Watt, 1950). There is still a long way to go. By taking advantage of such supplementary data, normal yield tables can be very useful. Johnson (1955) compared the accuracy of several methods of applying normal yield tables to well-stocked stands of Douglas-fir and recommends a method called "normal growth."

Variable Density Yield Tables. To correct one of the major deficiencies of normal yield tables, variable density yield tables (sometimes called "non-normal" or "empirical" yield tables) have been developed. They use density as a third independent variable, along with age and site. Various measures of density such as basal area and stand density index have been employed for this purpose; a discussion of density measurement appears later in this paper. Examples of variable density yield tables are those for loblolly pine developed by MacKinney *et al.* (1937); tables for northern hardwoods by Duerr and Gevorkiantz (1938); tables for certain Canadian species by Mulloy (1944, 1947); and Douglas-fir tables prepared by McKeever (1947). Some of these tables have added corrections for density changes with time based on data from permanent sample plots (Mulloy, 1947; McKeever, 1947).

Other Growth Tables. Because growth of a forest depends upon many interrelated variables, it is to be expected that many and varied methods have been developed for estimating it. Conditions of the forest itself, the particular facilities at hand, and the anticipated uses of the data determine the method to be used. For example, the growth of cutover stands has been predicted simply on the basis of the residual volume and time since cutting (Meyer, 1930, 1934; Hornibrook, 1939, 1940, 1942; Roe, 1952). Gross yield can be adjusted for site quality, stand structure, mortality and number of poles. Lexen (1935) predicted growth of ponderosa pine stands 15 years after cutting, on the basis of residual volume plus the volume of the average tree as a second variable.

Stand density rather than volume has been used as a basis for predicting growth of cutover stands for certain periods following cutting. The method can be refined by adding composition index and site index as additional variables (Westveld, 1941; Bowman, 1944; Long, 1947). Bole area has been suggested by Lexen (1943) as an ideal variable for predicting growth.

Height alone or height and density can be used to predict growth, particularly in the application of aerial photographs (Spurr, 1946).

Considerable use has been made of average diameter as a basis for growth prediction. For example, average diameter, number of trees, and height replaced the conventional units of age and site in revised yield tables for Douglas-fir (McArdle *et al.*, 1949). Growth estimates from these tables should be more accurate than those obtained from conventional tables based on age and site because of the more realistic description of the stand at the beginning and end of the growth period.

Bruce and Schumacher (1950) describe a graphic method of growth prediction in which average diameter, basal area, age, and volume-basal area ratio are used to construct freehand, harmonized curves based on temporary plot data. From these curves future average diameter is first estimated from which future basal area and volume-basal area ratio are estimated. These, then, lead directly to future stand volume. The method makes ingenious use of data that can be readily collected and analyzed with a minimum of office computation.

Growth tables based on diameter classes also have been used. These, of course, are similar to the stand tables and have the same disadvantage of requiring corrections for mortality and ingrowth. Krouch (1930) developed the individual tree approach for ponderosa pine in the Southwest. He computed growth by d.b.h. classes for various site, age, vigor, and crown classes. Mortality corrections were determined from permanent growth plots. Briegleb (1945, 1950) used a similar approach for ponderosa pine in the Northwest and introduced Keen tree class as an additional factor.

Gevorkiantz and Olsen (1948) described a method of growth prediction in which the past 10-year growth of individual trees was used to predict future 10-year growth after making adjustments for age and decadal growth during the entire life of the tree. Thus, a table of diameter growth or volume growth by diameter classes and age can be constructed. In such a table, stand density, and site to a certain degree, are accounted for in the age-diameter relation. This method was used successfully in second growth ponderosa pine in the Inland Empire (Lynch 1954, 1958b). Accurate net growth estimates, as with all diameter class systems, depend upon an accurate prediction of mortality.

The growth percentage technique has often been used to express the past growth of a stand and to predict future growth. Two old, well-known formulas that foresters have studied are Pressler's and Schneider's. Also, both simple interest and compound interest formulas have been advocated, and to this day a controversy exists over the appropriateness of these two methods. (Grosenbaugh, 1958; Meyer, 1959). These formulas and their limitations should be clearly understood if faulty applications are to be avoided. The unit of measure concerned, the length of the period, net growth rates or gross growth rates, and the base upon which the percentages are computed must be stipulated. For various management and economic considerations, growth percentage has its place.

Two-Way Growth Prediction. Spurr (1952) makes a strong case for what he terms a "two-way growth prediction." The system employs only basal area and height growth, and because of their independence, each is estimated separately. Ideally, these estimates are based on permanent sample-plot data from which a regression of stand basal area growth on existing basal area is computed. The accuracy of the regression can be improved by introducing age as a second independent variable. Gross basal area growth can also be determined from increment borings on temporary plots. Spurr shows the desirability of obtaining cores from representative trees and provides a correction factor to apply if the average diameter of sample trees differs from that of the full stand. However, estimation of mortality still remains the one major problem. All methods that use any form of prediction based on past performance face this "bugaboo" of mortality, and accurate mortality data become the key to their success. Spurr's proposal to sidestep the mortality problem by applying predictions only to trees above a certain diameter class is a questionable procedure, but in the absence of reliable mortality data, it is a possible solution.

The Schumacher Method of Growth Prediction. Combining the advantages of the yield table approach to growth predictions with a method of accounting for changes in stocking with time (or approach to normal), Schumacher and Coile (1960) used a formula method in a growth and yield study of six southern pine species. The same method has been applied to second-growth stands of ponderosa pine in the Inland Empire (Lynch, 1958a). It requires data from a series of temporary sample plots covering the desired range of age, site, and density. Thus, it has the advantage over normal yield studies of not being restricted to fully stocked stands which at best are difficult to find, are atypical, and are highly subjective.

First, an expression of stocking is calculated, using the tree area ratio concept. If the sample plot area is considered 100, then stocking can be calculated by a linear equation using basal area, height, and age as independent variables. The stocking is calculated directly in percentage with the average stocking of all the plots in the study being 100.

The next step is to estimate future stocking at the desired future age. Schumacher does this with the following equation (Fig. 26–1):

$$\log S_1 = 2 + (\log S_0 - 2)\frac{A_0}{A_1}$$

where S = stocking percentage and
A = age

and in which subscript 1 refers to the future and subscript 0 to the present. This equation satisfies the following characteristics of stocking change with time:

1. Understocked stands increase in stocking.
2. Overstocked stands decrease in stocking.
3. Young stands change stocking faster than old stands.
4. Rate of stocking change is related to the degree of under- or over-stocking.

With future stocking predicted, future basal area can be calculated from the original stocking equation in which basal area was a variable. Next, the ratio of future number of trees to present number can be expressed in a logarithmic equation involving height, age, and basal area, each one of which can now be predicted for a future date. The tree of average basal area follows directly from the future basal area and number of trees.

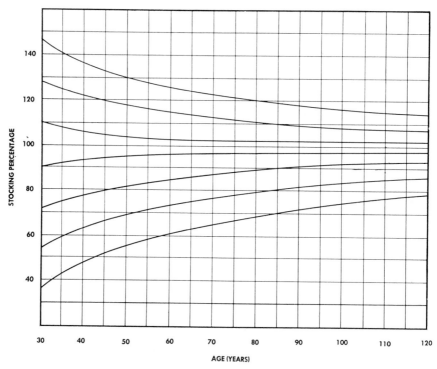

FIG. 26–1. Change in stocking with time as given by the equation,

$$\text{Log } S_1 = 2 + (\log S_0 - 2)\frac{A_0}{A_1}$$

Future stand volume in cubic feet is calculated from a logarithmic expression of volume per tree, based on diameter squared and height, and by the number of trees already determined. Other measures of volume can be derived from cubic-foot volume by a ratio process that is superior to calculating board feet or cords directly. Converting ratios can be determined for any portion of the stand and for any purpose desired using total cubic feet as the basic volume measure.

The Schumacher method of growth prediction answers a very real need for variable density yield tables with provisions for stocking changes with time. It employs the basal area and height variables shown to be superior in growth determinations, and the results can be presented readily by graphic means for a full range of initial densities. Until more accurate yield tables based on permanent sample plots become available, tables based on this system should be very useful.

A Look at Techniques

Changes and improvements in the techniques of doing any job seem to be the modern pattern. This is as true in forestry as in other scientific activities, although perhaps not in such a spectacular manner. Since the publishing of Spurr's *Forest Inventory* in 1952, the great increase in use of electronic computing processes alone has strongly influenced procedures in forest measurement. Another rather revolutionary development is the process of point sampling—or variable plot cruising. These and other advanced techniques should at least briefly be pointed out at this time.

ELECTRONIC COMPUTERS. Probably no other tool has opened up such a wide vista of opportunity in data computing as the modern electronic computer. Problems that were feared a few years ago now can be solved in minutes. There no longer need be concern about multiple correlations with a large number of variables. All possible actions and interactions, combinations, and transformations can be handled with relative ease. The use of these machines has revolutionized and will continue to revolutionize much of forest mensuration. Where simplified relations, single all-purpose variables, rules of thumb, and short cuts were once sought, we now should look for more variables to measure, more combinations of variables, and more complex interactions in order to reduce the variation in estimates and measurements of trees and forests. Forests are complex biological units and complex methods will be required to measure their growth and yield with a high degree of accuracy. With modern electronic computers, this job should no longer be feared.

POINT SAMPLING. A timber cruising technique known as point sampling, or variable plot cruising, entered the American scene in the early 1950's, and after a rather slow start has been accepted in a remarkable way. Its theory is credited to Bitterlich (1947), but Grosenbaugh (1952) was responsible for introducing it to American foresters. The process gives a measure of stand basal area directly and can be extended to give stand volume, basal area, volume by diameter classes, and a stand table if desired. Its great advantage over conventional plot cruising is its speed and accuracy in measuring basal area. As indicated throughout this report, basal area is the most important single variable in measuring tree and stand growth. Point sampling techniques should become important in future growth studies, both in temporary and permanent plots or points. Point sampling provides an ideal technique for measuring variation in basal area, or spatial distribution within stands, a factor that should receive increased attention in future growth studies.

MEASURES OF STOCKING. Since the density of a timber stand is a key variable in its growth and yield, the accurate measurement of density or stocking is important. Although basal area is probably the most satisfactory single variable in density measurement, it does not provide the complete measure often needed. Stand density index includes two variables: number of trees and average diameter, and has been extensively used. Since forest stands have different densities on different sites and at different ages, a satisfactory density measure should reflect these differences. The desired precision can be obtained only by adding more variables to the stocking expression.

Tree area ratio is a measure of stocking that deserves more use than it has had. This ratio is ideally suited to describing relative stocking of stands based on data from temporary sample plots. With the availability of machine methods, as discussed above, a formula approach to stocking using several variables should not be the burden that it once was. Many variables can be added to the tree area ratio formula in addition to the commonly accepted number of trees, average diameter, average diameter squared (or basal area), age, and height. Site index, crown length, some objective measure of tree vigor, and a measure of basal area variation (or spatial distribution) are but a few variables that should be tested in selecting the ideal tree area ratio equation for a particular stand or type. Briegleb (1952), for example, points out the importance of both diameter and height in density measurements of managed Douglas-fir stands.

An example of a tree area ratio equation used in second-growth ponderosa pine is the following (Lynch, 1958a):

$$S = b_1(N) + b_2(B) + b_3(BH) + b_4\left(\frac{BH}{A}\right) + b_5\left(\frac{B}{A}\right)$$

in which N = number of trees,
B = basal area,
H = dominant height, and
A = age

The contribution of each of these variables in reducing the residual variance is shown in the following tabulation:

Source of Variation	Explained Variation (Per Cent)
Regression on (B)	87.2
Adding the effect of (BH)	89.9
Adding the effect of $\dfrac{(B)}{(A)}$	90.3
Adding the effect of $\dfrac{(BH)}{(A)}$	91.7
Adding the effect of (N)	92.0

Although basal area alone explains 87 per cent of the variation, one need not be content with this. The addition of other commonly measured variables gives a highly accurate equation. Undoubtedly, more precision is possible by including still more factors.

Since the tree area ratio concept considers many variables and is well suited to such modern techniques as point sampling and machine computing, it should be an ideal method.

SITE MEASUREMENT. The site index concept of site measurement is an indispensable tool of the mensurationist. However, some improvements in the technique of developing site index curves should not be overlooked. For example, it is increasingly apparent, as height growth data become available, that stands on different sites have different growth patterns. The old method of constructing a set of site curves from one basic curve by anamorphosis has largely been replaced, but techniques need to be improved still further. The best site curves eventually will be obtained from permanent growth plots for all types on all sites and at all densities. This, of course, is an ideal for which we cannot wait. When facilities permit, however, the next best method of site curve construction is by complete stem analysis. It provides independent curves for each site class and also provides for special growth conditions that may be present in the stand such as Stage (1959) found in grand fir.

Another approach, which is suited to modern computing techniques, is to include additional variables in the conventional site index equation in an effort to develop more accurate curves. This approach was used to construct variable density site curves for second-growth ponderosa pine (Lynch, 1958a).

Another improvement in site curve construction is the use of only dominant trees, or perhaps the tallest given number of trees on a plot, as the basis for the curves. The subjective nature of the dominant and codominant tree approach and the added difficulty of measuring codominant heights in dense stands have ruled against this former method. Just as growth patterns change from site to site, they also change from place to place; so, ideally, site curves based on local conditions should be available.

When site quality cannot be determined by the usual methods because of the absence of trees or the uneven-aged or disturbed character of a stand, alternate methods such as the use of soil and plant indicators become valuable. In recent years soil-site studies conducted in many forest types have provided useful correlations.

McLintock and Bickford (1957) have developed site index curves for red spruce using diameter as the independent variable in place of age. This method has promise for other uneven-aged types, particularly if a measure of density can be added. Heiberg and White (1956) make a plea for using all available information in evaluating sites. They point out the complex and dynamic nature of site quality.

FOREST SURVEY TECHNIQUES. In addition to improving methods of growth measurement and prediction, foresters are continually improving survey methods of collecting data. Advanced sampling procedures taking full advantage of stratification, randomization, and double sampling should be used. For example, the relation of volume to basal area requires detailed and expensive measurements. Once this relation is established at a desired level of accuracy for a given type and age class, additional measurements are not necessary. An intensive sample of basal area alone, which is easily and inexpensively obtained, can raise the overall sampling accuracy.

Double sampling can be used, also, in establishing a relation between aerial photo classes and stand volume, the costly phase, then building up sampling accuracy by classifying a large number of photo plots, the inexpensive phase (Bickford, 1952).

The relocation and remeasurement of permanent sample plots are more costly than measurement of temporary plots. Bickford (1959) points out that a few remeasured permanent sample plots will provide reliable growth data, while additional temporary plots can be measured to obtain accurate current volume estimates.

Important as a knowledge of growth is to the forest manager, he also needs considerable additional information for management purposes. He must employ survey methods that will give such information as thinning and pruning needs, timber quality, stand structure, and other diagnostic data in addition to growth (Grosenbaugh, 1955). The modern trend, then, will be to measure more variables, measure them more accurately, and analyze them with the aid of electronic computers.

Summary

The important methods and techniques of measuring and predicting growth of even-aged stands are briefly reviewed and discussed. The older methods such as stand table projection, continuous inventory, and normal yield tables are treated rather briefly. More emphasis is placed on methods that have been developed in the last decade.

The advantages of constructing variable density yield tables are pointed out, and the importance of measuring and predicting changes in stocking with time is emphasized. Data on stocking change (or approach to "normal") are gradually being obtained from permanent sample plots, but other methods are urgently needed in the interim. One method of estimating these changes in a yield table approach has been developed by Schumacher and Coile (1960).

An appeal is made to take full advantage of modern electronic computers in mensurational studies. Modern techniques in site index studies, stocking studies, and timber surveys are discussed and their easy adaptation to modern computing methods pointed out.

LITERATURE CITED

BARNES, G. H. 1956. Intermediate yields of Douglas-fir as interpreted from British yield tables. Jour. Forestry 54: 177–179.

BICKFORD, C. A. 1952. The sampling design used in the forest survey of the Northeast. Jour. Forestry 50: 290–293.

———. 1959. A test of continuous inventory for national forest management based upon aerial photographs, double sampling, and remeasured plots. Jour. Forestry Proc. 1959: 143–147.

BICKFORD, C. A., et al. 1957. Stocking, normality, and measurement of stand density. Jour. Forestry 55: 99–104.

BITTERLICH, W. 1947. Die Winkelzählmessung. (Measurement of basal area per hectare by means of angle measurement.) Allg. Forst u. Holzwirtschaftliche Ztg. 58: 94–96. Forestry Abs. 10: 1473.

BOWMAN, A. B. 1944. Growth and occurrence of spruce and fir on pulpwood lands in northern Michigan. Mich. Agr. Expt. Sta. Tech. Bull. 188. 82 pp.

BRIEGLEB, P. A. 1942. Progress in estimating trend of normality percentage in second-growth Douglas-fir. Jour. Forestry 40: 785–793.

———. 1945. Calculating the growth of ponderosa pine forests. U.S. Forest Serv., Pacific Northwest Forest Range Expt. Sta. Prog. Rpt. 60 pp.

———. 1950. Growth of ponderosa pine. Jour. Forestry 48: 349–352.

———. 1952. An approach to density measurement in Douglas-fir. Jour. Forestry 50: 529–536.

BRUCE, D., and F. X. SCHUMACHER. 1950. Forest mensuration. 3d ed. McGraw-Hill Book Co., Inc., New York. 483 pp.

CHAIKEN, L. E. 1939. The approach of loblolly and Virginia pine stands toward normal stocking. Jour. Forestry 37: 866–871.

DUERR, W. A., and S. R. GEVORKIANTZ. 1938. Growth predictions and site determination in uneven-aged timber stands. Jour. Agr. Res. 56: 81–98.

GEVORKIANTZ, S. R. 1937. The approach of northern hardwood stands to normality. Jour. Forestry 35: 487–489.

GEVORKIANTZ, S. R., and L. P. OLSEN. 1948. An improved increment-core method for predicting growth of forest stands. U.S. Forest Serv., Lake States Forest Expt. Sta. Paper 12. 19 pp.

GRAVES, H. S. 1899. Practical forestry in the Adirondacks. U.S. Dept. Agr., Div. Forestry Bull. 26. 84 pp.

GROSENBAUGH, L. R. 1952. Plotless timber estimates—new, fast, easy. Jour. Forestry 50: 32–37.

———. 1955. Better diagnosis and prescription in southern forest management. U.S. Forest Serv., South. Forest Expt. Sta. Occas. Paper 145. 27 pp.

———. 1958. Allowable cut as a new function of growth and diagnostic tallies. Jour. Forestry 56: 727–730.

———. 1959. Quantification and estimation in future forest management. Soc. Amer. Foresters Proc. 1959: 117–121.

HALL, O. F. 1959. The contribution of remeasured sample plots to the precision of growth estimates. Jour. Forestry 57: 807–811.

HEIBERG, S. O., and D. P. WHITE. 1956. A site evaluation concept. Jour. Forestry 54: 7–10.

HORNIBROOK, E. M. 1939. Preliminary yield tables for selectively cut ponderosa pine in the Black Hills. Jour. Forestry 37: 807–812.

———. 1940. A preliminary yield table for selectively cut lodgepole pine stands. Jour. Forestry 38: 641–643.

———. 1942. Yields of cutover stands of Engelmann spruce. Jour. Forestry 40: 778–781.

JOHNSON, F. A. 1955. Predicting future stand volumes for young well-stocked Douglas-fir forests: A comparison of methods. Jour. Forestry 53: 253–255.

JOHNSON, F. A., and W. H. CARMEAN. 1953. Sampling error in the estimation of site index. Jour. Forestry 51: 26–27.

KRAUCH, H. 1930. The determination of increment in cut-over stands of western yellow pine in the Southwest. Jour. Forestry 28: 978–986.

LEXEN, B. 1935. Some factors influencing the yield and mortality of ponderosa pine in the Southwest. Jour. Agr. Res. 50: 777–787.

———. 1943. Bole area as an expression of growing stock. Jour. Forestry 41: 883–885.

LONG, H. D. 1947. Short period growth predictions. Pulp and Paper Res. Inst. Canada, Woodlands Sect. Res. Index 921. 5 pp.

LYNCH, D. W. 1954. Growth of young ponderosa pine stands in the Inland Empire. U.S. Forest Serv., Intermountain Forest Range Expt. Sta. Res. Paper 36. 16 pp.

———. 1958a. Effects of stocking on site measurement and yield of second-growth ponderosa pine in the Inland Empire. U.S. Forest Serv., Intermountain Forest Range Expt. Sta. Res. Paper 56. 36 pp.

———. 1958b. Diameter growth of young ponderosa pine stands in the Inland Empire. U.S. Forest Serv., Intermountain Forest Range Expt. Sta. Res. Note 59. 3 pp.

McARDLE, R. E., W. H. MEYER, and D. BRUCE. 1949. The yield of Douglas-fir in the Pacific Northwest. Rev. U.S. Dept. Agr. Tech. Bull. 201. 74 pp.

McKEEVER, D. G. 1947. Empirical yield tables for Douglas-fir, board feet Scribner rule by site and stocking classes. Weyerhaeuser Timber Co., Tacoma, Wash.

MacKINNEY, A. L., F. X. SCHUMACHER, and L. E. CHAIKEN. 1937. Construction of yield tables for nonnormal loblolly pine stands. Jour. Agr. Res. 54: 531–545.

McLINTOCK, T. F., and C. A. BICKFORD. 1957. A proposed site index for red spruce in the Northeast. U.S. Forest Serv., Northeast. Forest Expt. Sta. Paper 93. 30 pp.

MEYER, W. H. 1930. A method of constructing growth tables for selectively cut stands of western yellow pine. Jour. Forestry 28: 1076–1084.

———. 1934. Growth of selectively cut ponderosa pine forests of the Pacific Northwest. U.S. Dept. Agr. Tech. Bull. 407. 64 pp.

————. 1942. Yields of even-aged stands of loblolly pine in northern Lousiana. Yale Univ., School Forestry Bull. 51. 39 pp.

————. 1959. Comments on "allowable cut as a new function of growth and diagnostic tallies." Jour. Forestry 57: 210–211.

MULLOY, G. A. 1944. Empirical stand density yield tables. Canada Dom. Forest Serv. Silvic. Res. Note 73. 22 pp.

————. 1947. Empirical stand density yield tables. Canada Dominion Forest Serv. Silvic. Res. Note 82. 54 pp.

PINCHOT, G. 1898. The Adirondack spruce. New York. 157 pp.

ROE, A. L. 1952. Growth of selectively cut ponderosa pine stands in the upper Columbia Basin. U.S. Dept. Agr. Handb. 39. 28 pp.

SCHUMACHER, F. X., and T. S. COILE. 1960. Growth and yields of natural stands of the southern pines. T. S. Coile, Inc., Durham, N. C. 115 pp.

SPURR, S. H. 1946. Volume tables for use with aerial photographs. Harvard Forest. 16 pp.

————. 1952. Forest inventory. The Ronald Press Co., New York. 476 pp.

STAEBLER, G. R. 1955. Gross yield and mortality tables for fully stocked stands of Douglas-fir. U.S. Forest Serv., Pacific Northwest Forest Range Expt. Sta. Res. Paper 14. 20 pp.

STAGE, A. R. 1959. Site index curves for grand fir in the Inland Empire. U.S. Forest Serv., Intermountain Forest Range Expt. Sta. Res. Note 71. 4 pp.

WATT, R. F. 1950. Growth in understocked and overstocked western white pine stands. U.S. Forest Serv., North. Rocky Mountain Forest Range Expt. Sta. Res. Note 78. 3 pp.

WELLWOOD, R. W. 1943. Trend toward normality of stocking for second-growth loblolly pine stands. Jour. Forestry 41: 202–209.

WESTVELD, M. 1941. Yield tables for cut-over spruce-fir stands in the Northeast. U.S. Forest Serv., Northeast. Forest Expt. Sta. Occas. Paper 12. 18 pp.

27

Estimating Growth of Forest Stands from Samples

Marshall N. Palley

Complete enumeration is seldom feasible in measuring growth of forest stands. It is necessary, in most cases, to use sampling methods. Several of the methods of sampling for change in the forest stand will be considered in this paper. Their suitability, sampling properties, and possible application will be outlined. Such applications will include the case of applying the estimate of past stand growth to expected growth in the future.

The Population and Its Characteristics

If forest sampling is done at a certain moment in time, the forest may be viewed either as a collection of trees or as a tract of land containing a collection of trees. If, on the other hand, interest centers in the change in the forest over a time interval, then the make-up of the population of trees may itself have changed during that time interval. Here there are advantages in considering the forest as a land area rather than as a fixed collection of trees. The change is taken as the difference between the aggregate of tree values at the end of the interval and the aggregate value of the trees represented at the beginning. This view has the advantage of simplifying problems of dendro-accounting. It coincides with the net growth concept of forestry literature (Meyer, 1953). Net growth may be positive, showing an increase, or it may be negative, indicating loss or diminution.

Some of the stand characteristics are measured directly on each component tree. If it is desirable to measure stand average diameter, then the diameter of each tree is measured initially and again

417

at the end of the growth period. Characteristics which are difficult
to measure may be estimated by regression: some auxiliary characteristics, u_j ($j = 1, 2, \ldots, p$) are measured, and a relationship between y, measured, and these sets of values of u_j is developed. For
example, the height and the diameter of each tree may be measured
and expected value of the volume associated with this height and
this diameter may be read from a volume table. Or, the weight of
a tree may be estimated by regression from the specific gravity of a
core, the age, the diameter, and the height.

The stand characteristics of interest are typically aggregated from
tree characteristics. For certain characteristics such as frequency,
basal area, and volume, a contribution to the stand total is made by
each tree in the stand. There also are stand characteristics which
depend upon only certain trees or classes of trees. Top height and
stand age are examples of stand measures of this kind.

Growth is the change in the state of a forest system from one moment in time to another. One may accordingly sample at each of
these two moments and express the growth for the interval as the
difference of the values on the two occasions. The two samples might
be drawn independently of one another. But it is usually preferable
to make the second observation on the sampling units drawn in the
original survey. Estimates of growth having lower variance are
achieved in this way. (Cochran, Chap. 12, 1953). In the formula
for the variance of a difference

$$\sigma^2(X - Y) = \sigma^2(X) + \sigma^2(Y) - 2 \operatorname{Cov} XY$$

the covariance term is zero when the samples on the two occasions
are independent. When, however, X and Y represent the state of a
common set of sampling units at the two points in time, then the
covariance term has the effect of reducing the variance, since there
is usually a positive correlation between the values X and Y. Accordingly, consideration will be limited to the case of remeasured
sampling units, or to the equivalent case of a stand in which the
initial measurements are reconstructed by increment borings and
stem analysis.

Simple Random and Stratified Random Sampling

Consider a forest whose land area is made up of N units of equal
area and let y_{ti} be the value of a characteristic of the forest stand on
the ith unit at time t. Call the mean of the population for this characteristic

$$\bar{Y}_t = \frac{1}{N} \sum_{i=1}^{N} y_{ti}$$

at the time t; and the mean of this same population at the end of one growth period

$$\overline{Y}_{t+1} = \frac{1}{N} \sum_{i=1}^{N} y_{t+1\,i}$$

Then the growth of the ith unit may be represented by the relation

$$y_{t+1\,i} - y_{ti} = \overline{Y}_{t+1} - \overline{Y}_t + \epsilon_i$$

One may choose to estimate the $\overline{Y}$ by taking a simple random sample of size n out of the population. In this case the model will be:

$$y_{t+1\,i} - y_{ti} = \bar{y}_{t+1} - \bar{y}_t + \delta_{ij}$$

The residual δ_{ij} now contain a further component relating to the variability of sample means.

A model for the mean growth per unit based on the estimate from two successive samples on the same units could be written:

$$\overline{Y}_{t+1} - \overline{Y}_t = \bar{y}_{t+1} - \bar{y}_t + \delta_j$$

where δ_j is the error corresponding to the jth random sample. The errors are normally distributed with an expected value of zero and a variance of σ^2, likely to be large because the growth of the forest is variable from place to place.

In order to reduce the variance of such a growth estimate, it may be possible in many cases to map the stands into several strata which are reasonably homogeneous and then to sample each of the strata so recognized on a random sampling basis. Mapping systems which are based on site-type indicators are likely to be the relevant ones in stratifying forest stands for growth determination rather than those which stratify on a volume basis. The differences in productivity of the several site types may be postulated on theoretical grounds. For the hth stratum, the model for the ith acre is similar to that for the simple random sampling case:

$$y_{t+1\,hi} - y_{thi} = \overline{Y}_{t+1\,h} - \overline{Y}_{th} + \gamma_{hi}$$

Once again, the stratum means may be estimated from random sampling. In estimating the variance of the stratified mean over the whole forest it is necessary to weight each stratum variance by the square of the ratio of its area to the forest area (Cochran, 1953).

Regression Sampling

An alternative to either of the methods so far given which has several important advantages is regression sampling (Osborne, 1950). In the first stage a set of sampling units is measured at time

t and again at time $t + 1$. In addition, certain auxiliary variables are measured. In the second stage the auxiliary variables are measured on another and perhaps larger sample. The growth in y is predicted from the regression relationship which has been developed out of the sampling done in the first stage. There is as a model for the growth of the ith sampling unit:

$$y_{t+1i} - y_{ti} = \beta_0 + \beta_1 X_{1i} + \beta_2 X_{2i} + \cdots + \beta_s X_{si} + v_i$$

where the β's are the population regression coefficients for the particular sets of X's involved. The β's are estimated from a sample selected so as to sample the ranges of the X's in a way deemed satisfactory and adequate. Some estimated $\hat{\beta}$'s from the first stage samples are calculated and their respective estimated variances are also computed. Those variables are retained in the model for which the β's differ from zero at a chosen level of significance.

In the more inclusive second sample, the significant X's are observed at each one of a number of representative sampling units. The average growth is estimated from the following equation:

$$\bar{y}_{t+1i} - \bar{y}_{ti} = \hat{\beta}_0 + \hat{\beta}_1 \bar{X}_1 + \hat{\beta}_2 \bar{X}_2 + \cdots + \hat{\beta}_s \bar{X}_s + v_{ij}$$

in which the $\bar{X}$'s are estimated from the second stage sample. Interval estimates of this average growth per acre or of the total growth on the tract are possible. It must be kept in mind that both the β's and the $\bar{X}$'s are estimated from samples. Some recent work suggests an approach to showing how these estimates are distributed (O'Regan, 1960).

This double-sampling method is most directly relevant to estimating the growth of the stand and the particular growth period from which the samples have been taken. On the other hand, if the first-stage sample covers several time periods l years in length, and if the sets of X's used are similar to those in an existing stand for which an estimate of future growth is desired, one may undertake to predict future growth for such a stand, using the estimated regression coefficients and the estimated $\bar{X}$'s of the stand in question. In any such sampling it is altogether essential that the X-variables be defined and measured precisely as they were in the initial survey which led to the estimated regression coefficients.

Criteria are needed to guide the choice of candidate auxiliary variables. In general, a theoretical basis should exist for the proposal of any such variable. Depending on the growth characteristic which is being estimated, one or another of the more readily measurable stand or site characteristics may be observed and tested. These stand variables may be observed either at the initial or at the terminal state of the system. Variables taken at the initial state are the more useful in the framework of predicting future growth. For most growth characteristics, some measure of stocking, such as basal area, is likely to be an important variable, as are stand age and measures of site quality. The work of Clements has shown that species composition may also prove to be a significant variable in certain types of stands (Roy, 1955). Within certain forest regions, such physiographic features as aspect assume importance (Nash, 1959).

It will be of great interest, as time goes on and more studies of this kind are made, to compile a list of the stand variables which, in particular cases, have been found to be associated with stand growth. Further, it will be of value to discover what proportion of the large amount of variation in the admittedly intricate process of stand growth can be accounted for by relatively simple growth regressions of the form described here.

LITERATURE CITED

Cochran, W. G. 1953. Sampling techniques. John Wiley & Sons, Inc., New York.

Meyer, H. A. 1953. Forest mensuration. Pennsylvania Valley Publishers, Inc., State College, Pa.

Nash, A. J. 1959. Growth in well-stocked natural oak stands in Missouri. Mo. Agr. Expt. Sta. Res. Bull. 700.

O'Regan, W. G. 1960. Personal communication.

Osborne, J. G. 1950. A continuous inventory basis for determining growth, mortality, and yield. In: Timber Management Plans on the National Forests. L. S. Gross (ed.). U.S. Department of Agriculture, Washington.

Roy, D. F. 1955. The Clements growth prediction charts for residual stands of mixed conifers in California. Calif. Forest Range Expt. Sta. Tech. Paper 9.

Participants

Sharlene R. Agerter, Macalester College
G. S. Allen, University of British Columbia
Martin B. Applequist, Arizona State College, Flagstaff
M. W. Bannan, University of Toronto
Bryant Bannister, University of Arizona
C. Allen Bickford, U.S. Forest Service, Upper Darby, Pennsylvania
F. H. Bormann, Dartmouth College
Robert Z. Callaham, U.S. Forest Service, Spokane, Washington
John P. Decker, U.S. Forest Service, Tempe, Arizona
Robert Jack Downs, U.S. Department of Agriculture, Beltsville,
   Maryland
Charles W. Ferguson, University of Arizona
H. A. Fowells, U.S. Forest Service, Washington, D. C.
Donald A. Fraser, Petawawa Forest Experiment Station, Chalk
   River, Ontario, Canada
George M. Furnival, Yale University
Stanley P. Gessel, University of Washington
J. L. Giddings, Brown University
Waldo S. Glock, Macalester College
Edward Hacskaylo, U.S. Department of Agriculture, Beltsville,
   Maryland
Emil W. Haury, University of Arizona
Henry Hellmers, U.S. Forest Service, Pasadena, California
Philip N. Knorr, University of Arizona
Theodore T. Kozlowski, University of Wisconsin
Paul J. Kramer, Duke University
Edwin B. Kurtz, Jr., University of Arizona
Olof Langlet, The Forest Research Institute, Stockholm, Sweden
Philip R. Larson, U.S. Forest Service, Rhinelander, Wisconsin
Donald W. Lynch, U.S. Forest Service, Boise, Idaho

Andrew L. McComb, University of Arizona
Paul S. Martin, University of Arizona
Elias Melin, University of Uppsala, Uppsala, Sweden
François Mergen, Yale University
Peitsa Mikola, University of Helsinki, Helsinki, Finland
Charles O. Minor, Arizona State College, Flagstaff
Marshall N. Palley, University of California, Berkeley
C. W. Ralston, Duke University
F. I. Righter, U.S. Forest Service, Berkeley, California
Taisitiroo Satoo, University of Tokyo, Tokyo, Japan
M. Schaffalitzky de Muckadell, Erikshåb, Højrup, Denmark
Henry Schneider, Citrus Experiment Station, Riverside, California
Cherng-jiann Shiue, University of Minnesota
H. Lee Silvey, University of Arizona
Terah L. Smiley, University of Arizona
Frank H. Smith, Oregon State University
Marvin A. Stokes, University of Arizona
G. K. Voigt, Yale University
Robert F. Wagle, University of Arizona
Robert Wellwood, University of British Columbia
Fritz W. Went, Missouri Botanical Garden, St. Louis
Hugh Wilcox, State University of New York, Syracuse
Robert W. Wilson, U.S. Forest Service, Upper Darby, Pennsylvania
D. J. Wort, University of British Columbia
Robert Zahner, University of Michigan

Author Index

425

Subject Index

433